W9-BSZ-376

DRAMA
for Reading & Performance

Collection One

Seventeen Full-length
Plays
for Students

including information, lessons,
and assignments for
understanding and
performance

DRAMA
for Reading & Performance
Collection One

Perfection Learning

Logan, Iowa 51546-0500

Editorial Director   Julie A. Schumacher
Senior Editor   Gay Russell-Dempsey
Design   Mary Ann Lea
Electronic Technology   Pegi Bevins, Digital Talkies
Permissions   Laura Pieper, Meghan Schumacher, Oliver Oertel

Cover Image A masked character from Carlo Gozzi's *commedia dell'arte* play *The King Stag*. Produced at the American Repertory Theater, Cambridge, Massachusetts, by Julie Taymor, 1984.

Warning
The editors have made every effort to trace the ownership of all copyrighted materials found in this book and to make full acknowledgment for their use.

Acknowledgments
The Arkansaw Bear by Aurand Harris. Copyright © 1980 by Anchorage Press, Inc. Reprinted by permission of Anchorage Press, Inc. CAUTION: All performance inquiries should be directed to Anchorage Press, Inc. Post Office Box 8067, New Orleans, Louisiana 70182.

The Dancers by Horton Foote from *Selected One-Act Plays of Horton Foote*. Copyright © 1955, 1983 by Horton Foote, Copyright © renewed 1989 by Sunday Rock Corp. Reprinted by special arrangement with Horton Foote and the Barbara Hogenson Agency. CAUTION: Information regarding stock and amateur production rights must be obtained from Dramatists Play Service, Inc., 440 Park Avenue South, New York, NY 10016.

(Continued on page 340.)

Copyright © 2000 by Perfection Learning ® Corporation
1000 North Second Avenue
P.O. Box 500
Logan, Iowa 51546-0500
Tel: 1-800-831-4190 • Fax: 1-712-644-2392

All rights reserved. No part of this book may be used or reproduced in any manner whatsoever without written permission from the publisher.

Printed in the United States of America

Paperback ISBN: 0-7891-5204-5
Cover Craft ® ISBN: 0-7807-9531-8

Contents

How to Read a Play   vii

The Arkansaw Bear *by Aurand Harris*
Symbolism in Literature / Mime in Theatre   2

The Dancers *by Horton Foote*
Plot in Literature / Movement in Theatre   26

Novio Boy *by Gary Soto*
Characterization in Literature / The Set in Theatre   46

Chekhov's **The Man in a Case** *by Wendy Wasserstein*
Diction in Literature / Listening and Reacting in Theatre   80

Variations on the Death of Trotsky *by David Ives*
Comic Irony in Literature / Burlesque in Theatre   90

A Conversation with My Dogs *by Merrill Markoe*
Tone in Literature / Physical Acting in Theatre   100

He Who Says Yes and He Who Says No *by Bertolt Brecht*
Theme in Literature / The Chorus in Theatre   106

I Never Saw Another Butterfly *by Celeste Raspanti*
Dramatic Monologue in Literature / Sound in Theatre   118

Painted Rain *by Janet Allard*
Mood in Literature / Props in Theatre   146

Avi's **Nothing But the Truth** *Dramatized by Ronn Smith*
Protagonist and Antagonist in Literature / Creating a Character in Theatre   164

This Is a Test *by Stephen Gregg*
Style in Literature / Pacing and Timing in Theatre   222

The Frog Prince *by David Mamet*
Dialogue in Literature / Voice in Theatre   240

The Love of Three Oranges *by Carlo Gozzi*
adapted by Lowell Swortzell
Archetypes in Literature / Improvisation in Theatre   258

Maggie Magalita *by Wendy Kesselman*
Foreshadowing in Literature / Costumes and Makeup in Theatre   270

The Drummer *by Athol Fugard and*
The Big Black Box *by Cleve Haubold*
Beginning, Middle, and End in Literature / Lighting in Theatre   308

The Hitch Hiker *by Lucille Fletcher*
Suspense in Literature / The Radio Play in Theatre   320

Glossary   332

How to Read a Play

R eading a play is different from reading other kinds of literature because a play is different from other kinds of literature. Short stories, poems, novels, and so on are all complete on the printed page. But a printed play—also called a *script*—is not complete. It becomes complete when it is performed by actors for an audience. The play is what happens on the stage or screen.

Because of this, you—as reader—must bring a little more of yourself to reading a play. Of course you will bring your imagination, as you do to reading short stories and novels. And you will also make an effort to visualize the characters and actions, and to imagine their thoughts and emotions. What else can you do to help make your reading more complete and satisfying? Here are some tips.

Reading Tips

- Read the **stage directions.** *(They are often in parentheses and printed in italic type, like this.)* Stage directions are not meant for an audience; they are messages from the playwright to the people who stage the play. They may tell the actors when and where to move, what emotions to express, what props (hand-held objects, such as a newspaper or a coffee cup) to pick up and what to do with them. They may tell the director where to position the actors or what the overall mood of a scene should be. They may tell the designers what the set looks like, what costumes the actors should wear, what music or sounds are heard, or what time of day the lighting should suggest. Stage directions are usually not read aloud, even when the actors rehearse a show.

UR Upstage Right	UC Upstage Center	UL Upstage Left
R Right	C Center	L Left
DR Downstage Right	DC Downstage Center	DL Downstage Left

- Understand the **stage areas.** Stage directions often include abbreviations like *R* for *right* or *L* for *left.* (These mean the actors' right or left sides as they face the audience.) Other abbreviations are *U* for *upstage* or *D* for *downstage* or *C* for *center.* (*Downstage* means toward the audience; *up* and *down* are terms left over from the days when stages actually slanted.)

- Pay attention to the characters' names. They tell who says what speeches.

- Read the speeches aloud. They are, after all, meant to be heard. Read with as much feeling as you can, to get the most out of the speeches. Even if you're reading the play by yourself, you can play all the parts, changing your voice for the different characters. This will give you a better understanding of the characters, who they are and what they are doing.

- Look for a **subtext.** This is, simply, what the characters are thinking or feeling, and it is not always the same as what they are saying. For example, a character may say, "Of course I'll take my little sister to the movie, Dad," but actually be thinking, "How can you *do* this to me? What will my friends think?"

Theatre Conventions

A **convention** is an accepted way of doing things. The more plays you see on stage, the better you will understand the conventions, the things that make a play a play. Here are some common conventions.

Narrator Sometimes an actor will speak directly to the audience, to explain who the characters are or what is happening. Sometimes a character will speak directly to the audience and then go back to speaking to the other characters. When they do, they serve the function that a narrator serves in short stories or novels.

The "Fourth Wall" In realistic plays, the actors may behave as if the audience simply isn't there. It's as if the audience is eavesdropping on the action through an invisible "fourth wall" of a room, whether the set is actually an enclosed room or not.

Dramatic Time The time an action is supposed to take onstage isn't necessarily the time that same action would take in real life. For example, actors may take seven minutes to eat a meal that they would spend twenty-five minutes on in reality. Just accept what the play tells you about how much time has elapsed.

Lapses of Time If you go to the movies, you're probably familiar with the convention that several minutes or days or even years elapse from one scene to another. It's the same with plays—a curtain or change of lighting may suggest that any amount of time has passed. When you read a play, the stage directions will usually specify what is happening.

The World Offstage Actors are trained to keep in mind, when they enter or exit, just where it is they're supposed to be coming from or going to. This helps them create their characters more realistically. When you're reading a play, try to imagine the lives the characters are leading when they're not onstage. This will help you understand the characters and their subtexts better, and will give you a better understanding of the play as a whole.

Sharing the Experience

Seeing a play performed live onstage can be a truly thrilling experience. As a reader, you can share some of that thrill if you read attentively, with imagination, and if you try actively to enter into the world of the characters and of the play. In this book are many different kinds of plays in different styles from playwrights all over the world. Enjoy them.

THE ARKANSAW BEAR

The Play as Literature: Symbolism

The Arkansaw Bear is a story about life and death. Think about words and images that represent or symbolize life and death to you. Use a graphic organizer to list or illustrate your symbols. Then, as you read the play, think about what symbols the characters in the play encounter.

The Play as Theatre: Mime

A child stomps her feet and slams a door. A man sits slumped in a chair, head in his hands, shoulders shaking. A woman stands with her hands on her hips quickly tapping her foot. None of these people has spoken a word, yet we understand them perfectly. We often communicate quite powerfully without words. In the theatre, this is called *pantomime*, or simply *mime*.

In ancient Greece, the word *mimes* meant an actor who imitated life in an effort to communicate thoughts and feelings. Later, when performers became more extravagant, the word *panto*, meaning "all," was added. *Pantomime* refers to the performance and *mime* to the performer. Today people use both words to mean the same thing.

Marcel Marceau is a famous mime. He usually performs on a bare stage with few or no props. His face is painted in makeup called clown white to highlight his expressions. Marceau has the ability to make his audience feel what his character is feeling and see the imagined world that he has created.

Marcel Marceau

WARM UP!

Think about a treasured possession from your childhood. Maybe it's an old stuffed animal, a picture, or a favorite book. Remember the weight, feel, shape, smell, and sound of the object. Write a detailed description of it. When you have finished writing, imagine holding the object in your hand, turning it over, and putting it on your desk.

THE ARKANSAW BEAR

by Aurand Harris

SETTING	CHARACTERS	TIME
Somewhere in Arkansas	**TISH** **STAR BRIGHT** **MIME** **WORLD'S GREATEST DANCING BEAR** **GREAT RINGMASTER** **LITTLE BEAR** **VOICES: MOTHER** **AUNT ELLEN** **ANNOUNCER**	The present

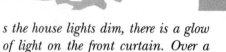

As the house lights dim, there is a glow of light on the front curtain. Over a loudspeaker a man's whistling of "Oh! Susannah" is heard. The curtains open. Tish walks into a large spot of warm light at L. The whistling dims out. TISH is a little girl and carries some hand-picked flowers. She listens to the voices, heard over a loudspeaker, and reacts to them as if MOTHER and AUNT ELLEN were on each side of her, downstage.

TISH. I've come to see Grandpa.

MOTHER'S VOICE. No, dear. No. You can't go in.

TISH. But Mother—

MOTHER'S VOICE. No, Tish! You can't see Grandpa now.

TISH. I picked him some flowers. These are Grandpa's favorites.

AUNT ELLEN'S VOICE (She is TISH'S great-aunt, elderly, gentle, and emotional.) Quiet, child.

TISH. But Aunt Ellen—

AUNT ELLEN'S VOICE. The doctor is here.

TISH. The doctor?

MOTHER'S VOICE. Tish dear.

TISH. Yes, Mother?

MOTHER'S VOICE. Grandpa had a turn for the worse. His heart—

AUNT ELLEN'S VOICE. Oh, it's the end. (Cries quietly)

TISH. The end?

AUNT ELLEN'S VOICE. The doctor said . . . no hope.

(TISH reacts.)

MOTHER'S VOICE. Don't cry, Aunt Ellen.

TISH. Is Grandpa going . . . to die?

AUNT ELLEN'S VOICE. Yes.

TISH. No! He can't.

MOTHER'S VOICE. We all have to die, dear.

TISH. I know. But not Grandpa. (Starts to move)

MOTHER'S VOICE. Stop. You can't go in.

TISH. Why can't he live forever!

AUNT ELLEN'S VOICE. You're too young to understand. Too full of life.

TISH. I have to tell him there's a circus coming. I saw a poster with a bear.

MOTHER'S VOICE. It doesn't matter now.

TISH. Yes, it does! Do something!

MOTHER'S VOICE (*firmly*). We've done all we can.

TISH (*softly*). Yes, if I'd been quiet so he could sleep. And—Oh! Once when I was mad, I said . . . I wish he was dead. Oh, I didn't mean it, Grandpa. I didn't mean it.

MOTHER'S VOICE. Hush, dear. It's not your fault. Grandpa loved you.

TISH. Then why is he . . . leaving me?

(*Pulls away as if being held*)

TISH. Oh, let me go!

MOTHER'S VOICE (*sharply, becoming edgy with emotion*). Yes. Go put the flowers in some water.

TISH. He liked the pink ones. Now . . . he'll never see them. Oh, why . . . why does Grandpa have to die?

MOTHER'S VOICE (*sternly,*[1] *trying to control and cover her grief*). Run along, dear. Run along.

AUNT ELLEN'S VOICE. Keep away. Away from his door. Away . . . away.

(*The voices of* MOTHER *and* AUNT ELLEN *overlap and mix together, as they keep repeating,* "Run along," "Away," "Run . . . run," "Away . . . away," "Run," "Away," "Run . . . away; run . . . away." *They build to a climax in a choral chant,* "Run . . . away.")

TISH. I will. I'll run away. Up the hill . . . to my tree . . . my tree.

(*She runs, circling to the tree which is at R, and on which the lights come up. The circle of light on the first scene dims out, and the chanting of the voices stops.* TISH *stands alone by her tree in the soft light of evening. She brushes back a tear, shakes her head, and throws the flowers on the ground.*)

(*She sinks to the ground by the tree, hugs her knees, and looks up. She sees the first star, which is out of sight. Quickly she gets up, points to the star and chants.*)

Star light, star bright,

First star I see tonight,

I wish I may, I wish I might,

Have the wish I wish tonight.

I wish . . . I wish . . . Oh, Grandpa . . . why?

(*Goes back to tree*)

Why do you have to die?

(*There is star music, tinkling with bells. From above, a small swing starts descending. Magic star light spots on it.* STAR BRIGHT *stands on the swing, which stops in mid-air. Music dims out.*)

STAR BRIGHT. Repeat, please.

TISH. I wish. . . I wish. . .

STAR BRIGHT. I know you are wishing. That's why I'm here. But WHAT? Repeat, please.

TISH (*sees and goes near him*). Who are you?

STAR BRIGHT (*slowly and proudly*). I am the first star out tonight!

(*Happily*)

I did it! I did it! I did it again!

(*Excitedly*)

First star. . . first star. . . first star out tonight!

(*To* TISH)

It's the early star, you know, who gets the wish. What is yours? Repeat, please.

TISH. Can you make a wish come true?

---

1. sternly (stėrn′ lē), harshly firm

STAR BRIGHT. I've been making wishes come true for a thousand years.

TISH. A thousand years! You're older than Grandpa.

STAR BRIGHT (*sits on swing*). Old? Oh, no. I'll twinkle for another thousand years.

TISH. And then?

STAR BRIGHT (*cheerfully*). Then my light will go out.

TISH. Like Grandpa.

STAR BRIGHT. But there will be a new star. It's the great pattern . . .

TISH. I'll never have another Grandpa.

STAR BRIGHT. . . . the great circle of life. In every ending there is a new beginning.

TISH (*fully realizing it*). I'll never see Grandpa again. I'll never hear him whistle. (*Begins to whistle "Oh! Susannah"*)

STAR BRIGHT. Your wish? What is your wish?

TISH. I wish. . . I wish Grandpa could live a thousand years!

STAR BRIGHT (*startled*). What? Repeat, please!

TISH (*excited*). I wish he'd never die. Nobody would ever die! Everyone would live forever!

STAR BRIGHT. Oh no, no, no! Think what a mixed up world it would be!

TISH (*speaks intently*[2]). I wish. . . I wish I knew why. . . why Grandpa has to die.

STAR BRIGHT. That is not a quick one-two-buckle-my-shoe wish. No. That is a think-and-show-it, then-you-know-it, come-true wish.

TISH. Please.

STAR BRIGHT (*with anticipated*[3] *excitement*). Close your eyes. Whisper the words again. Open your eyes. And your wish will begin.

(TISH *closes her eyes.* STAR BRIGHT *claps his hands, then motions. There are music and beautiful lights.* STAR BRIGHT *is delighted with the effect.*)

Very good! Repeat, please.

(*He claps and waves his hand. Again there are music and beautiful lights.*)

Excellent! Thank you!

T he swing with STAR BRIGHT *is pulled up and out of sight. The full stage is seen, lighted brightly and in soft colors. [Never is the stage dark, eerie, or frightening.] It is* TISH's *fantasy. There are the large tree at R, and open space with beautiful sky.*

MIME *appears at R. He is a showman, a magician, and an accomplished*[4] *mime who never speaks. He wears a long coat with many colorful patch pockets. He is NOT in white face, but his face is natural, friendly, and expressive. He enters cautiously, carrying a traveling box, which he sets down at C. On the side the audience sees is painted the word* BEAR. *On the other side is painted the word* DANCING. *He beckons off R. The* WORLD'S GREATEST DANCING BEAR *enters R. He is a star performer, amusing, vain, and lovable like a teddy bear. He does NOT wear an animal mask, nor is the actor's face painted, frightening or grotesque,*[5] *with*

---

2. intently (in tent'lē), in a determined manner
3. anticipated (an tis'ə pāt id), expectant
4. accomplished (ə kom'plisht), expert; skilled
5. grotesque (grō tesk'), odd or unnatural in shape or appearance

animal make-up. He wears his traveling hat. He hurries in, worried and out of breath.)

BEAR. I must stop and get my breath. *(Pants heavily)* My heart is pounding. *(Looks about)* Are we safe? *(Frightened)* I don't see him. I don't hear him. Yes, we have outrun him.

(He motions and MIME *places box for* BEAR *to sit.)*

Where . . . where in this wide whirling wonderful world . . . do you think we are? Switzerland?

*(*MIME *makes pointed mountain with his wrist, runs his fingers up and down the "mountain," then shakes his head.)*

You are right. No mountains. England?

*(*MIME *opens and holds up imaginary umbrella, holds hand out to feel the rain, shakes his head.)*

You are right. No rain. India?

*(*MIME *leans over, swings one arm for a trunk, then other for his tail and walks.)*

No elephants.

TISH. Excuse me.

(They freeze. She comes to them.)

I can tell you where you are. You are in Arkansas.

BEAR. Quick! Disguise. Hide.

(He and MIME *hurry to R.* MIME *quickly takes from one of his pockets a pair of dark glasses and gives them to* BEAR, *who puts them on; then stands beside* BEAR *to hide him.)*

TISH *(recites with pride).* Arkansas was the twenty-fifth state to be admitted to the union. It is the twenty-seventh in size, and the state flower is the apple blossom.

BEAR. Who is it?

*(*MIME *pantomimes a girl.)*

A girl?

*(*MIME *pantomimes a small girl.)*

A little girl? Tell her to go away. To run away.

*(*MIME *pantomimes to* TISH. BEAR *hides behind tree.)*

TISH. I have. I have run away. Have you run away, too?

*(*MIME *nods.)*

Why?

*(*MIME *looks frightened off R, then puts finger to lips.)*

Who are you?

*(*MIME *takes a card from a pocket and presents it to her. She reads.)*

"A Mime." You never speak.

*(*MIME *shakes his head, and "walks" in one spot and tips his hat.)*

"A Magician." You do tricks!

*(*MIME *pulls handkerchief from sleeve.)*

"Friend." You give help.

*(*MIME *touches handkerchief under her eyes.)*

Thank you. I was crying because my grandpa . . . he's going to . . .

*(*BEAR, *without glasses, steps out from behind the tree, does a loud tap dance step, and poses.* MIME *turns the traveling box around and with a flourish[6] points to the word painted on that side of the box.* TISH *reads it with amazement.)*

Dancing.

*(*MIME *turns box around again. She reads.)*

Bear.

*(*MIME *motions to* BEAR, *who steps forward.)*

_____

6. flourish (flėr′ish), act of waving about

I've never met a bear. I've never seen a DANCING bear.

BEAR *(to* MIME*).* Should I?

*(*MIME *nods.)*

Shall I?

*(*MIME *nods.)*

I will! My Spanish hat.

*(*MIME *jumps with joy and gets hat from box.* BEAR *motions to* TISH, *who sits on ground.)*

Be seated please.

*(*MIME *holds up hand mirror, which he takes from a pocket. He holds it up for* BEAR *to look at himself, and fixes the hat.)*

To the right . . . to the right . . . Ah, just right!

*(*MIME *motions and a spotlight comes on. An* ANNOUNCER'S VOICE *is heard over a loud-speaker.)*

ANNOUNCER'S VOICE. Ladies and Gentlemen: Presenting in his spec-tacular, special, Spanish dance, the World's famous, the World's favorite, the World's Greatest Dancing Bear!

*(*MIME *motions and Spanish music is heard.* BEAR *steps into the spotlight. He dances with professional perfection a Spanish dance, but he does not finish. At a climactic moment, he stops, holds his hand against his heart, and speaks with short breaths.)*

BEAR. Stop the music.

*(*MIME *motions. Music stops.)*

Dim the light.

*(*MIME *motions. Spot dims out.)*

TISH. What is it?

BEAR. *(breathing heavily).* He is near. He is coming.

TISH. Who?

BEAR. He is almost here. Hide. I must hide. He must not find me.

*(*MIME *points to tree.)*

Yes, the tree. Hurry!

*(*MIME *helps* BEAR *to tree.)*

TISH. Who? Who is coming?

BEAR. The box. Cover the box.

(He disappears behind the tree. MIME *sits on traveling box.* BEAR's *head appears.)*

Talk.

*(*MIME *mime-talks with hands and face.)*

Louder!

*(*BEAR's *head disappears.* MIME *motions for* TISH *to talk.)*

TISH. Talk? What about?

BEAR *(head appears).* Arkansas.

(Head disappears)

TISH *(recites nervously).* Arkansas has mineral springs, natural caves, and . . . and . . . diamond mines. *(Looks off R and whispers, frightened)* I don't hear anyone. I don't see any-one.

*(*MIME *motions for her to talk.)*

Arkansas was first known as the state of many bears. *(Looks and whispers mysteriously)* There isn't anyone. Nothing. Just quiet, nothing. Who is he running away from?

*(*MIME *motions "Sh," then runs L to R and looks, then motions for* BEAR *to come out.)*

BEAR *(comes from behind tree).* He didn't find me. I escaped . . . this time. *(Pleased, but short of breath)* My travel-ing hat. We must go on.

*(*MIME *takes Spanish hat and gives* BEAR *traveling hat.)*

TISH. Where? Where will you go?

BEAR *(looks off R, afraid).* I must keep ahead of him.

TISH. Ahead of who? Who?

BEAR *(cautiously).* Never speak his name aloud. *(Looks around)* He may be listening, and come at once.

(MIME gives him hat.)

Oh, my poor hat. You and I have traveled together for many a mile and many a year. We are both beginning to look a little weary. *(Puts hat on)*

TISH. Grandpa has an old hat.

BEAR. Perhaps, if it had a new feather. Yes! A bright new feather!

TISH. I think your hat is very stylish.

BEAR *(pleased).* You do?

TISH. And very becoming.

BEAR *(flattered).* Thank you. You are a very charming little girl. What is your name?

TISH. Tish.

BEAR. Tish-sh-sh! That is not a name. That is a whistle. Ti-sh-sh-sh-sh.

TISH. It's short for Leticia. It was my grandmother's name.

BEAR. Leticia. Ah, that is a name with beauty.

TISH. Grandpa calls me "Little Leticia."

BEAR. I shall call you . . . *(Rolling the "R")* Princess Leticia.

TISH. Princess?

BEAR. All my friends are important people. Kings and Queens . . . Command performances for Ambassadors and Presidents . . . *(To MIME)* The velvet box, please.

(MIME takes from a pocket a small box.)

I will show you my medals, my honors.

TISH. My grandpa won a medal.

BEAR. Ah?

TISH. He was the best turkey caller in Arkansas.

BEAR. Turkey caller?

TISH. He won first prize!

BEAR *(to MIME).* Pin them on me so she can see. And so that I can remember . . . once again . . . all my glories.

(Royal music begins and continues during the scene. MIME puts ribbons and jeweled medals on BEAR as VOICE announces each decoration. Two are pinned on. One is on a ribbon which is fastened around BEAR's neck.)

ANNOUNCER'S VOICE. The Queen's highest honor, the Royal Medallion.

BEAR. I danced in the Great Hall. It was the Queen's birthday party.

ANNOUNCER'S VOICE. The Diamond Crescent of the East.

BEAR. Fifteen encores. Fifteen encores and they still applauded.

ANNOUNCER'S VOICE. The Royal Ribbon of Honor for Distinguished[7] Service.

BEAR. It was during the war. I danced for the soldiers.

ANNOUNCER'S VOICE. And today, a new decoration. Her Royal Highness, Princess Leticia presents, in honor of her grandfather, the highest award in the State of Arkansas—the Turkey Feather.

(MIME takes a bright feather from a pocket and gives it to TISH. BEAR parades to her,

_____

7. distinguished (dis ting′wisht), marked by excellence

with a few dance steps, and she puts the feather in his hat. Royal music stops.)

BEAR. Thank you. A party! We will celebrate my new honor! *(To* MIME*)* Food and festivities! Honey bread!

(MIME nods.)

Thick with honey spread!

(MIME nods twice, then makes magic motions toward BEAR. *Suddenly* MIME *turns and points to* LETICIA. *She puts out her hand which, magically, holds a honey bun.)*

TISH *(delighted).* O-o-oh! It looks delicious.

(MIME turns and points to BEAR, *who puts out his hand which, also magically, holds a colorful honey bun.)*

BEAR. A-a-ah! It IS delicious. *(BEAR puts finger in it, then licks finger.* MIME *raises his hand.)*

Yes, give us a toast.

(BEAR and TISH *hold honey buns up.* MIME *pantomimes "A toast . . . " holds up his hand; "to the winner . . ." clasps his hands and shakes them high in the air; "of the turkey feather," walks like a turkey, bobbing his head, then* MIME *pulls out an imaginary feather from his hip.)*

Thank you.

TISH. What did he say?

BEAR. You didn't listen?

TISH. How can I hear when he doesn't speak?

BEAR. You listen with your eyes, and then YOU say the words. Listen. He will repeat the toast.

TISH *(MIME pantomimes the toast again. She watches and speaks aloud.)* "A toast . . . to the winner . . . of the turkey feather!"

BEAR. Thank you. Now entertainment! *(To* MIME*)* You tell us a story. *(To* TISH*)* You listen and say the words.

TISH. Me?

BEAR. And I will eat! *(Wiggles with excitement and sits on box)*

TISH *(MIME pantomimes a story which* TISH, *watching him, repeats in words.)* "Once there was . . . a princess . . . a beautiful princess!"

BEAR. Named *(Sings it)* Leticia. *(Takes a bite)*

TISH. "One day . . . in the woods . . . she met . . . *(Doubtful)* . . . a cat?"

(MIME shakes his head. Mimes again.)

A . . . goosey-gander?

(MIME shakes his head. Mimes again.)

TISH. A . . . bear!

BEAR. The World's Greatest Dancing Bear! *(Seated, he makes his own vocal music and dances with his feet.)*

TISH. "Under a spreading tree . . . they had a party . . . with honey bread, thick with honey spread."

BEAR *(licks his five fingers, one on each word).* Yum . . . yum . . . TO . . . the . . . last . . . crumb. *(Licks his hand and picks and eats crumbs from his lap)*

TISH. "Now honey bread, thick with honey spread . . . made the bear . . . very . . . sleepy. He yawned."

(BEAR follows action of the story and goes to sleep.)

". . . gave a little sigh . . . and took a little nap."

(BEAR snores.)

He's asleep. Who . . . who is he running away from?

(MIME *goes to sleeping* BEAR, *puts his finger to his lips, then mimes.*)

"The World's Greatest Dancing Bear . . . is old and tired . . . and his heart . . . is tired." (*To herself*) Like Grandpa.

(*Speaking for* MIME)

"He is running away from . . ." Who? "Someone is coming to take him away . . . forever." Does that mean if he's caught, he will die?

(MIME *nods.*)

TISH. Is he running away . . . from death?

(MIME *nods.*)

Oh! I'll help him. Yes, I'll help him.

(*Faint music of a calliope is heard.* BEAR *stirs.*)

He's waking up.

BEAR (*slowly wakes up*). Music . . . the calliope . . . circus music . . . of the Great Center Ring! (*Rises*) The Ringmaster is coming!

TISH (*to* MIME). Death?

(MIME *nods.*)

BEAR. He is near. I hear the music.

TISH. I don't hear it. (*To* MIME) Do you?

(MIME *shakes his head.*)

BEAR. Only I can hear him. Only I can see him. He is coming for me. Quick! We must go.

TISH. Yes, I'll help you.

BEAR. This way. Hurry!

(MIME *carries box. Led by* BEAR *they start L, but stop when the music becomes louder.*)

No! No! The music is here. Quick! Turn! Run the other way.

(*They rush to R and are stopped by music becoming louder.*)

No! The music is coming from here. It is all around us! Here! There! Look! (*He points off R.*)

TISH. What?

BEAR. The Great Ringmaster. He is there! He is coming . . . for me!

(RINGMASTER *enters slowly from R. He wears an ornate[8] ringmaster's jacket, boots, and a tall hat. He has a friendly face, a pleasant voice, but walks and speaks with authority. He stops. Music stops.*)

Quick! Hide me! Hide me!

(BEAR *runs to L.* TISH *and* MIME *follow. He quickly hides behind them when they stop.* BEAR *peeks over* TISH's *shoulder.*)

Tell him to go away.

TISH. I can't see him. Where is he?

BEAR. There. (*Hides*)

TISH (*bravely speaks, facing front talking into space*). Excuse me . . . sir. This is my secret place . . . by the big tree. You must leave at once. Go away. Now. (*Whispers to* BEAR) Did he go?

BEAR (*peeks*). No. (*Hides*)

RINGMASTER (*distinctly and with authority*). I have come for the Dancing Bear. I have come to take him to the Great Center Ring.

BEAR. Tell him he has made a mistake.

TISH. Excuse me . . . sir. You have made a mistake.

RINGMASTER (*opens book*). No. It is written plainly in the book. The date is today. The name is . . . the Dancing Bear.

---

8. ornate (ôr nāt′), having much decoration

BEAR (*who was hidden by* MIME *at the side, now steps into view, wearing boxing gloves and a sport cap*). You HAVE made a mistake. I am a BOXING bear.

(MIME *blows a whistle and continues to blow it, as* BEAR *shadow boxes, comically, with a few dance steps and kicks thrown in. He ends in a heroic pose.*)

Goodbye.

RINGMASTER. A boxing bear? (*Looks in his book*) There has never been a mistake.

TISH (*whispers*). Have you tricked him? Outwitted him?

BEAR (*nods, then calls loudly*). Yes. Training time. On your mark; get set; ready—talleyho! (*Starts jogging off R*)

RINGMASTER (*reads*). The book says: His father, born in Russia, a dancing bear.

BEAR (*stops, indignant*). Correct that. He was Russia's most honored dancing bear.

RINGMASTER. His mother, born in Spain, also a dancing bear.

BEAR. She was prima ballerina bear of all Spain!

RINGMASTER. He, only son—

BEAR. Is the World's Greatest Dancing Bear!

RINGMASTER. Then you are the one I have come for!

BEAR. Yes!

RINGMASTER. Then we will have no more tricks or games.

(BEAR *realizes he has revealed himself.*)

Come. Take my hand.

(BEAR *always reacts with fear to the* RING-

MASTER'*s white gloved hand.*)

I will show you the way to the Great Center Ring.

BEAR. No! No!

TISH. What is he saying?

BEAR. He is going to take me away.

RINGMASTER. Come. You must. And it is easier if you go quietly.

BEAR. No! I will not go with you. I will fight! (*Holds up boxing gloves*)

TISH. Fight him! I'll help you!

BEAR. I have fought all my life. Battled my way to the top. Look at my medals. I will fight to the end.

RINGMASTER. This, my friend, is the end.

BEAR. No! No! Not for me. Not yet! Stay away! I have new dances to do.

RINGMASTER. Today you will take your last bow.

BEAR. No! No! (*Savagely*) I will claw! I will eat! I will crush! I will kill! Kill to live! (*Violently throws boxing gloves away*) To live! To live!

RINGMASTER. Everyone shouts when he is frightened of the dark.

BEAR. I WILL NOT DIE!

RINGMASTER. You have no choice.

BEAR. But . . . why! Why me? ME!

RINGMASTER. You are like all the others. Everyone thinks HE will live forever. Come.

BEAR. No! What did I do wrong? What can I do now? To stop it?

RINGMASTER. Death comes to all. It has never been IF you will die. The only question has been WHEN you will die. Now you know.

BEAR *(runs).* I will run. I will hide.

RINGMASTER *(with authority).* You cannot escape from death.

BEAR *(bargaining desperately).* More time. Give me more time. I have so much to do.

RINGMASTER *(slightly annoyed).* There is always that which is left undone.

BEAR. I don't know how . . . to die. I need to rehearse.

RINGMASTER. No one has to rehearse. It is very simple . . . very easy. *(Holds out hand)* Come. It is growing late.

BEAR. No! *(Desperate for any excuse)* I must write my memories! Tell the world the glories of my life. My life . . .

(Pause. TISH *and* MIME *rush to him as he falters,*[9] *place box, and help him sit.)*

It is almost over. And what was it? A few medals that will be lost. No. There must be more to life. Give me time. Time to find the answer.

TISH *(kneeling by him, pleads into space).* Please . . . let him live.

RINGMASTER. Your life is over. Today is the day.

BEAR. But my day is not over. *(To* TISH*)* The day is not ended, is it?

TISH. Give him to the END of the day!

BEAR. Yes! To the end. Oh, you are a very smart little girl!

RINGMASTER. Well . . . *(Looks in his book)*

TISH. What did he say?

BEAR. He's looking in his book.

RINGMASTER. The day you are to die is written plainly. But not the hour.

BEAR. Then give me the full day.

TISH. Please.

RINGMASTER *(pause).* I will give you until midnight. Until the last hour of your last day.

BEAR. YES!

TISH. Can you live?

BEAR. YES! Oh, let me shout to the world! I AM ALIVE! *(To* MIME*)* Give me my brightest, my happiest hat! *(To* RINGMASTER, *who has gone)* Oh, thank you . . . thank you . . . He is gone . . . for a while.

(To TISH*)* Oh, let me touch you. Let me feel the warmth . . . the life in you. There is much yet to do! And so little time. My life . . . it went too fast. I didn't stop to listen . . . I didn't stop to see.

*(*MIME *waves clown hat in front of* BEAR.*)*

Oh, yes! I will be the clown!

(Puts hat on. To TISH.*)* Come. Dance with me! And we will make the world spin round and round with joy!

TISH. Grandpa taught me how to whistle and how to dance a jig.

(Quickly she whistles "Oh! Susannah," and does a little jig, looking at her feet.)

BEAR. No, no, no. To dance is a great honor. Hold your head high.

(He follows his own instructions.)

And first you smile to the right . . . then you smile to the left . . . and you bow to the center . . . and then . . . begin.

*(*MIME *motions. A spotlight comes on* BEAR. *Music is heard.* BEAR *does short, charming soft-shoe dance. Spotlight and music dim out.* TISH *applauds.* BEAR *sits on box which*

---

9. falter (fôl′tər), move unsteadily; stumble

MIME *places for him.* BEAR *is happy, breathless.*)

TISH. Oh, how wonderful!

BEAR. Thank you.

TISH. You're better than Grandpa! He can only do a little jig.

BEAR. But he taught you?

TISH. Yes.

BEAR. And he taught you how to whistle?

TISH. Yes.

BEAR *(rises).* If I could teach my dances to someone . . . if someone could carry on the fame of my family . . . All my hats . . . there will be no one to wear my hats. They, too, will be put in a box and forgotten. Tell me, are you like your grandfather?

TISH. Daddy says I'm a chip off the old block.

BEAR. You are part of him. And you will carry on for him in life.
(Excited) Yes! Yes, that is the answer to the riddle.

TISH. What riddle?

BEAR. The riddle of life. I must leave my dances! They will be a part of me that will live on! But who? Where? How?

TISH. Make a wish!

BEAR. A wish?

TISH. On the first star you see. And it will come true. It will. It will!

BEAR *(wanting to believe).* You are sure it will?

(TISH nods. To MIME.*)* Do you believe it will?

*(*MIME *nods.)*

I could try.

TISH. Quick!

BEAR. Of course I don't believe in superstitions. But I did get up on the right side of the bed.

*(*MIME *nods.)*

I did find a four-leaf clover.

*(*MIME *nods.)*

And I haven't sneezed once.

*(*MIME *shakes his head.)*

Yes, luck is with me today! So . . . let me knock on wood—three times— and I will do it!

*(*MIME *takes off hat.* BEAR *knocks on* MIME*'s head three times, with sound effects.)*

What do I say?

TISH. Point to the first star you see.

BEAR *(looks about, then points).* There! I see a bright twinkling one.

TISH. Say, "Star light, star bright . . ."

BEAR *(to* MIME*).* The rabbit's foot! This wish must come true.

(Looks up)

"Star light, star bright."

TISH. "First star I see tonight."

BEAR. "First star I see tonight." *(Takes rabbit's foot from* MIME *and rubs it vigorously)* Oh, bring me luck. Make my wish come true.

TISH. "I wish I may, I wish I might . . ."

BEAR. "I wish I may, I wish I might." Oh, it won't work. It's nothing but a nursery rhyme.

TISH. "Have the wish I wish tonight." Say it. Say it!

BEAR. "Have the wish I wish tonight." *(Pause)* Nothing. Nothing. I told you so.

TISH. Look. Look! It's beginning to happen.

STAR BRIGHT *(star music and lights begin as* STAR BRIGHT *enters on swing. He is joyously happy.)* Tonight I'm blinking. Tonight I'm winking. Wishes are flying past. Wishes are coming quick and fast! I'm twinkling bright and RIGHT tonight! *(Laughs)* Your wish, please.

BEAR *(lost in happy memories).* Look. It is like the circus. The trapeze high in a tent of blue . . . the music of the band . . .

*(*MIME *motions. Soft band music of the circus is heard. Colorful lights play on the backdrop.)*

the acrobats; the jugglers tossing, catching bouncing balls . . .

*(*MIME *pantomimes juggling.)*

the delicious smell of popcorn . . . the dance on the high wire . . .

*(*TISH *holds up an imaginary umbrella and walks on an imaginary tight rope.)*

the sweet taste of pink lemonade . . . Oh, the beauty, the wonder of life. Let me look at it. The happiness of living . . . Oh, let me feel it. The joy of being alive! Let me keep it. Let me hold it forever.

(Holds out his arms to embrace it all)

STAR BRIGHT *(claps his hands. Music and circus scene stop.)* Your wish. Your wish. Repeat, please.

BEAR *(confused, he is led by* MIME *to star.)* I wish to leave a footprint.

STAR BRIGHT *(puzzled).* Repeat, please.

TISH. The answer to the riddle.

BEAR *(intently).* I wish to leave with someone my dances so that I . . . so

that they . . . will be remembered.

STAR BRIGHT. This is a wish I hear every night . . . every night. A wish to shine on earth . . . and leave behind a trace . . . to learn, to earn the grace . . . of immortality.[10] Of your wish, half I can do. The other half is left for you. But quick! You must start. Because all wishes on a star must be done before the star is overshadowed by the sun. *(He claps his hands. Magic music and lights begin.)*

One, two;

Sunset red;

Midnight blue;

The wish you wish

I give to you.

agic lights and music end as STAR BRIGHT *exits up and out of sight. From off L,* LITTLE BEAR *is heard singing. All look to L.* LITTLE BEAR *enters, finishing his song to the tune of "Turkey in the Straw." He is a small cub, wearing country overalls and a little turned-up straw hat. Over his shoulder he carries a small fishing pole.*

LITTLE BEAR *(sings).*

Turkey in the straw, haw, haw, haw;

Turkey in the hay, hay, hay, hay;

Bait the hook, give the line a swish;

Jumpin' jiggers, I caught a fish.

TISH. A little bear.

*(*LITTLE BEAR *does a few dance steps of joy, and continues walking and singing.)*

BEAR. A little dancing bear. *(To* MIME*)* Meet him. Greet him. Make him

---

10. immortality (im ôr′tal′ət ē), fame that lasts forever

welcome. (*To* TISH) Quick, the hand mirror.

(TISH *holds mirror which* MIME *gives her and* BEAR *preens.* MIME *hurries to* LITTLE BEAR *and pantomimes a big and friendly greeting.* LITTLE BEAR, *as if it were a game, imitates every movement of the* MIME. *It ends with both shaking hands. Then* LITTLE BEAR *gives a friendly goodbye wave and starts off R, singing.*)

Stop him!

(MIME *rushes in front of* LITTLE BEAR *and turns him around.*)

I am ready to be presented.

(MIME, *with a flourish, presents* BEAR.)

How do you do.

LITTLE BEAR. Howdy-do to you.

BEAR. You have come from my WISH-ING on a star.

LITTLE BEAR. Huh uh. I've come from my FISHING in the river.

BEAR. Oh, my little one, I am going to give you the treasure of my life. Bestow on you all my gifts.

LITTLE BEAR. I could use a new fishing pole.

BEAR. I am going to teach you all my dances. You will wear all my hats. Oh-ho, I have never felt so alive in my life!

(*He gives a joyous whoop and jumps and clicks his heels.* LITTLE BEAR *is bewildered.*[11] BEAR, *with the eyes of a dancing master, looks* LITTLE BEAR *over.*)

Yes, you have a good build. Good stance.[12] Relaxed torso.[13]

(*Taps* LITTLE BEAR's *waist.* LITTLE BEAR *wiggles and giggles from the tickling.*)

Legs sturdy. Up! Leg up. Up!

(LITTLE BEAR *cautiously lifts leg.*)

Up! Up!

(BEAR *raises* LITTLE BEAR's *leg high.*)

LITTLE BEAR. Whoa!

BEAR. Point. Point!

LITTLE BEAR (*points with finger*). Point where?

BEAR (*holding* LITTLE BEAR's *foot high.*) Point your foot. Ah, feet too stiff . . . too stiff.

(*Lets leg down.* LITTLE BEAR *stands in profile, stomach pushed out.*)

Stomach flat!

(*Taps stomach.* LITTLE BEAR *pulls stomach in, but pushes hips out.*)

Rear push in!

(*Smacks* LITTLE BEAR *on the bottom.* LITTLE BEAR *pulls hips in, and turns facing audience.*)

Stretch . . . up . . . up!

(*Pulls* LITTLE BEAR *up, who tries to stretch. His face is tense.*)

Relax.

(*Pats* LITTLE BEAR *on the forehead.* LITTLE BEAR *slowly sinks to the ground.* BEAR *lifts him up.*)

Smile.

(LITTLE BEAR *forces a tortured smile.*)

Walk! Walk!

(LITTLE BEAR *starts walking stiffly.*)

TISH. Will he be a good dancer?

BEAR. He will be magnificent!

(*Puts arm out and stops* LITTLE BEAR's *escape*)

---

11. bewildered (bi wil′dərd), completely confused
12. stance (stans), a manner of standing; posture
13. torso (tôr′sō), the human body from the shoulders to the hips

He will be—ME! My rehearsal hat. My father's Russian dancing hat!

(He dances a few steps of a Russian dance, and shouts a few Russian words.)

To the dressing room. *(He continues the dance steps and shouting as he exits at R.* MIME, *with traveling box, follows him, imitating the dance steps.)*

LITTLE BEAR. Who . . . who is he?

TISH. He is the greatest dancing bear in the world.

LITTLE BEAR. Oh!

TISH. And . . . he's going to die.

LITTLE BEAR. Oh.

TISH. My grandpa is going to die and I don't know what to do.

LITTLE BEAR. Up in the hills, I've seen a lot of them die.

TISH. You have?

LITTLE BEAR. Old ones, little ones, and big ones, too. And there ain't nothing you can do about it. 'Cause as sure as you're born, you're as sure of dying.

TISH. It's sad.

LITTLE BEAR. Course it's sad.

TISH. It's frightening.

LITTLE BEAR *(thinking it out).* No. It ain't dying that you're afraid of. It's not knowin' what comes AFTER you die. That's what scares you.

TISH *(tearful).* I'll never see Grandpa again.

LITTLE BEAR *(with gentle understanding).* You go on. You have yourself a good cry. It'll help you to give him up. And you got to. *(With emphasis)* You got to let him go.

TISH. No.

LITTLE BEAR. You have to! 'Cause he is gone . . . forever.

TISH. You don't know what it's like to have your grandpa die.

LITTLE BEAR. Yes, I do. My grandpa died last winter. And my papa . . . I saw a hunter shoot my papa.

TISH *(shocked).* Shoot your papa! Oh, what did you do?

LITTLE BEAR. First, I cried. Yes, I cried, and then I started hatin' and I kicked and clawed 'cause I felt all alone.

TISH *(nods).* All by yourself.

LITTLE BEAR. Then my mama said, "You have to go on living, so . . . do your best. Give yourself to the livin'. 'Cause that's the best way to say goodbye to your pa." So I made my peace.

TISH. Your peace?

LITTLE BEAR. Inside myself. Oh, it don't mean I understand about dyin'. I don't. But you do go on living. The next day. The next year. So if you love your grandpa like I loved my papa . . .

TISH. Oh, I do.

LITTLE BEAR. Then show him you do.

TISH. How?

LITTLE BEAR. Tell him goodbye . . . by giving your most to the living. I'm wanting to do something . . . something big . . . just for Papa.

BEAR *(off).* All is ready!

TISH. Please, dance with him. He needs you.

LITTLE BEAR. Well, I like to help folks.

TISH. You said, "Give to the living."

LITTLE BEAR. And I do like to dance!

TISH (*excited with a new idea*). This is the big thing you can do for your papa.

LITTLE BEAR. For Papa?

TISH (*points with her hand as she visualizes it*). Your name will be in lights. You will be the NEW World's Greatest Dancing Bear!

(BEAR *and* MIME *enter.* BEAR *wearing his Russian Cossack hat.*)

BEAR. Let the flags fly! Let the band play! (*To* LITTLE BEAR) We will start with a simple waltz. My mother's famous skating waltz. One, two, three; one, two, three . . . (*He dances, continuing during the next speeches.*)

LITTLE BEAR (*tries to do the step, then stops*). No. I'm just a country bear, with no schoolin'.

TISH. You will be the famous . . . "Arkansas Bear!" (*Urges him on*)

LITTLE BEAR. Arkansas. I ain't right sure how to spell Arkansas.

(*He moves in one spot to the beat of the music, wanting to dance, but afraid.*)

TISH. Like it sounds. A—R—K—A—N—

LITTLE BEAR (*shouts, eager to dance*). S—A—W!

(*With a burst of energy he follows* BEAR *and dances with joy, counting loudly and happily.*)
One! Two! Three! One! Two! Three! I'm doing it!

(*The first chime of midnight is heard, loud and distinct. The other chimes follow slowly.* MIME *runs to* BEAR, *motions for him to listen.*)

TISH. What is it?

BEAR. The chimes are striking twelve.

LITTLE BEAR. It's the end of the day. Midnight.

BEAR. No! No! Not yet! I have not taught you my dances. Stop the clock!

TISH. Run! Hide! Before he comes back!

BEAR. Where?

LITTLE BEAR. In the caves! In the hills!

TISH. Hurry!

(TISH *and* LITTLE BEAR *help* BEAR. MIME *carries box. All start toward back. Soft calliope music is heard.* RINGMASTER *enters R.*)

RINGMASTER. Twelve.

(*They stop.*)
Your day is ended. Your time is up. Come. I will take you to the Great Center Ring.

BEAR. No! No!

TISH. Is he here?

BEAR. Yes, he has come for me.

(*Comes downstage. Backs off towards L.*)
Stop him.

RINGMASTER. There is no way to stop death.

TISH. I know a way.

(*Grabs* MIME *and points up toward star.*)
You! Make a wish on the first star you see. Say,

(*Shouts*)
"Star light, star bright,
First star I see tonight . . . "

(MIME *quickly points and looks up, rapidly miming the words of the rhyme.*)

STAR BRIGHT (*off*). Louder, please.

RINGMASTER. Come. (*Holds out his hand and slowly crosses toward* BEAR *at far L*)

TISH (MIME *pantomimes, repeating with larger gestures, while* TISH *says the words.*)
"I wish I may, I wish I might,

Have the wish I wish tonight."

STAR BRIGHT *(quickly descends into view).*
Wish quickly chanted. Wish quickly
granted.

TISH *(MIME pantomimes her words.)* Stop
death!

(With a sound effect of a roll on a cymbal,
STAR BRIGHT *points at* RINGMASTER, *who
has advanced almost to* BEAR. RINGMASTER
stops in a walking position.)

Make him go away!

(A roll on a cymbal is heard, as STAR BRIGHT
makes a circle with his hand. RINGMASTER
slowly turns around.)

LOCK HIM UP IN THE TREE!

(Another roll on the cymbal)

STAR BRIGHT. Walk to the tree.

*(*RINGMASTER *slowly walks to a tree.)*

Your home it will be . . . for a time.

*(*RINGMASTER *stops.* STAR BRIGHT *points to
tree again. There is a roll on a cymbal as the
trunk slowly opens.)*

It is open wide . . . to welcome you.
Step inside.

*(*RINGMASTER *faces tree and slowly steps
inside the tree trunk, and turns and faces
audience.)*

Let it enfold and hold you . . . for a
time.

*(Waves his hand. There is a last roll on a
cymbal. The tree trunk slowly closes shut.)*

Locked, blocked, and enclosed!

(He laughs.)

BEAR *(to* TISH*).* You did it! You stopped
death!

TISH *(She and* BEAR *shout together, while*
MIME *jumps with joy and blows whistle.)*
We did it!

BEAR. We did it!

STAR BRIGHT *(claps his hands).*
Remember . . . soon will come the
morning sun, and then . . .
Remember that is when . . . all wishes become . . . undone.

*(Star music and light begin as he ascends out
of sight, and then stop.)*

BEAR *(Their joy changes to concern.)* It is
true! Time is short! Quick. I must
teach the little one— *(Looks about.*
LITTLE BEAR *has, unnoticed, slipped
away when* RINGMASTER *appeared.)*
Where is he?

TISH. Little Bear!

(Pause. There is no answer.)

BEAR. Little Bear, come back!

TISH *(She and* MIME *run looking for him.)*
Little Bear?

BEAR. He was frightened . . . *(Looks at
tree)* of death. He is gone. And with
him all my hopes are gone.

(He slumps, wearily.)

TISH *(concerned, rushes to him).* You must
rest, like Grandpa.

BEAR. Your grandfather has you.
(Amused) A chip off the old
block, eh? *(She nods.)* You gave
him happiness in life . . . peace
in death.

TISH. Are you all right?

BEAR. I am old, and weary and tired.
And I am going to die.

TISH. No. We stopped death.

BEAR. But only for a brief time. Death,
they say is a clock. Every minute our
lives are ticking away. Now . . .
soon . . . my clock will stop.

TISH. No.

BEAR. When I was young like you, I wondered, "Where did I come from?" And now when I am old, I wonder, "Where am I going?"

(MIME *looks and listens off R, then runs to them and excitedly mimes that* LITTLE BEAR *is coming.*)

BEAR. What is it?

(MIME *pantomimes more.*)

Who? Where?

(MIME *points to R. All watch as* LITTLE BEAR *enters.*)

You have come back.

LITTLE BEAR. I left my fishing pole.

BEAR. Have no fear. Death is locked in the tree.

(LITTLE BEAR *reacts with fright at tree.*)

TISH. You have come back to help.

LITTLE BEAR. I come back to learn all your fancy dancin'.

TISH (*runs to* LITTLE BEAR *and hugs him*). Oh, you are the best, the sweetest, the most wonderful little bear in the world!

(LITTLE BEAR *is embarrassed.*)

BEAR. Yes! Quick! We must begin the lesson. There is so little time and much to learn. (*Looks frightened off R. To* MIME.) Stand watch. Yes, watch for the first rays of the sun!

(MIME *stands at R, anxiously looking off.* TISH *sits on box.* BEAR *motions to* LITTLE BEAR.)

Come! Come! Attention! I will teach you all I know.

(*Takes position*)

First, you smile to the right.

(BEAR *does the action with the words.* LITTLE BEAR *watches and tries to do the action.*)

You smile to the left. You bow to the center. And then . . . begin . . . to dance. I will start with my father's famous Russian dance. Master this and all else will be easy.

(*to* MIME) How many more minutes?

(MIME *holds up ten fingers.*)

Ten! Position. Position!

(LITTLE BEAR *imitates him.*)

Listen to the beat . . . the beat . . . (*Taps foot*)

LITTLE BEAR. Beat what?

BEAR. Your feet! Your feet! The beat . . . the beat . . .

(*Taps foot.* LITTLE BEAR *slowly and timidly taps beat.*)

Too slow. Too slow.

(LITTLE BEAR *pivots*[14] *in a circle, weight on one foot while tapping fast using the other foot.*)

Too fast. Too fast.

(LITTLE BEAR *does it right.*)

Ah! Ah! Ah! Good! Good!

LITTLE BEAR. I'm doing it right!

BEAR (*shows him next Russian step*). The first step. Hop, hop, hop, switch, hop.

(LITTLE BEAR *tries, awkward at first, then better.*)

Hop, hop, hop, switch, hop. Yes, hop, hop, hop, switch, hop. Yes! Yes!

(*Shows him next step*)

Deep knee, hop.

(LITTLE BEAR *shakes his head.*)

Try. Try.

---

14. pivot (piv′ət), turn while keeping one foot in place and moving the other foot in another direction

(LITTLE BEAR *tries deep knee bends with a hop.*)

Deep knee, hop. Lower. Lower.

(LITTLE BEAR *puts hands on floor in front of him and does step. He smiles at the audience at the easiness of it.*)

No, no, no! No hands!

(*Lifts* LITTLE BEAR *up.* LITTLE BEAR *continues to kick his feet.*)

The next step. The finale.

(*Shows step*)

Turn, two, up, two. Turn, two, up, two.

LITTLE BEAR. Oh, my!

BEAR. Turn, two, up, two.

(LITTLE BEAR *tries.*)

Turn, two, up, two. Faster. Faster.

LITTLE BEAR (*falls*). I can't do it. I can't do it.

BEAR. You will. You must do it. I must leave my dances with you.

TISH. Try, please. Please, try.

LITTLE BEAR. Well . . .

(*Gets up*)

BEAR. Again. Again. Ready. Turn, two, up, two.

(BEAR *keeps repeating the count, and* LITTLE BEAR *does the step better and better, until he is perfect—and happy.*)

He did it! He did it!

TISH. He did it!

LITTLE BEAR. I did it!

BEAR (*to* MIME). How many minutes are left?

(MIME *holds up eight fingers.*)

Eight minutes. Time is running out. Quick. The polka. The dance of the people. Music!

(MIME *motions. Music is heard.* BEAR *dances a few steps.* LITTLE BEAR *quickly follows him and masters them. Music stops.* BEAR *breathes heavily.*)

How many more minutes?

(MIME *holds up seven fingers.*)

Only seven minutes left! Hurry. My famous tarantella.

(MIME *motions and music is heard.* BEAR *does a few steps.* LITTLE BEAR *again quickly does them and they dance together. Music stops.* BEAR *pants for breath.* MIME *runs to him and holds up six fingers.*)

Six minutes. And at the end take your bow. The first bow.

(BEAR *bows, short of breath.*)

The second bow.

(BEAR *bows, pauses, then with trembling voice he speaks with emotion, knowing it is his last bow.*)

And the last and final bow.

TISH. More, more! Encore! Encore!

(BEAR *slumps to the floor. She rushes to him.*)

He's fallen.

(*She and* MIME *cradle* BEAR *on either side.*)

Are you all right?

BEAR (*stirs, weakly*). How . . . many more minutes . . . do I have left?

(MIME *holds up five fingers.*)

My little one, you will do my dances, you will carry on for me?

LITTLE BEAR. Yes. Yes.

BEAR. Take my father's hat . . . and it was HIS father's hat . . .

LITTLE BEAR. No, you must wear it.

BEAR. I will not need it where I am going. I have taken my last bow.

TISH. No. (*Buries her head on his shoulder*)

BEAR. Ah, tears can be beautiful. But there is no need to cry. I am content. I was a part of what went before and I will be a part of what is yet to come. That is the answer to the riddle of life. *(Weakly)* How many more minutes?

(MIME holds up two fingers.)

Two. Bring me my traveling hat. I will wear it on my last journey.

(LITTLE BEAR gets traveling hat from box, as MIME and TISH help BEAR to stand.)

I must look my best when I enter the Great Center Ring.

(MIME puts hat on BEAR, who smiles at TISH.)

Does it look stylish?

TISH. Yes.

BEAR. Is it becoming?

(She nods.)

Then I am ready. *(Gently pushes TISH and MIME away)*

No. This journey I must go alone.

(Extends hand to MIME)

Goodbye, good friend. Thank you for everything. And sometimes when the band plays . . . think of an old bear.

(MIME motions for BEAR to wait. MIME quickly gets a pink balloon on string from the side and holds it out to BEAR.)

Yes, I remember when once we said, "Life is like a bright balloon." Hold it tight . . . Hold it tight. Because . . . once you let it go . . . it floats away forever. *(Breathless)* How many more minutes? *(MIME holds up one finger. BEAR turns to TISH.)*

I have one last request. When the end comes . . . when I enter the Great Center Ring . . . I want music. I want you to whistle the tune your grandfather taught you.

TISH. "Oh! Susannah."

BEAR *(nods and smiles)*. You will find that when you whistle you cannot cry at the same time.

(A rooster is heard crowing.)

Listen.

LITTLE BEAR. It's a rooster crowin'. It's almost mornin'.

TISH. The sun is up. The stars are fading away.

STAR BRIGHT *(Star music is heard as STAR BRIGHT descends into view. He speaks softly.)* Announcing: the first ray of sun is peeping out. Warning: all wishes end as the sun begins. The new day is starting, the old departing. That is the great pattern . . . the circle of life. Tomorrow is today.

(He points at the tree, and claps his hands. The tree trunk slowly opens.)

And the night and the stars fade away . . . fade away.

(There is star music as STAR BRIGHT disappears. Soft calliope music is heard which continues during the scene.)

RINGMASTER *(Steps out from tree trunk. He speaks with authority.)* There is no more time. The book is closed.

BEAR. Poets tell us death is but a sleep, but who can tell me what I will dream?

RINGMASTER *(walks slowly to bear)*. Take my hand.

BEAR. Tell me, tell me what is death?

RINGMASTER. When there is no answer,

you do not ask the question. Come.

BEAR. Yes, I am ready.

(*To* LITTLE BEAR) My little one . . . I give you my feather . . . and you . . . give joy . . . to the world. (*Gives turkey feather to* LITTLE BEAR. *He whispers.*) Let the balloon go.

RINGMASTER *holds out his hand, which* BEAR *takes. Together they walk off L slowly.* MIME *lets the balloon go. He,* TISH, *and* LITTLE BEAR *watch as it floats up and out of sight. At the same time the calliope music builds in volume. There is a second of silence. Then the* ANNOUNCER'S VOICE *is heard, loud and distinctly.*)

ANNOUNCER'S VOICE. Ladies and gentlemen: presenting for your pleasure and entertainment, the new dancing bear, the world's famous, the world's favorite, the world's greatest—The Arkansaw Bear!

(*During the announcement,* MIME *points to* LITTLE BEAR. LITTLE BEAR *looks frightened, amazed, and pleased.* MIME *holds up mirror and* LITTLE BEAR *puts feather in his hat.* MIME *motions for* LITTLE BEAR *to step forward, then motions a circle of light on the floor. Spotlight comes on and* LITTLE BEAR *steps into the light.*)

BEAR'S VOICE (*Over the loudspeaker,* BEAR'*s voice is heard. He speaks softly and with emotion.* LITTLE BEAR *follows his instructions.*) You smile to the right . . . smile to the left . . . bow to the center . . . and then begin to dance!

(*Music begins, lively "Turkey in the Straw."* LITTLE BEAR *begins his dance.*)

My dances . . . your dances . . . and make the world spin round and round with joy.

(LITTLE BEAR *dances with fun, excitement, and joy, a wonderful short dance. During this,* TISH *exits, and* MIME *exits with box. At the end of the dance,* LITTLE BEAR *bows as the audience applauds, and exits at L, peeks out and waves again. Spotlight goes out. Fantasy music is heard and a soft night light illuminates the tree.* TISH *is leaning against it. She looks up, sighs, picks up the flowers, and slowly circles back to the downstage area of the first scene, which becomes light as the tree area dims out. Fantasy music also fades out.* MOTHER'*s and* AUNT ELLEN'*s voices are heard, and* TISH *answers as if they were standing on each side of her downstage.*)

MOTHER'S VOICE (*worried*). Tish? Tish, is that you?

TISH. Yes, Mother.

MOTHER'S VOICE. Where have you been?

TISH. I went up the hill to my tree. I want to see Grandpa.

AUNT ELLEN'S VOICE. He's dead . . . dead.

TISH (*trying to be brave*). Dead. Tears can be beautiful, Aunt Ellen. But you have to give him up. Let the balloon go.

AUNT ELLEN'S VOICE. What?

TISH (*trying to keep back her tears*). I know everyone . . . everything has a time to die . . . and it's sad. But Grandpa knew the answer to the riddle.

AUNT ELLEN'S VOICE. The riddle?

TISH. He left his footprint. He left a chip off the old block.

MOTHER'S VOICE. What, dear? What did he leave?

TISH. Me! And I want to do something . . . something big for Grandpa. Because that's the best way to say goodbye. *(Softly)* Let me give him his flowers . . . the pink ones.

MOTHER'S VOICE *(positive, and with a mother's love and authority).* All right, dear. Come along. We'll go together and see Grandpa.

(TISH starts L, and begins to whistle.)

What are you doing?

TISH. Whistling . . . for the bear . . . and for Grandpa. Because it helps . . . when you are afraid and in the dark. And . . . when you whistle, you can't cry. *(Whispers)* Goodbye, Grandpa, I . . . I love you.

(TISH exits L, bravely trying to control her crying. At the same time lights slowly come up so the full stage is seen. The lights on TISH's area dim out. The stage is bright with soft beautiful colors. The lone whistling of "Oh! Susannah," the same as at the beginning of the play, is heard. There is a moment of a final picture—the living tree standing, as it has through the years, against a beautiful endless sky. The whistling continues as the curtains close.)

THE ARKANSAW BEAR

Responding To the Play

1. What part of the play did you find most memorable? Why?
2. Look back at the diagram you made before reading the play. Which symbols might you add based on Tish and Little Bear's experiences?
3. Draw a picture of Dancing Bear based on the description of him on page 6. Consider the movement and actions required of the character as well as the colors that would be most appropriate.
4. If you were the director, how would you instruct the actor playing Star Bright to be "magical"? Be aware of how the use of the voice, body movement, props, and costume pieces might help achieve the qualities of enchantment.
5. Design a program cover for the play. Think about Dancing Bear, the magic of Star Bright, Tish, the tree, and other significant characters, images, and events in the play.

More About Mime

Mimes use exaggerated gestures to communicate their stories. These gestures are clear and concise so they won't confuse the audience and so they can be seen in the last row of the theatre. Reread the scene on page 10 in which Dancing Bear demands that Mime "tell" them a story. Think about the actions that could be performed in conjunction with the story Tish is narrating. One person tells the story using words and the other person tells the story using mime.

CREATING AND PERFORMING

1. Look back at page 7, when Mime and Bear first appear. Read again the descriptions of Switzerland, England, and India. Share with the class how you would act out Mime's part in this exchange.
2. Pick one of the characters in the play and freeze in a position that best illustrates that character's personality.
3. Working with a partner, write a short scene that is not in the play but that could be. For example, write a scene in which Tish goes fishing with her grandfather. Then present your scene to the class.

Before Reading

The Dancers

The Play as Literature: Plot

If a work of literature were an automobile, the plot would be its engine. The plot gives any literary work its drive. It moves forward a series of related actions that build to and then resolve a conflict. As the plot gathers speed, the conflict builds to a dramatic climax, or turning point. This is followed by the resolution. The diagram under *plot* in the glossary helps you visualize how the plot rises and falls.

As you read *The Dancers*, try to decide where the turning point occurs in the plot.

The Play as Theatre: Movement

When you act, you have more than lines to think about on stage. How, where, and when to move is also a major consideration. Always be aware of your position in relation to others on stage. Where you position yourself tells the audience something about the importance of your character in the scene as well as your relationship to the other characters.

The actor who is moving or talking is generally the one the audience focuses on, so if you are not the dominant character in the scene try not to move. If you are directed to move, you should do so behind the dominant actor. Make eye contact with the audience only if the script directs you to do so.

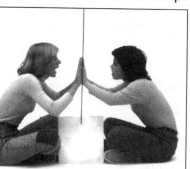

Always sit, stand, and move naturally and with good posture. Try to move in character while maintaining a natural balance. Practice shifting your weight smoothly as you move.

Warm Up!

To help you with body awareness and movement, play the "mirror image" game. Stand facing a partner. The person who is designated "the mover" slowly makes a broad movement, such as lifting one leg or raising both arms. The "follower" must duplicate the movement as though he or she were a mirror reflection of the mover.

The Dancers

by Horton Foote

Place	*Characters*	*Time*
Harrison, Texas	A WAITRESS INEZ STANLEY ELIZABETH CREWS EMILY CREWS HERMAN STANLEY HORACE MARY CATHERINE DAVIS VELMA MORRISON TOM DAVIS MRS. DAVIS	Early summer, 1952

*T*he stage is divided into four acting areas. *DL is the living room of* INEZ *and* HERMAN STANLEY. *DR is part of a small-town drugstore. UR is the living room of* ELIZABETH CREWS. *UL is the yard and living room of* MARY CATHERINE DAVIS. *Since the action should flow continuously from one area to the other, only the barest amount of furnishings should be used to suggest what each area represents. The lights are brought up on the drugstore, DR. A* WAITRESS *is there.* INEZ STANLEY *comes into the drugstore. She stands for a moment thinking. The* WAITRESS *goes over to her.*

WAITRESS. Can I help you?

INEZ. Yes, you can if I can think of what I came in here for. Just gone completely out of my mind. I've been running around all day. You see, I'm expecting company tonight. My brother Horace. He's coming on a visit. (ELIZABETH CREWS *and her daughter* EMILY *come into the drugstore.* EMILY *is about seventeen and very pretty. This afternoon, however, it is evident that she is unhappy.*) Hey . . .

ELIZABETH. We've just been by your house.

INEZ. You have? Hello, Emily.

EMILY. Hello.

ELIZABETH. We made some divinity[1] and took it over for Horace.

INEZ. Well, that's so sweet of you.

ELIZABETH. What time is he coming in?

INEZ. Six-thirty.

ELIZABETH. Are you meeting him?

INEZ. No—Herman. I've got to cook supper. Can I buy you all a drink?

ELIZABETH. No, we have to get Emily over to the beauty parlor.

INEZ. What are you wearing tonight, Emily?

ELIZABETH. She's wearing that sweet little net I got her the end of last summer. She's never worn it to a dance here.

INEZ. I don't think I've ever seen it. I'll bet it looks beautiful on her. I'm gonna make Horace bring you by

---

1. divinity (də vin′ət ē), a kind of fudge made with whipped egg whites, sugar, and nuts

the house so I can see you before the dance.

WAITRESS. Excuse me. . . .

INEZ. Yes?

WAITRESS. Have you thought of what you wanted yet? I thought I could be getting it for you.

INEZ. That's sweet, honey . . . but I haven't thought of what I wanted yet. (*To* ELIZABETH *and* EMILY) I feel so foolish, I came in here for something, and I can't remember what.

WAITRESS. Cosmetics?

INEZ. No . . . you go on. I'll think and call you.

WAITRESS. All right. (*She goes.*)

INEZ. Emily, I think it's so sweet of you to go to the dance with Horace. I know he's going to be thrilled when I tell him.

ELIZABETH. Well, you're thrilled too, aren't you, Emily?

EMILY. Yes ma'am.

ELIZABETH. I told Emily she'd thank me someday for not permitting her to sit home and miss all the fun.

EMILY. Mama, it's five to four. My appointment is at four o'clock.

ELIZABETH. Well, you go on in the car.

EMILY. How are you gonna get home?

ELIZABETH. I'll get home. Don't worry about me.

EMILY. O.K. (*She starts out.*)

INEZ. 'Bye, Emily.

EMILY. 'Bye. (*She goes on out.*)

ELIZABETH. Does Horace have a car for tonight?

INEZ. Oh, yes. He's taking Herman's.

ELIZABETH. I just wondered. I wanted to offer ours if he didn't have one.

INEZ. That's very sweet—but we're giving him our car every night for the two weeks of his visit. Oh—I know what I'm after. Flowers. I have to order Emily's corsage for Horace. I came in here to use the telephone to call you to find out what color Emily's dress was going to be.

ELIZABETH. Blue.

INEZ. My favorite color. Walk me over to the florist.

ELIZABETH. All right.

(*They go out as the lights fade. The lights are brought up DL on the living room of* INEZ STANLEY. HERMAN STANLEY *and his brother-in-law,* HORACE, *come in.* HERMAN *is carrying* HORACE*'s suitcase.* HERMAN *is in his middle thirties.* HORACE *is eighteen, thin, sensitive, but a likable boy.*)

HERMAN. Inez. Inez. We're here. (*He puts the bag down in the living room.* INEZ *comes running in from R.*)

INEZ. You're early.

HERMAN. The bus was five minutes ahead of time.

INEZ. Is that so? Why, I never heard of that. (*She kisses her brother.*) Hello, honey.

HORACE. Hello, Sis.

INEZ. You look fine.

HORACE. Thank you.

INEZ. You haven't put on a bit of weight though.

HORACE. Haven't I?

INEZ. Not a bit. I'm just going to stuff food down you and put some weight on you while you're here. How's your appetite?

HORACE. Oh, it's real good. I eat all the time.

INEZ. Then why don't you put on some weight?

HORACE. I don't know. I guess I'm just the skinny type.

INEZ. How are the folks?

HORACE. Fine.

INEZ. Mother over her cold?

HORACE. Yes, she is.

INEZ. Dad's fine?

HORACE. Just fine.

INEZ. Oh, Herman, did you ask him?

HERMAN. Ask him what?

INEZ. Ask him what? About his tux.[2]

HERMAN. No, I didn't. . . .

INEZ. Honestly, Herman. Here we have him a date with the prettiest and most popular girl in Harrison and Herman says ask him what. You did bring it, didn't you, Bubber?

HORACE. Bring what?

INEZ. Your tux.

HORACE. Oh, sure.

INEZ. Well, guess who I've got you a date with. Aren't you curious?

HORACE. Uh huh.

INEZ. Well, guess. . . . *(A pause. He thinks.)*

HORACE. I don't know.

INEZ. Well, just try guessing. . . .

HORACE. Well . . . uh . . . uh . . . *(He is a little embarrassed. He stands trying to think. No names come to him.)* I don't know.

INEZ. Emily Crews. Now isn't she a pretty girl?

HORACE. Yes. She is.

INEZ. And the most popular girl in this town. You know her mother is a very close friend of mine and she called me day before yesterday and she said, "I hear Horace is coming to town," and I said yes you were, and she said that the boy Emily is going with is in summer school and couldn't get away this weekend, and Emily said she wouldn't go to the dance at all but her mother said that she had insisted and wondered if you'd take her. . . .

HORACE. Her mother said. Does Emily want me to take her?

INEZ. That isn't the point, Bubber. The point is that her mother doesn't approve of the boy Emily is in love with and she likes you. . . .

HORACE. Who likes me?

INEZ. Emily's mother. And she thinks you would make a very nice couple.

HORACE. Oh. *(A pause)* But what does Emily think?

INEZ. Emily doesn't know what to think, honey. I'm trying to explain that to you. She's in love.

HORACE. Where am I supposed to take her to?

INEZ. The dance.

HORACE. But, Inez, I don't dance well enough. . . . I don't like to go to dances . . . yet . . .

INEZ. Oh, Horace. Mother wrote me you were learning.

HORACE. Well . . . I am learning. But I don't dance well enough yet.

---

2. tux (tuks), tuxedo; a very formal man's suit, usually black

INEZ. Horace, you just make me sick. The trouble with you is that you have no confidence in yourself. I bet you can dance.

HORACE. No, I can't. . . .

INEZ. Now let's see. (INEZ *goes to the radio and turns it on. She comes back to him.*) Now come on. Show me what you've learned. . . .

HORACE. Aw, Sis . . .

HERMAN. Inez. Why don't you let the boy alone?

INEZ. Now you keep out of this, Herman Stanley. He's my brother and he's a stick. He's missing all the fun in life and I'm not going to have him a stick. I've sat up nights thinking of social engagements to keep him busy every minute of these next two weeks—I've got three dances scheduled for him. So he cannot not dance. Now come on, dance with me. . . . (*He takes her by the arm awkwardly. He begins to lead her around the room.*) Now that's fine. That's just fine. Isn't that fine, Herman?

HERMAN. Uh huh.

INEZ. You see all you need is confidence. And I want you to promise me you'll talk plenty when you're with the girl, not just sit there in silence and only answer when you're asked a question. . . . Now promise me.

HORACE. I promise.

INEZ. Fine. Why, I think he dances real well. Don't you, Herman?

HERMAN. Yes, I do. Just fine, Inez.

INEZ. Just a lovely dancer, all he needs is confidence. He is very light on his feet. And he has a fine sense of rhythm—why, Brother, you're a born dancer—

*H*ORACE *is smiling over the compliments, half wanting to believe what they say, but then not so sure. He is dancing with her around the room as the lights fade. They are brought up on the area UR.* EMILY CREWS *is in her living room. She has on her dressing gown. She is crying. Her mother,* ELIZABETH, *comes in from UR.*

ELIZABETH. Emily.

EMILY. Yes ma'am.

ELIZABETH. Do you know what time it is?

EMILY. Yes ma'am.

ELIZABETH. Then why in the world aren't you dressed?

EMILY. Because I don't feel good.

ELIZABETH. Emily . . .

EMILY. I don't feel good. . . . (*She begins to cry.*) Oh, Mother. I don't want to go to the dance tonight. Please, ma'am, don't make me. I'll do anything in this world for you if you promise me . . .

ELIZABETH. Emily. This is all settled. You are going to that dance. Do you understand me? You are going to that dance. That sweet, nice brother of Inez Stanley's will be here any minute. . . .

EMILY. Sweet, nice brother. He's a goon. That's what he is. A regular goon. A bore and a goon. . . .

ELIZABETH. Emily . . .

EMILY. That's all he is. Just sits and doesn't talk. Can't dance. I'm not going to any dance or anyplace else with him and that's final. *(She runs out R.)*

ELIZABETH. Emily . . . Emily . . . You get ready this minute. . . . *(The doorbell rings. Yelling.)* Emily . . . Emily . . . Horace is here. I want you down those stairs in five minutes . . . dressed. *(She goes out L and comes back in followed by* HORACE, *all dressed up. He has a corsage box in his hand.)* Hello, Horace.

HORACE. Good evening.

ELIZABETH. Sit down, won't you, Horace? Emily is a little late getting dressed. You know how girls are.

HORACE. Yes ma'am. *(He sits down. He seems a little awkward and shy.)*

ELIZABETH. Can I get you something to drink, Horace?

HORACE. No ma'am.

(A pause. ELIZABETH *is obviously very nervous about whether* EMILY *will behave or not.)*

ELIZABETH. Are you sure I can't get you a Coca-Cola or something?

HORACE. No. Thank you.

ELIZABETH. How's your family?

HORACE. Just fine, thank you.

ELIZABETH. I bet your sister was glad to see you.

HORACE. Yes, she was.

ELIZABETH. How's your family? Oh, I guess I asked you that, didn't I?

HORACE. Yes, you did.

*(ELIZABETH *keeps glancing off* R, *praying that* EMILY *will put in an appearance.)*

ELIZABETH. I understand you've become quite an accomplished dancer. . . .

HORACE. Oh . . . well . . . I . . .

ELIZABETH. Inez tells me you do all the new steps.

HORACE. Well—I . . .

ELIZABETH. Excuse me. Let me see what is keeping that girl. *(She goes running off R.* HORACE *gets up. He seems very nervous. He begins to practice his dancing. He seems more unsure of himself and awkward. . . . We can hear* ELIZABETH *offstage knocking on* EMILY's *door. At first* HORACE *isn't conscious of the knocking or the ensuing[3] conversation and goes on practicing his dancing. When he first becomes conscious of what's to follow he tries to pay no attention. Then gradually he moves over to the far L side of the stage. The first thing we hear is* ELIZABETH's *genteel tapping at* EMILY's *door. Then she begins to call, softly at first, then louder and louder.)* Emily. Emily. Emily Crews. Emily Carter Crews. . . . *(The pounding offstage is getting louder and louder.)* Emily. I can hear you in there. Now open that door.

EMILY *(screaming back).* I won't. I told you I won't.

ELIZABETH. Emily Carter Crews. You open that door immediately.

EMILY. I won't.

ELIZABETH. I'm calling your father from downtown if you don't open that door right this very minute.

EMILY. I don't care. I won't come out.

ELIZABETH. Then I'll call him. *(She comes running in from R.* HORACE *quickly gets back to his chair and sits.)*

---

3. ensuing (in sü′ng), happening afterward; taking place as a result

Excuse me, Horace. *(She crosses through the room and goes out UR. HORACE seems very ill at ease. He looks at the box of flowers. He is very warm. He begins to fan himself. ELIZABETH comes back in the room from UR. She is very nervous, but she tries to hide her nervousness in an overly social manner. ELIZABETH has decided to tell a fib.)* Horace, I am so sorry to have to ruin your evening, but my little girl isn't feeling well. She has a headache and a slight temperature and I've just called the doctor and he says he thinks it's very advisable that she stay in this evening. She's upstairs insisting she go, but I do feel under the circumstances I had just better keep her in. I hope you understand.

HORACE. Oh, yes ma'am. I do understand.

ELIZABETH. How long do you plan to visit us, Horace?

HORACE. Two weeks.

ELIZABETH. That's nice. *(They start walking offstage L.)* Please call Emily tomorrow and ask her out again. She'll just be heartbroken if you don't.

HORACE. Yes ma'am. Good night.

ELIZABETH. Good night, Horace. *(HORACE goes out. ELIZABETH calls out after him.)* Can you see, Horace? *(In the distance we hear HORACE answer.)*

HORACE. Yes ma'am.

ELIZABETH. Now you be sure and call us tomorrow. You hear? *(She stands waiting for a moment. Then she walks back across stage to UR, screaming at the top of her voice.)* Emily Carter Crews. You have mortified me. You have mortified me to death. I have, for your information, called your father and he is interrupting his work and is coming home this very minute and he says to tell you that you are not to be allowed to leave this house again for two solid weeks. Is that perfectly clear?

(She is screaming as she goes out UR. The lights are brought down. They are brought up immediately DR on the drugstore. It is half an hour later. HORACE comes in. He seats himself at the counter. He still has the box of flowers. The drugstore is deserted. A WAITRESS is up near the front with her arms on the counter. She keeps glancing at a clock. HORACE is examining a menu. . . .)

HORACE. Can I have a chicken salad sandwich?

WAITRESS. We're all out of that.

HORACE. Oh. *(He goes back to reading the menu.)*

WAITRESS. If it's all the same to you, I'd rather not make a sandwich. I'm closing my doors in ten minutes.

HORACE. Oh. Well, what would you like to make?

WAITRESS. Any kind of ice cream or soft drinks. *(She looks up at the ice cream menu.)* Coffee is all gone.

HORACE. How about a chocolate ice cream soda?

WAITRESS. O.K. Coming up. *(She starts to mix the soda. She talks as she works.)* Going to the dance?

HORACE. No.

WAITRESS. The way you're all dressed up I thought for sure you were going.

HORACE. No. I was, but I changed my mind.

*M*ARY CATHERINE DAVIS *comes in the drugstore from* DR. *Somehow she has gotten in her young head the idea that she is a plain girl and in defiance for the pain of that fact she does everything she can to make herself look plainer.*

WAITRESS. Hello, Mary Catherine. Been to the movies?

MARY CATHERINE. Yes, I have.

(*The* WAITRESS *puts the drink down in front of* HORACE. *He begins to drink.*)

WAITRESS. What'll you have, Mary Catherine?

MARY CATHERINE. Vanilla ice cream.

WAITRESS. O.K. (*She gets the ice cream. She talks as she does so.*) There weren't many at the picture show tonight, I bet. I can always tell by whether we have a crowd in here or not after the first show. I guess everybody is at the dance.

MARY CATHERINE. I could have gone, but I didn't want to. I didn't want to miss the picture show. Emily Crews didn't go. Leo couldn't get home from summer school and she said she was refusing to go. Her mother made a date for her with some bore from out of town without consulting her and she was furious about it. I talked to her this afternoon. She said she didn't know yet how she would get out of it, but she would. She said she had some rights. Her mother doesn't approve of Leo and that's a shame because they are practically engaged.

WAITRESS. I think Emily is a very cute girl, don't you?

MARY CATHERINE. Oh, yes. I think she's darling.

(HORACE *has finished his drink and is embarrassed by their talk. He is trying to get the* WAITRESS'*s attention but doesn't quite know how. He finally calls to the* WAITRESS.)

HORACE. Miss . . .

WAITRESS. Yes?

HORACE. How much do I owe you?

WAITRESS. Twenty cents.

HORACE. Thank you. (*He reaches in his pocket for the money.*)

WAITRESS. Emily has beautiful clothes, doesn't she?

MARY CATHERINE. Oh, yes. She does.

WAITRESS. Her folks are rich?

MARY CATHERINE. She has the prettiest things. But she's not a bit stuck up.

(HORACE *holds the money out to the* WAITRESS.)

HORACE. Here you are.

WAITRESS. Thank you. (*She takes the money and rings it up on the cash register.* HORACE *goes on out. The* WAITRESS *shakes her head as he goes.*) There's a goofy nut if I ever saw one. He's got flowers under his arm. He's wearing a tux and yet he's not going to the dance. Who is he?

MARY CATHERINE. I don't know. I never saw him before.

(*The* WAITRESS *walks to the edge of the area and looks out. She comes back shaking her head. She sits on the stool beside* MARY CATHERINE.)

WAITRESS (*while laughing and shaking her head*). I ought to call the sheriff and have him locked up. Do you know what he's doing?

MARY CATHERINE. No. What?

WAITRESS. Standing on the corner. Dancing back and forth. He's holding his arm up like he's got a girl and everything. Wouldn't it kill you? (MARY CATHERINE *goes to the front and looks out.*) See him?

MARY CATHERINE. No. He's stopped.

WAITRESS. What's he doing?

MARY CATHERINE. Just standing there. Looking kind of lost. (MARY CATHERINE *comes back to the counter. She starts eating her ice cream again.*)

WAITRESS. Well—it takes all kinds.

MARY CATHERINE. I guess so.

(*She goes back to eating her ice cream. The lights are brought down. The lights are brought up on the area DL. The living room of the* STANLEYS. INEZ *is there reading a book.* HERMAN *comes in.*)

HERMAN. Hi, hon.

INEZ. Hello. . . .

HERMAN. What's the matter with you? You look down in the dumps.

INEZ. No. I'm just disgusted.

HERMAN. What are you disgusted about?

INEZ. Horace. I had everything planned so beautifully for him and then that silly Emily has to go and hurt his feelings.

HERMAN. Well, honey, that was pretty raw, the trick she pulled.

INEZ. I know. But he's a fool to let that get him down. He should have just gone to the dance by himself and proved her wrong. . . . Why, like I

told him. Show her up. Rush[4] a different girl every night. Be charming. Make yourself popular. But it's like trying to talk to a stone wall. He refused to go out anymore. He says he's going home tomorrow.

HERMAN. Where is he now?

INEZ. Gone to the movies.

HERMAN. Well, honey. I hate to say it, but in a way it serves you right. I've told you a thousand times if I've told you once. Leave the boy alone. He'll be all right. Only don't push him. You and your mother have pushed the boy and pushed him and pushed him.

INEZ. And I'm going to keep on pushing him. I let him off tonight because his feelings were hurt, but tomorrow I'm going to have a long talk with him.

HERMAN. Inez. Leave the boy alone.

INEZ. I won't leave him alone. He is my brother and I'm going to see that he learns to have a good time.

HERMAN. Inez . . .

INEZ. Now you just let me handle this, Herman. He's starting to college next year and it's a most important time in his life. He had no fun in high school. . . .

HERMAN. Now he must have had some fun. . . .

INEZ. Not like other people. And he's not going through four years of college like a hermit with his nose stuck in some old book. . . . (*She jumps up.*) I'll never forgive Elizabeth for letting

---

4. rush (rush), date enthusiastically; court

Emily behave this way. And I told her so. I said, "Elizabeth Crews, I am very upset." . . .

(She is angrily walking up and down as the lights fade. They are brought up DR on the drugstore area. The WAITRESS *is there alone.* MARY CATHERINE *comes in from DR.)*

WAITRESS. Did you go to the movies again tonight?

MARY CATHERINE. Uh huh. Lila, do you remember when I was telling you about Emily's date and how she wouldn't go out with him because he was such a bore?

WAITRESS. Uh . . .

MARY CATHERINE. Oh. I just feel awful. That was the boy sitting in here. . . .

WAITRESS. Last night? . . .

MARY CATHERINE. Yes. I went riding with Emily and some of the girls this afternoon and we passed by his sister's house and there sat the boy.

WAITRESS. Shh . . . shh . . . *(She has seen* HORACE *come into the area from DR. He comes to the counter. He seems very silent. He picks up a menu.)* Back again tonight?

HORACE. Uh huh.

WAITRESS. What'll you have?

HORACE. A cup of coffee. . . .

WAITRESS. All out. We don't serve coffee after eight unless we happen to have some left over from suppertime. . . .

HORACE. Thanks. *(He gets up.)*

WAITRESS. Nothing else?

HORACE. No, thanks.

(He goes over to the magazine rack. He picks up a magazine and starts looking through it. EMILY CREWS *comes in from DR. She doesn't see* HORACE. *She goes right over to* MARY CATHERINE.)*

EMILY. Leora and I were riding around the square and we saw you sitting here. . . .

(MARY CATHERINE points to HORACE. EMILY *turns around and sees him. She looks a little embarrassed. He happens to glance up, and sees her.)*

HORACE. Hello, Emily.

EMILY. Hello, Horace. . . . Do you know Mary Catherine Davis?

HORACE. No. How do you do.

EMILY. I feel awfully bad about last night, Horace. My mother says that you know I wasn't really sick. I just wanted to tell you that it had nothing to do with you, Horace. It was a battle between me and my mother. Mary Catherine can tell you. I promised the boy I go with not to go out with any other boys. . . .

HORACE. Oh, that's all right. I understand.

EMILY. You see, we've gone steady for two years. All the other boys in town understand it and their feelings are not a bit hurt if I turn them down. Are they, Mary Catherine?

MARY CATHERINE. No.

EMILY. Mary Catherine is my best friend and she can tell you I'm not stuck up. And I would have gone anyway, except I was so mad at my mother. . . .

MARY CATHERINE. Emily is not stuck up a bit. Emily used to date all the boys before she began going with Leo steadily. She even had a date with Gus Meredith. All the other girls wouldn't go with him because they thought he was so fat and unattractive, but Emily said she wouldn't hurt his feelings for the world and she went with him. Didn't you, Emily?

EMILY. Uh huh. How long are you going to be here, Horace?

HORACE. Well, I haven't decided, Emily.

EMILY. Well, I hope you're not still hurt with me.

HORACE. No, I'm not, Emily.

EMILY. Well, I'm glad for that. Mary Catherine, can you come with us?

MARY CATHERINE. No, I can't, Emily. Velma came in after the first show started and I promised to wait here for her and we'd walk home together.

EMILY. Come on. We can ride around and watch for her.

MARY CATHERINE. No. I don't dare. You know how sensitive Velma is. If she looked in here and saw I wasn't sitting at this counter she'd go right home and not speak to me again for two or three months.

EMILY. Velma's too sensitive. You shouldn't indulge her in it.

MARY CATHERINE. I'm willing to grant you that. But you all are going off to college next year and Velma and I are the only ones that are going to be left here and I can't afford to get her mad at me.

EMILY. O.K. I'll watch out for you and if we're still riding around when Velma gets out, we'll pick you up.

MARY CATHERINE. Fine. . . .

EMILY. 'Bye. . . .

MARY CATHERINE. 'Bye. . . .

EMILY. 'Bye Horace.

HORACE. Good-bye, Emily.

(She goes out DR.)

MARY CATHERINE. She's a lovely girl. She was my closest friend until this year. Now we're still good friends, but we're not as close as we were. We had a long talk about it last week. I told her I understood. She and Eloise Dayton just naturally have a little more in common now. They're both going steady and they're going to the same college. *(A pause)* They're going to Sophie Newcomb. Are you going to college?

HORACE. Uh huh.

MARY CATHERINE. You are? What college?

HORACE. The University. . . .

MARY CATHERINE. Oh, I know lots of people there. *(A pause)* I had a long talk with Emily about my not getting to go. She said she thought it was wonderful that I wasn't showing any bitterness about it. *(A pause)* I'm getting a job next week so I can save up enough money to go into Houston to business school. I'll probably work in Houston someday. If I don't get too lonely. Velma Morrison's oldest sister went into Houston and got herself a job but she almost died from loneliness. She's back here now working at the courthouse. Oh, well . . . I don't think I'll get lonely. I think a change of scenery would be good for me.

(VELMA MORRISON comes in DR. She is about the same age as MARY CATHERINE. She is filled with excitement.)

VELMA. Mary Catherine, you're going to

be furious with me. But Stanley Sewell came in right after you left and he said he'd never forgive me if I didn't go riding with him. I said I had to ask you first, as I had asked you to wait particularly for me and that I knew you were very sensitive.

MARY CATHERINE. I'm very sensitive. You're very sensitive. . . . I have never in my life stopped speaking to you over anything.

(A car horn is heard offstage.)

VELMA. Will you forgive me if I go?

MARY CATHERINE. Oh, sure.

(VELMA goes running out.)

VELMA. Thank you. *(She disappears out the door.)*

MARY CATHERINE. I'm not nearly as close to Velma as I am to Emily. I think Emily's beautiful, don't you?

HORACE. Yes. She's very pretty.

MARY CATHERINE. Well, Lila's going to kill us if we don't stop holding her up. Which way do you go?

HORACE. Home.

MARY CATHERINE. I go that way too. We can walk together.

HORACE. O.K.

(They go out of the area.)

MARY CATHERINE. Good night, Lila.

WAITRESS. Good night.

*T*hey continue walking out as the lights fade. The lights are brought up on the living room of the CREWS's house. ELIZABETH CREWS is there, crying. EMILY comes in.

EMILY. Mother, what is it? Has something happened to Daddy?

ELIZABETH. No. He's in bed asleep.

EMILY. Then what is it?

ELIZABETH. Inez blessed me out and stopped speaking to me over last night. She says we've ruined the boy's whole vacation. You've broken his heart, given him all kinds of complexes and he's going home tomorrow. . . .

EMILY. But I saw him at the drugstore tonight and I had a long talk with him and he said he understood. . . .

ELIZABETH. But Inez doesn't understand. She says she'll never forgive either of us again. *(She starts to cry.)*

EMILY. Oh, Mother. I'm sorry. . . .

ELIZABETH. Emily, if you'll do me one favor . . . I promise you I'll never ask another thing of you again as long as I live. And I will never nag you about going out with Leo again as long as I live. . . .

EMILY. What is the favor, Mother?

ELIZABETH. Let that boy take you to the dance day after tomorrow. . . .

EMILY. Now, Mother . . .

ELIZABETH. Emily. I get down on my knees to you. Do me this one favor. . . *(A pause)* Emily . . . Emily . . . *(She is crying again.)*

EMILY. Now, Mother, please. Don't cry. I'll think about it. I'll call Leo and see what he says. But please don't cry like this. . . . Mother . . . Mother . . .

(She is trying to console her as the lights fade. The lights are brought up on UL. It is MARY CATHERINE's yard and living room. Music can be heard in the distance. HORACE and MARY CATHERINE come walking in DL and go up the C of the stage until they reach the upstage area.)

MARY CATHERINE. Well, this is where I live.

HORACE. In that house there?

MARY CATHERINE. Uh huh. *(A pause)*

HORACE. Where is that music coming from?

MARY CATHERINE. The Flats. . . .

HORACE. What's the Flats?

MARY CATHERINE. I don't know what it is. That's just what they call it. It's nothing but a bunch of barbecue restaurants and beer joints down there and they call it the Flats. There used to be a creek running down there that they called Willow Creek but it's all dry now. My father says when he was a boy, every time the river flooded, Willow Creek would fill up. The river doesn't overflow anymore since they took the raft out of it. I like to come out here at night and listen to the music. Do you like to dance? . . .

HORACE. Well . . . I . . .

MARY CATHERINE. I love to dance.

HORACE. Well . . . I don't dance too well.

MARY CATHERINE. There's nothing to it but confidence.

HORACE. That's what my sister says. . . .

MARY CATHERINE. I didn't learn for the longest kind of time for lack of confidence and then Emily gave me a long lecture about it and I got confidence and went ahead and learned. Would you like to come in for a while?

HORACE. Well . . . if it's all right with you. . . .

MARY CATHERINE. I'd be glad to have you.

HORACE. Thank you.

(They go into the area. MARY CATHERINE'*s father,* TOM DAVIS, *is seated there in his undershirt. He works in a garage.)*

MARY CATHERINE. Hello, Daddy.

TOM. Hello, baby.

MARY CATHERINE. Daddy, this is Horace.

TOM. Hello, son.

HORACE. Howdy do, sir. *(They shake hands.)*

MARY CATHERINE. Horace is Mrs. Inez Stanley's brother. He's here on a visit.

TOM. That's nice. Where's your home, son?

HORACE. Flatonia.

TOM. Oh, I see. Well, are you young people going to visit for a while?

MARY CATHERINE. Yes sir.

TOM. Well, I'll leave you then. Good night.

MARY CATHERINE. Good night, Daddy.

HORACE. Good night, sir. *(He goes out UL)* What does your father do?

MARY CATHERINE. He works in a garage. He's a mechanic. What does your father do?

HORACE. He's a judge.

MARY CATHERINE. My father worries so because he can't afford to send me to college. My mother told him that was all foolishness. That I'd rather go to business school anyway.

HORACE. Had you rather go to business school?

MARY CATHERINE. I don't know. *(A pause)* Not really. But I'd never tell him that. When I was in the seventh grade I thought I would die if I couldn't get there, but then when I was in the ninth, Mother talked to me one day and told me Daddy wasn't sleeping at nights for fear I'd be disappointed if he couldn't send me, so I told him the next night I decided I'd rather go to business school. He seemed relieved. *(A pause)*

HORACE. Mary Catherine. I . . . uh . . . heard you say a while ago that you didn't dance because you lacked confidence and uh . . . then I heard you say you talked it over with Emily and she told you what was wrong and you got the confidence and you went ahead. . . .

MARY CATHERINE. That's right. . . .

HORACE. Well . . . It may sound silly and all to you . . . seeing I'm about to start my first year at college . . . but I'd like to ask you a question. . . .

MARY CATHERINE. What is it, Horace?

HORACE. How do you get confidence?

MARY CATHERINE. Well, you just get it. Someone points it out to you that you lack it and then you get it. . . .

HORACE. Oh, is that how it's done?

MARY CATHERINE. That's how I did it.

HORACE. You see I lack confidence. And I . . . sure would like to get it. . . .

MARY CATHERINE. In what way do you lack confidence, Horace? . . .

HORACE. Oh, in all kinds of ways. *(A pause)* I'm not much of a mixer. . . .

MARY CATHERINE. I think you're just mixing fine tonight.

HORACE. I know. That's what's giving me a little encouragement. You're the first girl I've ever been able to talk to. I mean this way. . . .

MARY CATHERINE. Am I, Horace? . . .

HORACE. Yes.

MARY CATHERINE. Well, I feel in some ways that's quite a compliment.

HORACE. Well, you should feel that way. *(A pause)* Mary Catherine . . .

MARY CATHERINE. Yes, Horace?

HORACE. I had about decided to go back home tomorrow or the next day, but I understand there's another dance at the end of the week. . . .

MARY CATHERINE. Uh huh. Day after tomorrow.

HORACE. Well . . . I . . . don't know if you have a date or not . . . but if you don't have . . . I feel if I could take you . . . I would gain the confidence to go . . . I mean . . .

MARY CATHERINE. Well, Horace . . . You see . . .

HORACE. I know I'd gain the confidence. My sister is a swell dancer and she'll let me practice with her every living minute until it's time for the dance. Of course I don't know if I could learn to jitterbug by then or rumba or do anything fancy, you understand, but I know I could learn the fox-trot and I can waltz a little now. . . .

MARY CATHERINE. I'm sure you could.

HORACE. Well, will you go with me?

MARY CATHERINE. Yes, Horace. I'd love to. . . .

HORACE. Oh, thank you, Mary Catherine. I'll just practice night and day. I can't tell you how grateful Inez is going to be to you. . . . Mary Catherine, if we played the radio softly could we dance now?

MARY CATHERINE. Why certainly, Horace.

HORACE. You understand I'll make mistakes. . . .

MARY CATHERINE. I understand. . . . *(She turns the radio on very softly.)*

HORACE. All right.

MARY CATHERINE. Yes. . . . *(He approaches her very cautiously and takes her in his arms. He begins awkwardly to dance. MARY CATHERINE is very pleased and happy.)* Why, you're doing fine, Horace. Just fine.

HORACE. Thank you, Mary Catherine. Thank you.

*T**hey continue dancing.* HORACE *is very pleased with himself although he is still dancing quite awkwardly. The lights fade. The lights are brought up on the area DL. It is early next morning.* INEZ *is there reading.* HORACE *comes in whistling. He seems brimming over with happiness.*

INEZ. What are you so happy about?

HORACE. I'm just happy.

INEZ. Wait until you hear my news and you'll be happier.

HORACE. Is that so?

INEZ. Miss Emily has seen the light.

HORACE. What?

INEZ. She has succumbed.[5]

HORACE. What do you mean?

INEZ. She has crawled on her knees.

HORACE. She's crawled on her knees? I don't get it. . . .

INEZ. She has eaten dirt.

HORACE. Sister, what's this all about?

INEZ. Last night around ten o'clock she called in the meekest kind of voice possible and said, "Inez, I've called up to apologize to you. I have apologized to Horace in the drugstore." Did she?

HORACE. Uh huh.

INEZ. "And now I want to apologize to you and to tell you how sorry I am I behaved so badly."

HORACE. Well. Isn't that nice of her, Inez?

INEZ. Wait a minute. You haven't heard the whole thing. And then Her Highness added, "Tell Horace if he would like to invite me to the dance to call me and I'd be glad to accept." And furthermore, Elizabeth called this morning and said they were leaving for Houston to buy her the most expensive evening dress in sight. Just to impress you with.

HORACE. Oh . . . *(He sits down on a chair.)*

INEZ. Brother. What is the matter with you? Now are you gonna start worrying about this dancin' business all over again? You are the biggest fool sometimes. We've got today and tomorrow to practice.

HORACE. Inez . . .

INEZ. Yes?

HORACE. I already have a date with someone tomorrow. . . .

INEZ. You do?

---

5. succumbed (sə kumd′), yielded to a greater force; given in

HORACE. Yes. I met a girl last night at the drugstore and I asked her.

INEZ. What girl did you ask?

HORACE. Mary Catherine Davis. . . .

INEZ. Well, you've got to get right out of it. You've got to call her up and explain just what happened.

HORACE. But, Inez . . .

INEZ. You've got to do it, Horace. They told me they are spending all kinds of money for that dress. I practically had to threaten Elizabeth with never speaking to her again to bring this all about. Why, she will never forgive me now if I turn around and tell her you can't go. . . . Horace. Don't look that way. I can't help it. For my sake, for your sister's sake, you've got to get out of this date with Mary Catherine Davis . . . tell her . . . tell her . . . anything. . . .

HORACE. O.K. (A pause. He starts out.) What can I say?

INEZ. I don't know, Horace. (A pause) Say . . . well, just tell her the truth. That's the best thing. Tell her that Emily's mother is your sister's best friend and that Emily's mother has taken her into Houston to buy her a very expensive dress. . . .

HORACE. What if Mary Catherine has bought a dress? . . .

INEZ. Well, she can't have bought an expensive dress. . . .

HORACE. Why not?

INEZ. Because her people can't afford it. Honey, you'll be the envy of every young man in Harrison, bringing Emily Crews to the dance. . . . Why, everybody will wonder just what it is you have. . . .

HORACE. I'm not going to do it.

INEZ. Horace . . .

HORACE. I don't want to take Emily, I want to take Mary Catherine and that's just what I'm going to do.

INEZ. Horace . . .

HORACE. My mind is made up. Once and for all. . . .

INEZ. Then what am I gonna do? (She starts to cry.) Who's gonna speak to Elizabeth? She'll bless me out putting her to all this trouble. Making her spend all this money and time . . . (She is crying loudly now.) Horace. You just can't do this to me. You just simply can't. . . .

HORACE. I can't help it. I'm not taking Emily Crews—

INEZ. Horace . . .

HORACE. I am not taking Emily Crews.

(He is firm. She is crying as the lights fade. The lights are brought up on UL area. MARY CATHERINE's father is seated there. He is in his undershirt. In the distance dance music can be heard. MRS. DAVIS comes in from L.)

MRS. DAVIS. Don't you think you'd better put your shirt on, Tom? Mary Catherine's date will be here any minute.

TOM. What time is it?

MRS. DAVIS. Nine o'clock.

TOM. The dance has already started. I can hear the music from here.

MRS. DAVIS. I know. But you know young people, they'd die before they'd be the first to a dance. Put your shirt on, Tom.

TOM. O.K.

MRS. DAVIS. As soon as her date arrives we'll go.

TOM. O.K.

(MARY CATHERINE *comes in from L. She has on an evening dress and she looks very pretty.*)

MRS. DAVIS. Why, Mary Catherine. You look lovely. Doesn't she look lovely, Tom?

TOM. Yes, she does.

MRS. DAVIS. Turn around, honey, and let me see you from the back. *(She does so.)* Just as pretty as you can be, Mary Catherine.

MARY CATHERINE. Thank you. (HORACE *comes in DL in his tux with a corsage box. He walks up the C of the stage to the UL area.)* That's Horace. *(She goes to the corner of the area.)* Hello, Horace.

HORACE. Hello, Mary Catherine.

MARY CATHERINE. You've met my mother and father.

HORACE. Yes, I have. I met your father the other night and your mother yesterday afternoon.

MRS. DAVIS. Hello, Horace.

TOM. Hello, son.

MRS. DAVIS. Well, we were just going. You all have a good time tonight.

HORACE. Thank you.

MRS. DAVIS. Come on, Tom.

TOM. All right. Good night and have a nice time.

MARY CATHERINE. Thank you, Daddy. *(They go out L.* HORACE *hands her the corsage box. She takes it and opens it.)* Oh, thank you, Horace. Thank you so much. *(She takes the flowers out.)* They're just lovely. Will you pin them on for me?

HORACE. I'll try. *(He takes the corsage and the pin. He begins to pin it on.)* Will about here be all right?

MARY CATHERINE. Just fine. *(He pins the corsage on.)* Emily told me about the mix-up between your sister and her mother. I appreciate your going ahead and taking me anyway. If you had wanted to get out of it I would have understood. Emily and I are very good friends . . . and . . .

HORACE. I didn't want to get out of it, Mary Catherine. I wanted to take you.

MARY CATHERINE. I'm glad you didn't want to get out of it. Emily offered to let me wear her new dress. But I had already bought one of my own.

HORACE. It's very pretty, Mary Catherine.

MARY CATHERINE. Thank you. *(A pause)* Well, the dance has started. I can hear the music. Can't you?

HORACE. Yes.

MARY CATHERINE. Well, we'd better get going. . . .

HORACE. All right. *(They start out.)* Mary Catherine. I hope you don't think this is silly, but could we practice just once more?

MARY CATHERINE. Certainly we could. . . .

(They start to dance. HORACE *has improved although he is no Fred Astaire. They are dancing around and suddenly* HORACE *breaks away.)*

HORACE. Mary Catherine. I'm not good enough yet. I can't go. I'm sorry. Please, let's just stay here.

MARY CATHERINE. No, Horace. We have to go.

HORACE. Please, Mary Catherine . . .

MARY CATHERINE. I know just how you feel, Horace, but we have to go. *(A pause)* I haven't told you the whole truth, Horace. This is my first dance too. . . .

HORACE. It is?

MARY CATHERINE. Yes. I've been afraid to go. Afraid I wouldn't be popular. The last two dances I was asked to go and I said no.

HORACE. Then why did you accept when I asked you?

MARY CATHERINE. I don't know. I asked myself that afterwards. I guess because you gave me a kind of confidence. *(A pause. They dance again.)* You gave me confidence and I gave you confidence. What's the sense of getting confidence, Horace, if you're not going to use it?

(A pause. They continue dancing.)

HORACE. That's a pretty piece.

MARY CATHERINE. Yes, it is.

(A pause. They dance again. HORACE stops.)

HORACE. I'm ready to go if you are, Mary Catherine.

MARY CATHERINE. I'm ready. *(They start out.)* Scared?

HORACE. A little.

MARY CATHERINE. So am I. But let's go.

HORACE. O.K.

(They continue out the area down the C of the stage and off DR as the music from the dance is heard . . .and the lights fade.)

Responding to the Play

1. If you lived in Harrison, Texas, with whom would you be friends: Emily, Mary Catherine, or both? Why?
2. Discuss the turning point in the play. How was it resolved?
3. As either Mary Catherine or Horace, describe your first evening together at the drugstore.
4. Did the characters in this play seem believable to you? Back up your impressions with examples from the play.
5. Demonstrate how Horace would move and look while Mrs. Crews tries to persuade Emily to come out of her bedroom.

About Horton Foote

Horton Foote left his home in Wharton, Texas, at 16 to study acting in California. From there he went to New York to act and write. Since that time he has written plays for radio, television, stage, and film.

Foote identified strongly with great novelists. He successfully adapted John Steinbeck's *Of Mice and Men*, William Faulkner's *Tomorrow*, and Harper Lee's *To Kill a Mockingbird* into screenplays. Like them, Foote lets his plots unfold steadily and surely, never broadcasting his message. Foote's cycle of plays about the town of Harrison exemplifies this. He applied Sherwood Anderson's advice to William Faulkner to "find a small piece of land and write about it."

Foote won the 1995 Pulitzer Prize for Drama for his play *The Young Man from Atlanta*. His screenplays for *To Kill a Mockingbird* and *Tender Mercies* both won Academy Awards.

Creating and Performing

1. Reread the confrontation between Elizabeth and Emily on pages 31 and 32. With a partner, improvise the exchange, paying attention to your tone of voice, diction, and movement.
2. Working with a partner, develop dance steps for Horace and Mary Catherine. Practice your steps as you read the dialogue on page 44.
3. Horace goes home, but he and Mary Catherine promise to write to one another. Write a series of three letters from one to the other.

The Play as Literature: Characterization

Gary Soto is one of those rare adults who remembers vividly what life was like when he was fourteen. Soto's stories, as well as his first play, *Novio Boy*, are filled with the longings, friendships, fun, and misunderstandings of youth. Through the use of lively dialogue and description, Soto reveals much about his characters' personalities. The way a writer goes about acquainting us with his characters is called *characterization*.

As you read *Novio Boy*, contrast Soto's characterization of the young people (Rudy, Patricia, and their friends) with how he presents their elders (Rudy's mother, Uncle Juan, and Mama Rosa). Use a chart like the one below to help you organize your information.

Character	Looks	Speech	Behavior	Movement

The Play as Theatre: The Set

The space where a play is presented on a stage is called the *set*. Even before the play begins, the set gives the audience visual information about where and when the play occurs and how the people in the play live.

Some sets are very elaborate and ornate, full of backdrops, scenery, props, and furniture. Other sets are so sparse that no more than a chair is placed on the stage.

As you read *Novio Boy*, think about the kind of sets that would help the audience understand and become involved in the play.

Warm Up!

With a partner, discuss how two fourteen-year-old friends would meet and greet one another. Next, discuss a meeting between a teenager and an older person who lives down the street. How would they greet one another? How would the two meetings differ?

NovioBoy
by Gary Soto

SETTING	CHARACTERS	TIME
Fresno, California	**RUDY,** ninth grader, small, sweet, funny **ALEX,** ninth grader, big, awkward but wiser **PATRICIA,** eleventh grader, tall, romantic **ALICIA,** eleventh grader, dry-humored *chola* **RUDY'S MOTHER,** mid-thirties, attractive and perky **UNCLE JUAN,** a Chicano loafer; looks like a hippie **EL GATO,** a disc jockey **MAMA ROSA,** *curandera* of love **ESTELA,** woman in beauty parlor **CALLERS (6),** to radio show **OLD MAN,** crusty, but a good guy **WAITER,** quick and efficient	The Present

SCENE ONE

The scene begins in a backyard where two boys, both Mexican American, are philosophizing about girls. They are sloppy-looking, with holes in the knees of their pants. Stage right, two girls are silhouetted on a couch in a living room. The room is dim. Lights come up on RUDY and ALEX. RUDY paces back and forth and ALEX tries to keep up with him. RUDY throws himself down on a lawn chair. ALEX keeps pacing for a moment and then, noticing that his friend has sat down, joins him.

RUDY. What am I gonna talk about? She's older than me and good-looking.

ALEX. Just level with her. Tell her you're sorry you look like you do.

RUDY. Sorry? You mean I should be sorry that I look like Tom Cruise? *(Pause)* You're cold, homes. You're no help at all.

ALEX *(giggling).* Just joking, Rudy. Listen, man, you got to start simple.

Break the ice. Ask her . . . what her favorite color is or something.

RUDY. Color?

ALEX. Yeah, color. Like, red or white.

RUDY. You mean, like, blue or yellow?

ALEX. Lavender!

RUDY. Purple!

ALEX . Forest green!

RUDY. Chevy chrome!

ALEX. That's it, man.

(RUDY gets up and starts to pace. ALEX gets up, too.)

RUDY *(incredulous).* Colors?

ALEX. Colors. I picked up this little *secreto* from Mama Rosa on the Spanish station.

RUDY. Mama Rosa! You get your advice from her?

ALEX. She's for real. She's an expert about love and things. She says you got to get your *boca*[1] rattling. One

---

1. *boca* (bō′kä), mouth

thing leads to the next, you know.

RUDY. No, I don't know.

ALEX. Listen, man. Sometimes I'm talking about nothing and the next thing I know people are listening. Like I'm the President or something.

RUDY. You're not the President.

ALEX. I know that. What I'm saying is that you got to just talk stuff—anything!

(Pause. RUDY reflects.)

RUDY. I just start talking?

ALEX. That's right.

RUDY. Just . . . say things?

ALEX. Colors, start with colors. Just ask, "Patricia, what's your favorite color?"

RUDY. She won't think I'm weird?

ALEX. No. She'll know immediately you're trying to start something, so she'll play along. She'll say something like "Green" or "Pink."

RUDY. And I'll tell her that my favorite color is dark blue.

ALEX. There you go, homes. *(Pause)* So guess mine.

RUDY. Your what?

ALEX. My favorite color!

RUDY. Black and silver, like the Raiders?

ALEX. Nope.

RUDY. Blue and gold, like the Chargers?

ALEX. Nah. It's red, like my tongue.

(ALEX wiggles tongue at RUDY.)

RUDY *(punching ALEX).* That's *asco!*[2]

ALEX *(chuckling).* Don't worry, homes. Just be cool.

RUDY. Cool.

ALEX. Like an iceberg.

(The boys pace around the stage. They stop.)

RUDY. Man, I can't believe I'm going out with a girl in the eleventh grade. And yesterday, guess what I was doing.

ALEX. Helping your dad pour cement at a job site?

(RUDY shakes his head.)

ALEX. Lifting weights?

RUDY. You won't laugh if I tell you?

ALEX. Laugh at my best friend?

RUDY *(hesitates; long pause).* I was playing G.I. Joes with my cousin Isaac. Man, it was fun. G.I. Joe was beating up Ken, and Barbie was kicking back watching the *pleitos.*[3]

(ALEX laughs.)

RUDY. I got another problem. I told Patricia I was taking her to grub at Steaks, Steaks, y Más Steaks.

ALEX. You told her you were taking her there? What's wrong with you, homes? Those hamburgers cost twice as much as McDonald's. And you got to tip, too.

(RUDY reflects on his error.)

ALEX. You got enough money?

RUDY. How much do you think I'll need?

ALEX. At least fifteen bones.

RUDY. Fifteen dollars!

(RUDY shakes his head and shrugs his shoulders. ALEX starts to go through his pockets.)

ALEX *(teasing).* Here, this should help.

(RUDY takes ALEX's quarter and looks at it.)

RUDY *(sarcastically).* You're cool, Alex. This quarter might get me a piece of gum.

---

2. *asco* (äs′kō), sickening
3. *pleitos* (plā′tōs), fighting

(They sit and reflect on the dilemma.)

ALEX *(perks up)*. Let me give you some advice. You got to talk intelligent, like you know something.

RUDY. Like I know something?

ALEX. Remember, she's two years ahead of you and in eleventh grade. You got to be *suave,* kind of like—*pues,* like me. *(Hooks a thumb at himself)*

RUDY. Help me then, Alex.

ALEX *(thinking about it)*. It so happens I got this love letter from Sylvia Hernandez. Remember her?

RUDY. No.

ALEX. Yeah, you do. She threw up *huevos con* weenies in fifth grade. *(Imitates someone vomiting)* It was all over the classroom and down the hall. It was like that old movie *The Blob* after she was all done.

RUDY *(reflecting)*. Yeah, I remember that girl now. She got some on my shoes. *(Pause)* So what did the letter say?

ALEX *(reaches into his pocket)*. Got it right here.

(ALEX sniffs the letter for perfume, and RUDY sniffs it as well. ALEX starts to read letter.)

ALEX. "Alex, I think you have the coolest eyes. And the cutest nose."

RUDY. You got a fat *huango*[4] nose.

ALEX. Hey, dude, you want me to help you or not?

RUDY. I take that back. You got a real cute nose. *(Pulls up his own nose into the shape of a pig's snout)*

ALEX. That's better. *(Continues reading)* "I really care about you a lot, Alex. I really don't know how to say this, but here goes. I think that you like me but don't want to tell me because of what your friends might say. Forget them. They don't have to live your life. You do! Last year I fell totally in love with this guy Kendall—"

RUDY. What kind of name is Kendall?

(ALEX gives RUDY a look.)

ALEX *(continues reading)*. "At first Kendall was nice to me. Then he started being mean to me and talking behind my back. It hurt me when he told this girl from Selma that I was stuck-up. I guess it was to get me to stop liking him. But I didn't stop liking him for a long time. Now I like you, Alex. I dream about—"

RUDY. Man, she knows how to talk.

ALEX. *¡Cállate!*[5] You're interrupting the flow of my love letter. *(Pause)* Here's a good part. "Alex, you're nicer than Kendall. You're cute, too. All the boys from Roosevelt are cute, but you're the cutest. Please don't be like Kendall. I will shower you with kisses forever and ever."

RUDY *(takes the letter and examines it)*. Sounds like poetry. No, like *mi abuelita's telenovelas.*[6]

ALEX. This letter should be the floor plan for your love life. You got to lay it on thick. Be romantic, *ese.*[7] *Suave.*

RUDY *(reflecting)*. *Suave.* *(Pulls out a small notepad)* I better write some of this stuff down so I don't forget: "Be romantic." "Lay it on thick."

---

4. *huango* (wän′gō), stretched out
5. *¡Cállate!* (cä′yä tä), Be quiet; shut up!
6. *mi abulelita's telenovelas* (mē ä büä lē′täs tä lä nō bā′ läs), my grandmother's soap operas
7. *ese* (ā′sä), guy

ALEX. I went on a date once.

RUDY. You're lying.

ALEX. No, I did. *(Pause)* It wasn't exactly a date. Me and this girl went to the playground.

RUDY. Get serious.

ALEX. Yeah, I picked her up on my bike and . . . don't laugh.

RUDY. Why would I laugh at my best friend?

ALEX. I can see it. You're gonna laugh!

RUDY. No, I promise.

(RUDY and ALEX trade glances.)

ALEX. She had to pedal the bike because I didn't have enough leg strength. It's hard with two people!

(RUDY chokes, muffling his laugh.)

ALEX *(continuing)*. It was a lot of fun. We spent a couple hours on the monkey bars. Then we played tetherball, and then a game of chess. Yeah, it was going pretty good—until Frankie Torres came by and started teasing me.

RUDY. Frankie did that?

ALEX. Yeah. Because I was all dressed up. *(Laughs)* I had on this pink shirt, and a bow tie, and buckets of my dad's Aqua Velva.

RUDY. Dressed up at the playground?

ALEX. Yeah, plus . . .

RUDY. What?

(ALEX kicks at the ground, embarrassed.)

RUDY. Hey, I'm your *carnal.*[8]

ALEX. She was getting a drink of water, so I was holding her purse.

RUDY. And that's when Frankie saw you.

ALEX *(nodding his head)*. He called me a girl because I had her purse on my shoulder. *(Pause. ALEX stands up.)* That was my first date. Age nine.

(RUDY shakes his head sympathetically. He takes the letter from ALEX and reads it silently. Lights fade.)

Scene Two

ights come up on PATRICIA and ALICIA, *sitting on a couch with a magazine. They're playing the game of choosing the best-looking guy on the page.*

PATRICIA. I got this one.

ALICIA. I got this one.

PATRICIA. This gorgeous face.

ALICIA. This hot tamale.

PATRICIA. This enchilada.

ALICIA. This soft taco.

PATRICIA. Umm . . . this one.

ALICIA *(pouting)*. I wanted that one. His hair is so cute! *(Tosses magazine aside)*

PATRICIA. My brother, Eddie, and I used to pick toys like this. Me and my brother would go through the Toys "R" Us ads and—

ALICIA. —and pick the best toys. We played that, too.

PATRICIA. Now we're picking boys.

ALICIA. Toys or boys, it's all the same.

(The girls give each other high fives; they get up from the couch.)

ALICIA. Now you got this hot date.

PATRICIA. Rudy's really sweet. He's got these little dimples and hair that bounces when he walks.

---

8. *carnal* (kär näl′), buddy

ALICIA. Girl, you're lucky. Dimples are so cute!

PATRICIA. And long eyelashes.

ALICIA (*shivering*). Dimples *and* eyelashes.

PATRICIA. And get this. He's taking me to Steaks, Steaks, Y Más Steaks!

ALICIA. No, girl.

PATRICIA. Cross my heart.

ALICIA (*shaking her head*). You're lucky, Pat. You get a hamburger, and you get to fall in love, too.

PATRICIA. And he's extra nice to me when he's serving in the cafeteria. He really plops on those chili beans.

ALICIA. You mean that *escuincle*[9] in the cafeteria? Isn't he just in ninth grade?

PATRICIA. So?

ALICIA. What do you mean, "So"? You're robbing the cradle. He's a ninth grader. He's probably still carrying his Power Ranger lunch box to school.

PATRICIA. He's only two grades behind. It's nothing, girl. These are modern times. It's OK to date down.

ALICIA. It doesn't bother you?

PATRICIA. No, not really.

ALICIA. I mean, he's, like, just out of his high chair.

PATRICIA. It's just a date. (*Pause*) Life is really strange. Like, we've been alive sixteen years, almost seventeen. We're not kids anymore. (*Pause*) I can remember when I was playing with Barbie and Ken, and I was making Ken kiss Barbie really hard.

ALICIA. Ken was hot stuff, huh?

PATRICIA. But then I got my brother's G.I. Joe and had him beat up Ken. Kicked sand right in his face. ¡Híjole! G.I. Joe kissed even harder. I thought they would have to get married.

ALICIA. Yeah, I remember my Barbie. My stupid brother tore her head off and used it for a baseball with his stupid friends.

PATRICIA. That's sorry.

ALICIA. I got the dude back. When my parents were gone one day, I threw him outside with only his *chones*[10] on.

PATRICIA. No!

ALICIA. That's what he deserved. I made him stay out there on the porch.

PATRICIA. In his *chones*?

ALICIA. Dirty ones, too, all *fuchi y cochino*.[11] Then the mail lady came and my brother didn't know what to do, except pick up the cat and try to hide himself.

(*Pause. They look at a magazine.*)

PATRICIA. I'm going to get my hair done.

ALICIA. Short and with bangs?

(PATRICIA *shakes her head.*)

ALICIA. Long, with a little wave?

(PATRICIA *shakes her head again.*)

PATRICIA. Curls.

ALICIA. Curls?

PATRICIA. Lots of curls. I'm going to get my hair done at the House of Beauty.

(ALICIA *smiles. They turn the pages of the magazine.*)

---

9. *escuincle* (ās küēn′klā), little kid

10. *chones* (chō′nās), underwear

11. *fuchi y cochino* (fü′chē ē kō chē′nō), smelly and dirty; piglike

PATRICIA. Look at this one. He's good-looking.

ALICIA. Yeah, but my mom says don't trust any guy with green eyes. She says that men with green eyes can't be trusted.

PATRICIA (*clicking her tongue*). Parents are so superstitious.

ALICIA. Old-fashioned.

PATRICIA. Old, old-fashioned.

(*They turn the pages of the magazine.*)

ALICIA (*perks up*). I got him.

PATRICIA. Him?

ALICIA. The guy behind him.

PATRICIA. This little cutie.

(*They smile at the spread of handsome young boys in the magazine, then toss it aside.*)

ALICIA. Remember when I burned my report card?

PATRICIA (*searching her memory*). Your report card?

ALICIA. I got all those terrible grades and I knew my mom was gonna get mad at me. So I burned it on the front lawn and . . . *híjole*, I burned the whole front lawn.

PATRICIA. I remember. You tried to blame it on lightning.

ALICIA. That was stupid, huh? (*Pause*) I guess we are growing up. We're in eleventh grade. Now when I get a bad report card, I just type in some good grades.

(*The girls sit on the couch, each lost in her own thoughts. There is the sound of a low-rider car. The girls get up and look out the front window, watching the car cruise down the street.*)

PATRICIA. That's a nice ride.

ALICIA. He's hitting the switch. (*Calling to low-rider*) Hop it, brown boy! Hop it!

(*The girls' heads go up and down, watching the low-rider employ its hydraulics.*[12] *The noise of the low-rider fades and the girls turn away from the window.*)

ALICIA. What are you going to wear on your date?

PATRICIA (*reflecting*). Maybe my jeans and a white top. Keep it simple . . . Think I should help pay for lunch?

ALICIA. *Pues*, he invited you, *qué no?* Just leave the tip. That'll show you care about him.

PATRICIA. How do you know all this?

ALICIA. I read it in *Low-Rider*. They had a special on how to get guys to like you.

(*Music slowly rises. The girls freeze as lights come up on the other side of the stage to reveal* EL GATO, *the suave Chicano disc jockey.*)

EL GATO: We're coming to you *raza*[13] with heavy hitmakers from the sixties . . . It's dedication time . . .

(*A portion of a song plays.*)

EL GATO (*continuing*). Time for some love notes from you lovebirds. Here's one from Smiley to his girl in Dinuba . . . Here's one from Marta to her *novio*,[14] Samuel. She says, "Let's get together when I get out of juvie."[15] El Güero says to his little cookie, "Don't crumble 'cause I

---

12. hydraulics (hī drȯ′liks), system in certain cars that transmits pressure when oil is forced through a small tube, causing the car to move up or down.
13. *raza* (rä′sä), the Latino people
14. *novio* (nō′bēō), boyfriend
15. juvie (ju′vē or hü′bā), slang for juvenile detention, a place where a boy or girl, usually under 18 years of age, who has committed a legal offense is held

cheated on you." Ay, *este malo chavalo.*[16] Let's forget that dude. And here's one from Jesús to his baby love in Fowler, and we got something from as far away as Tulare . . . Yeah, it's a *quinceañera*[17] for Lupe de la Rosa. Way to go, girl. Fifteen and still pecking away at school, it says here. Here's a little *dedica* to Carolina from her secret admirer, who says, "I only got eyes for you." *(Pause)* I'm El Gato and I'm coming to you *vivo,*[18] *raza,* from K-Crudo . . .

(Lights fade on EL GATO *as the music fades. Lights on girls.)*

ALICIA. El Gato is cool.

PATRICIA. Why don't we call him up?

ALICIA. *Chale.*[19] I'm too scared.

PATRICIA. What's there to be scared of?

ALICIA. I don't know. Just talking to someone who's on the radio.

(Long pause as they look at magazines)

PATRICIA. Who's the most important person you've ever talked to?

ALICIA. What do you mean?

PATRICIA. You know, like a movie star or a rocker.

ALICIA *(thinks for a moment).* Don't laugh.

PATRICIA. I won't.

ALICIA. I can see that you're gonna laugh.

PATRICIA. *¡En serio!*[20] I promise.

ALICIA *(shyly).* Pues, it was Ronald McDonald.

(PATRICIA laughs.)

ALICIA. See, I knew you were going to laugh. I don't care. So who did you meet that was so big and important? Ed Olmos? Carlos Santana? Jimmy

Smits? Culture Clash?

PATRICIA. Well, he's just a notch below them.

ALICIA. Who, then?

PATRICIA. Promise you won't laugh? And if you do, I don't care.

(ALICIA crosses her heart.)

PATRICIA. Well, I met the San Diego Chicken.

ALICIA. The San Diego Chicken?

PATRICIA. You know, the chicken that's the mascot for the baseball team. The San Diego Padres.

ALICIA. The chicken? *¿El gallo?*

PATRICIA. I even got his autograph.

ALICIA. The dude's chicken scratch? *(Laughs)* I didn't know chickens could hold a pen. *(Pause)* We've never met anyone famous.

PATRICIA. I guess that's why we're scared to call El Gato.

ALICIA. What's there to worry about? *No te preocupes.* Let's call the *vato.* I want to hear "Ninety-six Tears." That's my favorite oldie.

PATRICIA. *Es mi favorito, también.* Hey, did you know that I cried exactly ninety-six tears when I broke up with Robert?

ALICIA. *Mentirosa.* You're lying, girl.

PATRICIA. Cross my heart, *flaca.*[21] Ninety-six *lágrimas!*

---

16. *este malo chavalo* (ās′tā mä′lō chä bä′lō), this bad kid
17. *quinceañera* (kēn sā ä nyā′rä), a party celebrating a girl's fifteenth birthday
18. *vivo* (bē′bō), live; alive
19. *Chale* (chä′lä), No way
20. *¡En serio!* (än sārēō), Seriously!
21. *flaca* (flä′kä), skinny girl

(PATRICIA *and* ALICIA *bury their heads and pretend to cry. Music plays briefly. Song fades. Lights darken.*)

Scene Three

ights come up on RUDY'S MOTHER *in the living room, lifting small weights.* RUDY *joins her in a comical imitation. After a "rep" she starts to jump rope and move around the stage comically.* RUDY *follows along. She drops on the floor and takes a swig from her squeeze bottle.*

MOTHER. Got to stay in shape, *m'ijo.*[22]

RUDY. Mom, you're already in shape.

(MOTHER *smiles at the compliment and starts to do sit-ups.*)

RUDY. Mom, who was your first boyfriend?

MOTHER. I had only one boyfriend—your daddy.

RUDY. Mom, level with me. I was born fourteen years ago. I know a lot.

(MOTHER *stops her sit-up routine.*)

MOTHER (*laughs*). What do you know?

RUDY. You know! Things! Like about the birds and the bees, and the cats and the dogs, and the 'Niners and the Raiders.

MOTHER (*dreamily*). *Pues,* I did have one boyfriend before your father.

RUDY. Really?

MOTHER. He was from Michoacán.[23] He had beautiful green eyes and red boots made from lizard skin. He was a gentleman, not a *borracho.* He had a thin little mustache. He danced beautifully and read poetry to me in the park. (*Snaps out of her dream*) *¿Por*

qué? Why do you want to know these things?

RUDY. I have something to tell you.

MOTHER. Don't tell me! You lost your gym clothes again.

RUDY. No, it's worse—I mean, better. (*Pause*) Mom, I'm going out with a girl tomorrow.

MOTHER. *¿Qué?*

RUDY. I told this girl that I would take her out for a hamburger. (*Quickly*) Can I borrow fifteen bucks?

MOTHER. *¡Espérate! ¿Quién es esta muchacha?*[24]

RUDY. Just a friend.

MOTHER. You're too little to have friends. (*Realizes she sounds ridiculous*) *Pues*, a friend like that.

RUDY. Come on, Mom. Make it ten dollars, then.

MOTHER. You think money grows on trees? (*Pause*) Who is this girl, anyway?

RUDY. Her name's Patricia Gomez. She's really, really, really, really, really cute. She's got this nose like this. (*Pushes up his nose*) She's smart and even president of the Spanish Club. (*Looks at audience, steps forward, and conjugates the verbs "to remember" and "to give"*) *Recuerdo, recuerdas, recuerda, recordamos, recordáis, y recuerdan; doy, das, da, damos, dais, y dan.*

MOTHER. *¡Cállate!* You sound like a broken record.

---

22. *m'ijo* (mē′hō), my son
23. Michoacán (mē chō ä kän′), a state in Southwest Mexico
24. *¡Esperate! ¿Quien es esta muchacha?* (äs pā rä te! kē än′ äs as′tä mü chä′chä), Wait! Who is this girl?

RUDY. Yeah, she's really nice. But there's one problem, Mom.

MOTHER. *¡Qué!* What is it?

RUDY. She's older than me.

MOTHER. Older?

(RUDY *nods his head.*)

MOTHER. How much older?

RUDY. Well, you know, she's an upperclassman in high school.

(MOTHER *sits down, shocked.* RUDY *tries to comfort her.*)

RUDY. Mom, you got nice biceps.

MOTHER. Never mind my muscles. How come you can't find a girl your own age?

RUDY. They're all taken. *(Pause)* Come on, Mom. You're a little older than Dad.

MOTHER. Just two years older than your *papi.* I look younger. That's what your *niña*[25] says. Do you see any wrinkles on my face?

(RUDY *takes his* MOTHER's *face between his hands and examines it.*)

MOTHER. And my hair? *Mira.* Black as the night.

RUDY. Naturally black?

MOTHER. *Pues,* I did touch it up at the parlor. Just around my ears.

RUDY. Touch it up?

MOTHER. All right, I mean dye! Can you tell?

RUDY *(sniffing).* The chemicals.

MOTHER. You can smell my hair? Come on!

(RUDY *nods his head.* MOTHER *touches her hair.*)

MOTHER *(walks around the stage).* So now you have a girlfriend?

RUDY. Nah, Mom, not a girlfriend. A friend. And she's just two years older. *(Pause)* Come on, Mom. I'll pay you back when I get a job.

MOTHER. Sure you will. You'll get married and move away and never think of your mommy.

RUDY. Mom, I'm just going out for a hamburger, not getting married.

MOTHER. Is she a nice girl?

RUDY. *Seguro que sí.*

MOTHER *(reflects).* If you go on this date, I want you to be nice. *¿Entiendes?*[26]

RUDY. Just like the dude you knew before you met Dad.

MOTHER. It's important that you act like a gentleman. Show some pride. Don't be a *mocoso.*[27]

RUDY. Was Dad a gentleman when you were dating him?

MOTHER. *Claro que sí.* Strong and clever and full of ideas about getting rich in America. Your *papi* is a clever man, just like you, *m'ijo.*

RUDY. And dedicated.

MOTHER. *Muy fuerte y bravo.* In only two years he got his own cement truck. Who would have ever thought? *Jefe*[28] of his own crew. *(Pause)* This is a good country.

RUDY. What do you mean?

MOTHER. Your *papi* has a job and I have my chair at the beauty parlor. One day you'll be going to college.

(*Examines* RUDY's *hair*) I need to cut your

---

25. *niña* (nē′nyä), godmother
26. *¿Entiendes?* (än tē än′däs), Do you understand?
27. *mocoso* (mō kō′sō), snotty kid; boy
28. *Jefe* (hā′fā), chief; boss

hair . . . (Sniffs the air) ¡Ay, los frijoles!

(MOTHER *runs from living room.* RUDY *starts lifting her weights. He does an aerobics routine comically and gets tired almost immediately. Enter* UNCLE JUAN *with his guitar.*)

JUAN (*sniffs the air*). Ay, your mommy must be cookin' her regular *cosa* of burnt beans. (*Pause*) Rudy-tudy. Bo-bo Bo-booty, banana, ramama-moody Rudy-tudy! *¿Qué pasa?*

RUDY (*downcast*). Hey, Uncle.

JUAN. How come you making *jeta.*[29]

RUDY. It's nothing.

JUAN. Nothing? What do you mean, nothing? Everything is something . . . Here, listen to my song that never made the top one million. (*He begins to play and sing with country-western twang.*) No menudo en mi bowl y nada en mi estómago.[30] Nothing in my wallet but a little crushed Lifesaver. *Nada, nada, nadaaaaaa!* Now you see why it was never a hit. So what's the problem?

RUDY. I'm going out with a girl.

JUAN. That's a problem? For a minute, I thought you didn't make the soccer team.

RUDY. *Tío,* I don't have any money for my date.

JUAN. *No problema,* Rudy!

RUDY. Uncle, you're playing with me.

JUAN. *En serio.* Money is the last thing you have to worry about when you go on a date. Worry about what you have to say, little Romeo.

RUDY. That's what Alex says. He says girls like it when you sound like you know something.

JUAN. Exactly. You got to move your *boca.* Whatever you do, don't get heavy on her or you'll scare her away.

RUDY. Break-the-ice kind of talk?

JUAN. *¡Simón!*[31] The first time I went with a girl, man, I freaked her out. I told her that I thought I had been captured by a UFO.

RUDY. No, you didn't!

JUAN. *Simón.* It was way back in the seventies. I told her about the UFO and this out-of-body experience. Freaked her out!

RUDY. Uncle, were you a hippie?

JUAN. A Chicano hippie, *lo mejor,* the best. (*Gives a peace sign and shouts to audience*) Peace . . . love . . . *¡Viva la raza!* (*To* RUDY) Man, I was a trip. I had these bad-looking bell bottoms and a tie-dyed T-shirt. Love beads and a peace sign. I wore these groovy glasses. Far out, man, that's how I was. (*Brings out a pair of John Lennon glasses, strums his guitar*)

(RUDY's *head bobs to the music.* MOTHER *returns from the kitchen.*)

JUAN. Hey, hey, here comes our money tree swaying real pretty. (*Sweetly*) Hey, *hermana,*[32] how are things? You looking tough.

MOTHER (*stops for a second and poses for them*). You think so?

JUAN. Like a model for pots and pans at

---

29. *jeta* (hā′fä), pout
30. *No menudo en mi* bowl *y nada en mi estómago* (nō mä nü′dō än mē bōl ē nä′dä än mē äs tō′mä gō), Not much tripe soup in my bowl and nothing in my stomach.
31. *¡Simón!* (sē mōn′), Yes!
32. *hermana* (är mä′nä), sister

the Kmart on Kings Canyon. You do something with your hair?

(RUDY *pulls his* UNCLE *away.*)

RUDY (*in near whisper*). Don't mention her hair.

JUAN (*confused*). *¿Qué?*

RUDY. She's dyeing it.

(JUAN *nods his head.*)

RUDY. Mom, Uncle's right. You're tough-looking.

JUAN. And dependable, like a five-year battery from Kragen's. (*Pause*) Sis, can you lend me a sweet twenty-five? Be a *pan dulce*—sweet!

MOTHER. You think money grows on trees? First Rudy and now you! And you compare me to a cheap battery?

JUAN. I'm talkin' in metaphors. (*Strums guitar to audience*) *Soy un poeta de* Aztlán.[33] *¡Viva la raza!* (*To sister*) Come on, *hermana.* How about *veinte dolares.*[34]

(MOTHER *gives him a stern look, hands on hips.*)

JUAN. How about ten bucks and that bag of crushed aluminum cans on the back porch?

MOTHER (*seriously*). Juan.

JUAN. *¿Qué, hermana?*

MOTHER. You got to stop your nonsense. It's about time you got a regular job.

JUAN. One from eight to five?

MOTHER. No, a job from six in the morning to eight at night. To make up for lost time.

JUAN. *¡Chale!* I can't work like that. What if my bum friends look up from the gutter and see me in a white shirt and a tie? Have you thought about that? The peer pressure? The alienation? Cultural rejection? *Angst y todo?*[35]

MOTHER (*softens*). Maybe some people aren't meant for regular jobs.

JUAN. That's me, *hermana.* (*Pause*) And I'll pay you back. I got a part-time job.

MOTHER. You? Working?

JUAN. I got a job playing *guitarra.* (*Pause*) The money's not for me. It's for Rudy. Come on, Sis, open up.

(MOTHER *softens even more. She goes through her purse for money and hands it over to* RUDY.)

MOTHER. It's a month early, but this is your birthday money.

RUDY. It's all clean, too. Thanks, Mom.

MOTHER. It went through the washer. It was in your *papi*'s pants.

JUAN (*bending over the ten-dollar bill*). I haven't seen a ten-dollar bill in ten years. I love the smell of money. (*Sniffs burning frijoles*) And your cooking, *hermana.* Rudy, go turn off the beans.

(RUDY *runs offstage.*)

MOTHER. You really got a job?

JUAN. *¡Simón!* I got a job playing guitar at Steaks, Steaks, y Más Steaks. I start tomorrow.

MOTHER. That's good news, Juan. (*Pause*) But, Juan, the seventies are

---

33. *Soy un poeta de* Aztlán (sōi ün pō ā′tä dā′ Ast län′), I'm a poet from Aztlan.
34. *veinte dolares* (bāēn′tā dō′lä räs), twenty dollars
35. *Angst y todo* (ängst ē tō′dō), anxiety and all

over. You got to get settled down. *¿Entiendes?*

JUAN. Don't talk like that, Sis. I just wanna play guitar. Bring *la música a la gente!*[36] (*Strums his guitar as he walks offstage*)

(MOTHER *sniffs her burning beans on the stove and runs offstage. Lights dim.*)

SCENE FOUR

ights come up on EL GATO. *Slow-dance music.*

EL GATO. We're coming to you, *raza*, from *el gran* station K-Crudo. We got a little romance happening in Orange Cove. It's Manuel and Manuela . . . Ay, the little brown M&M's . . . Got *una dedica* from Shirley to Louie, who's celebrating his driver's permit. Way to go, dude. We got some more *gente* on the road. Just be sure to stay between the lines. And now we got a special guest coming to you. It's the Doctor of Love, Mama Rosa, a *curandera*[37] who works out of her garage with her old man, a body-and-fender specialist. If you want to contact her, you can call her sister-in-law at *uno, dos, tres—pues.*

ROSA. That's right, El Gato. People can call me *cuando quieran* at *uno, dos, tres—pues.*

EL GATO (*into microphone*). OK, *raza*, listen up. She's got a special on broken hearts this week. If you bring in your *coche*,[38] you can get some Bondo work *también*. Think about it, *gente*. It's almost a two-for-one. You get to kick-start your love life and get a smooth-looking fender to boot.

(*Pause*) So, Rosa, how do opposites attract?

ROSA. By the shifting of stars and the moon lining up with Venus—

EL GATO. Check that out, *radiolandia*.

ROSA. —and the pull of the waves under a meteor shower.

EL GATO. That sounds pretty spacey, but can you give us some tips? Our listeners—and some of the lonely dudes *y chicas* in the audience—want to solve this problem of boy-meets-girl. So give it up, Mama Rosa. What's the secret?

ROSA. We're talking love potions, *qué no?*

EL GATO. You're the source, baby.

ROSA. I'll get to the potions soon enough. Let me start with the stare. (*Stands up and, bug-eyed, slowly approaches audience*) If a young woman sees a young man staring at her while he's touching his nose, that means he likes her for the moment. But later, you watch, he's going to thumb his nose at her.

EL GATO. That's cold. The old thumb-your-nose-at-your-ex-*vieja* trick.

ROSA. If a young woman is staring at a man while adjusting her purse strap, she wants money.

EL GATO. Is that so?

ROSA. *Sí, señor.* And if a man is staring at a woman while she's eating a burrito, it means that he just wants her to cook and clean for him. The *vato's* no good.

---

36. *la gente* (lä hän′tā), the people
37. *curandera* (kü rän dā′rä), healer, witch
38. *coche* (kō′chä), car

EL GATO. *¡Híjole!* This is valuable information, *gente*. So, if staring's no good, how can we get our people together in romance?

ROSA. Bingo.

EL GATO. *¿Qué?*

ROSA. *Sí,* bingo. Some of the nicest people in the world play bingo every week.

EL GATO. I thought you met nice people at church.

ROSA. No, El Gato, that's where the sinners go to make themselves feel better. Nice young people go to play bingo in the church basement. It's a lot of fun. You get a couple of cards, some coffee with Sweet 'N Low, maybe a basket of popcorn, and it's a beautiful atmosphere for discriminating people. *Pues,* you get to hear *chisme.*[39]

EL GATO. But tell us about those love potions.

ROSA. Un momento. I have something important to say to the young ladies out there. Advice, I mean. *(Leans toward the audience)* It's the *huevo* test.

EL GATO. The *huevo* test?

ROSA. It's not what you think, *hombre*. *(Pause)* Take a *huevo* and rub it on your old man's forehead when he's asleep and then cook it for him. If you crack the egg and some hair comes out, *pues,* it's a bad sign. *Muy malo.* Move out of town. Get back to Mexico if you have to.

EL GATO *(fanning himself).* Ay, *dios.* I don't know if I like this *huevo* exam.

ROSA *(Makes faces at* EL GATO*) Pero* if you crack the egg and the yolk comes out pretty and clean-looking, it means that he's a good guy.

EL GATO. My *huevos* are spanking clean, *mujer.*[40]

ROSA. Now, about potions. I recommend a simple one. Put three drops of lemon juice plus one or two of your tears in a glass of water. Place the glass under your *novio's* bed. In the morning, rush over to his house. If you discover that the water is dingy—*pues,* do I have to tell you he's no good?

EL GATO. *¡Chihuahua!*

ROSA. *De veras.*[41] The water will turn all ugly. *Pero* if the water is clear, have your *novio* drink half of it, and you drink the other half. Then the magic happens. You're no longer thirsty for other people. You're hooked.

EL GATO. Like a fish?

ROSA. You got it. As I say, love is eternal . . . as long as it lasts.

EL GATO. Wow, Mama Rosa. I want to thank you for coming on my show. For all your troubles, I got a couple of tickets for you to see the wrestling match at the fairgrounds. *Buena suerte.*[42] *Muchísimas gracias. (Into the microphone)* That was *muy interesante.* Our next guest is that cool, *suave* cat, that number-one *guitarrista del valle* who has finally, finally, finally found a job. I mean, the dude is working. Give it up, *gente,* for the *vato* Juan-Juan.

---

39. *chisme* (chēs′mā), gossip
40. *mujer* (mü hār′), woman
41. *de veras* (dā bā′räs), really; truthfully
42. *buena suerte* (bü ā′nä sü är′tā), good luck

(JUAN *walks out from stage left, waving to the audience. He strums his guitar. He blows a kiss to the audience.*)

EL GATO. How you doing, bro? Long time no see.

JUAN. Yeah, long time since I was on your show. What, two years?

EL GATO. I think you were playing *tu guitarra* on the street or at the swap meet, *qué no?*

JUAN. That's right, bro. I was taking the music to the people and collecting a little chump change for myself.

EL GATO. And now you got a job?

JUAN. Yeah, I'm playing over at Steaks, Steaks, y Más Steaks. I'm inviting everybody I don't owe money to to come over and hear me. I'm going to silence the critics about Chicano music. It's the best, *carnal. ¡Lo mejor!*

EL GATO. I like to hear that. That's a positive attitude.

JUAN. I can move them, the big ones and the skinny *flaca* ones, the tall ones and the short ones, the good-looking ones and the ugly ones. The smart ones y *estúpido* ones. *Toda la gente.* They just get down when they hear that Chicano music.

EL GATO. Juan, I understand you know Madonna.

JUAN. To be honest, in the music industry you meet all kinds of artists and celebrities.

EL GATO. Is that right? So what's Madonna like?

JUAN. You know, she's kind of like you and kind of like me, and she's sort of like all the people out there in *radiolandia.*

EL GATO. What else? Fill in the picture.

I'm sure *la gente en radiolandia* want to hear a little *chisme.*

JUAN. *Pues,* I don't know her for real. I mean, I met this dude from a record company who knows this guy who knows this other guy who saw her taking a sip from a soda. *(Pause)* The way he described it, it was like I was there for real.

EL GATO. A sip from her soda? You mean you talked to some dude who talked to another dude who talked to another *vato* who saw her nursing a Big Gulp?

JUAN. That's it, bro.

EL GATO. I guess I can picture it, bro. *(Pause)* It's been a while since you had a hit?

JUAN. Nah, last week me and *mis compas* was sitting in the backyard drinking a couple of cold ones—

EL GATO. No, *carnal!* A hit on the radio.

JUAN. Oh, yeah. *Pues,* not since my hit song "Tort Y Frijoles," way back in the seventies. Don't you remember the song?

EL GATO. Of course. You sold me a cassette at the swap meet.

(JUAN *stands up.*)

EL GATO. Will you sing for us now?
(JUAN *nods his head.*)

EL GATO. Go for it, Juanito! Share it with *la gente!*

JUAN (*sings with either a raplike beat or the rhythm of a ranchera a song of his choosing*).

(JUAN *returns to sit with* EL GATO.)

EL GATO. That was beautiful, man. Makes me hungry for a little *comida.*

JUAN. I haven't had breakfast myself. In fact, I skipped dinner last night. Times are tough in Fresno.

EL GATO. I can solve that, Juan. For being on my show, we got two coupons for you for dinner at Cuca's Restaurant.

(JUAN *takes the coupons and examines them.*)

JUAN. I wonder if I can use these for lunch. Dinner ain't for another five hours and my empty stomach is tripping out with some weird sounds. I'm hungry now.

EL GATO. Go for it, homes. (*To audience*) Let's give some *aplauso* for Juan-Juan. Catch him at Steaks, Steaks, y Más Steaks. He'll be playing there real soon.

(JUAN strums his guitar. Waves to the audience as lights fade.)

SCENE FIVE

Mexican American beauty parlor. RUDY'S MOTHER *is combing her customer* ESTELA's *hair.*

ESTELA. Yeah, the *hombre* was married, and telling me all along that he had to go home to his mother. I should have had eyes in the back of my head. No, *tonta*[43] me, I went along because of his pretty green eyes and red shoes. He could dance and talk a story so sweet it gave me goose bumps. *Pues,* I see him on the street pushing a stroller with a little *mosca* baby. Then I see his wife, big as a truck—no bigger, kind of like a couple of big rigs parked together. *(Pause as* MOTHER *combs hair)* Ay, you're pulling my hair!

MOTHER. *¡Cálmate* Estela! What color do you want your hair this time?

ESTELA. Red.

MOTHER. You sure?

ESTELA. *¡Seguro que sí!*[44] Lent[45] is over and I can get wild. *(Pause)* Do you think redheads have more fun?

MOTHER. *Qué loca,* Estela. Of course not. It's not the color of your hair, it's your attitude.

ESTELA. I don't have an attitude. My kids got attitudes and my first three husbands had attitudes. But not me. I'm sweet as *flan.*[46] *(Stares at mirror, snorting angrily)* Who's that *vieja*[47] staring at me?

MOTHER. Who?

ESTELA. Her!

MOTHER. Her who? What are you talking about?

ESTELA. Her, that ugly *vieja!* I'm going to scratch her eyes out!

MOTHER *(sees that* ESTELA *is staring at herself in the mirror).* *Loca,* that's you. You're looking in the mirror!

ESTELA *(laughs).* Oh yeah, I guess it is me. Attractive for her age.

(Pause as MOTHER *works on* ESTELA's *hair)*

MOTHER. *Mujer,* when I say "attitude" I'm talking about personality. It doesn't matter what you look like, it's how you are and how you take each day.

ESTELA. If that's true, how come you're in the business of making *viejas* like me pretty? Answer that!

MOTHER. Well, perhaps you're right. We all want beauty—and every now and then, to fall in love.

(MOTHER goes to a table, leaving ESTELA making a mean face as she stares in the direction of the mirror. MOTHER returns.)

MOTHER. I have a good husband. He works hard and doesn't fool around.

ESTELA. You're lucky, *flaca.* I've been there three . . . no, four times, and I tell you—*bastante!* Men, they're no good! *(Pause)* So, your lazy brother finally got a job?

MOTHER. He's playing tomorrow after-

---

43. *tonta* (tōn′tä), stupid
44. *¡Seguro que sí!* (sā gü′rō kā sē), of course, certainly
45. Lent (lent), the 40 weekdays between Ash Wednesday and Easter, observed in many Christian churches as a time of fasting and repenting for sins.
46. *flan* (flän), a custard dessert
47. *vieja* (bē ā′hä), old woman

noon. *(Brightly)* Let's go hear him, give him a little support.

ESTELA. *¡Cómo no!* If your brother wasn't such a lazy bum, I might hit on him. *(Hears* EL GATO*'s voice)* El Gato's on the radio. Turn it up!

(MOTHER *walks over to the radio and turns up the volume. Lights come up on the suave* EL GATO *sitting in the disc jockey's booth.)*

EL GATO. *Buenos días, gente.* I'm coming to you *vivo,* and it's *La Love* Hour for all of you at work. For those not at work, *pues,* get your *nalgas* [48] down to the unemployment office. Our topic today: love, *amor,* or whatever you want to call it. It's time we talk about man and woman, and the relationships that make us hate life. Ah, just kidding. We're here to spin some *discos,* and to answer large, universal *cuestiones.* We got someone on the line stung by Cupid. *¿Qué pasa?*

CALLER 1 *(offstage).* When is the best time to fall in love, El Gato?

EL GATO. Ahhh . . . when to fall in love . . . *Pues,* I think it's the first of the month, when the *cheque* comes in. *(Pause)* You're on *la línea.*

CALLER 2 *(offstage).* How do you know love is for real?

EL GATO. Good question! You can tell it's for real if she calls you the next day and remembers your name, not some other dude's. *(Pause)* You're on the line.

CALLER 3 *(offstage).* Do you always have to close your eyes when you kiss?

EL GATO. Yeah, if you want to pretend it's Jimmy Smits you got in your arms. *(Pause)* You're on the line.

CALLER 4 *(offstage).* How can I tell a salad fork from a dinner fork?

EL GATO. Sounds like you just ate at a fancy place. If you're faced with *este problema* in public, forget the forks and *usa una* tortilla. *(Pause)* You're on the line.

CALLER 5. El Gato, I just broke up with my fiancé. Should I return the engagement ring?

EL GATO. You know that pawnshop on Tulare Street? Just kidding. Yeah, for the sake of karma,[49] mail back the ring. It's probably imitation gold anyhow.

CALLER 6. I'm thirty-four years old and my *novio* is sixty-six years old. Will it last?

EL GATO. Sure, if he gets a triple bypass.

ESTELA *(gets up from the chair).* *Dáme el teléfono.* I got a question for the *vato.*

EL GATO. Yeah, what is love but some spring in your legs and a combination plate from El Pollo Loco? Yeah, love makes the world spin, just like *nuestra música. (Pause)* Let me get this next one.

(Thirty seconds of music plays.)

ESTELA. El Gato?

EL GATO. You're on the line, baby love.

ESTELA. Yeah. I'm calling to settle a little debate.

EL GATO. *¡Adelante!* Go ahead.

ESTELA. *Pues,* I'm over here at House of Beauty and I got to ask, do redheads really have more fun?

EL GATO. Let me get this straight.

---

48. *nalgas* (näl′gäs), buttocks
49. *karma* (kär′mä), all of a person's acts, words, and thoughts, believed to determine the form the person takes in the next life.

You're asking if the color of your hair improves your sex appeal?

ESTELA. Something like that.

EL GATO. Hair has nothing to do with enjoying life. It's your attitude.

ESTELA. I ain't got an attitude! How come everyone thinks I got an attitude? *¿Por qué?*

EL GATO. *Fíjate.*[50] I mean the way you are, your calmness, your inner self, *y todo.* You got to learn to go with the flow. That you got some smooth-looking hair means nothing. Shoot, I knew a bald woman who got a kick out of life more than any *mujer* I ever knew.

ESTELA. *Puro* nonsense.

EL GATO. I'm talking about personality. You got to be nice, not always staring down at other *viejas* because your old man looks at another woman. *¿Entiendes?*

(MOTHER nods in agreement.)

EL GATO. And you got to pick up the dinner tab now and then, not just expect the dudes to bring out their wallets. You've got to work on your inner self.

(ESTELA hangs up and turns off the radio. EL GATO looks at the telephone and places it back on the receiver. Lights fade from him.)

ESTELA. Inner self. What kind of nonsense it that?

(MOTHER shrugs her shoulders and puts ESTELA under an industrial-size hair dryer. PATRICIA enters and looks around shyly.)

MOTHER. *Buenos días.* Please come in.

PATRICIA. *Buenos días, señora.*

MOTHER. *Por favor, siéntese.*[51]

PATRICIA. Thank you. *(Looks about nervously.)* I've never been to a beauty parlor. Most of the time—

MOTHER. I know, your mother cuts your hair.

PATRICIA. Sometimes. Usually my dad does it.

MOTHER. *¿Su papi?* I'm impressed.

PATRICIA. He's got his own upholstery shop. He's pretty good with his hands.

(Pause as MOTHER examines PATRICIA's hair)

MOTHER. You have very fine hair.

PATRICIA. Thank you.

MOTHER. Glossy and smooth. No split ends and just a few flakes of dandruff.

PATRICIA. I don't do anything special. My mom has nice hair, and I guess I get it from her.

MOTHER. Let me guess. You want your hair curled?

PATRICIA. How did you know?

MOTHER. Instincts. And you're going out on a date? He's a good-looking *muchacho?*

PATRICIA. And sweet.

MOTHER. And you're going to dance the night away?

PATRICIA. Just a lunch date. *(Pause)* How tight will you make the curls?

MOTHER. Medium spring. A few precious loops near the back. *(Combing PATRICIA's hair)* Is your date—excuse me if I'm direct, *muchacha*—a special person?

---

50. *Fíjate* (fē′hä tä), pay attention
51. *Por favor, siéntese* (pōr fä bōr′ sē än′tä sē), please sit down

Novio Boy by Gary Soto   **65**

PATRICIA. He's a boy from school.

MOTHER. I guess you're testing the waters.

PATRICIA. What?

MOTHER. You know, kind of shopping around.

ESTELA. Yeah, shopping around. Like going to the Costco of life.

PATRICIA. Oh, I guess so. He's just really cute and sweet. I met him when he was working in the cafeteria. He served me an extra splotch of chili beans.

MOTHER. Sounds like a decent boy.

PATRICIA. I like him because he's honest.

MOTHER. That's good.

PATRICIA (looks cautiously at ESTELA, under hair dryer). But he's younger than me.

ESTELA. I heard that, muchacha. Stay away from younger men. They usually have bad credit.

MOTHER. Cállate, Estela. Let the girl talk. (To PATRICIA) So he's younger, and I guess cute because you're pretty yourself.

PATRICIA (blushing). Yeah, he's in ninth grade and I'm in eleventh.

MOTHER. Age is nothing, m'ija. It's a modern thing.

PATRICIA. That's exactly what I told my best friend, Alicia. I told her that he has personality, and that's what's important.

MOTHER. That's good.

PATRICIA. He doesn't smoke or cuss or scrawl placas[52] on walls. Rudy's smart, too, for a boy. I even had a dream

about Rudy. He was serving me two extra splotches of chili beans.

MOTHER (gives PATRICIA a look of surprise). This Rudy—ah, does he go to Roosevelt High?

PATRICIA. Yeah.

MOTHER. He's kind of small?

PATRICIA. True. He's a little short for his age.

MOTHER. He has a friend named Alex?

PATRICIA. I think so.

MOTHER. And you say he works in the school cafeteria?

PATRICIA. That's right. (Pause) How do you know all this?

MOTHER. Ah, you know, most kids go to Roosevelt High, and most boys have friends named Alex. Common names and common boys. (Pause) You're sure about this boy? He is younger?

ESTELA (butting in). I thought you told this muchacha that it's OK to date younger guys.

MOTHER (smiles). I did say that. (To PATRICIA) Do you know this boy's family?

PATRICIA. No, except that his mother is overprotective. Kind of strict. I mean, he can't go anywhere.

MOTHER (bug-eyed, to audience). Strict! Wait till I speak to that little mocoso. I give him ten dollars for his date, and now look at him. Putting down his poor mother. (Controls her anger before addressing PATRICIA again) But his sweet, loving mother must be really nice?

_____

52. placas (plä′käs), graffiti signatures

PATRICIA. Actually, he never talks about his mom, aside from her being really strict. I don't know if she's tall or short, or fat or skinny. Young or old. *Nada.*

MOTHER *(to audience).* See! Already he's forgotten his mommy!

PATRICIA. What?

MOTHER *(collects herself).* Nothing. *(Pause)* So you're in eleventh grade, and I guess you'll be going to college in a couple of years.

PATRICIA. Maybe. But I thought of joining the service.

MOTHER. Don't tell me—the army?

PATRICIA. You're pretty good at reading my mind. Yeah, I'd like to travel.

MOTHER. That's good. You should get out of town—I mean, you're young. You should travel. Maybe to Mongolia, or Saudia Arabia, or Timbuktu. Somewhere far, far away.

PATRICIA. Maybe I will. I'll see the world, then come back and marry Rudy. Won't that be something?

MOTHER *(to audience).* Oh, *m'ijito* is going to get married.

PATRICIA. What?

MOTHER *(collects herself).* You know, I think all you really need is a blow dry, some shaping here and there, a little off your bangs. But let's get Estela out of the hair dryer.

(MOTHER strolls over to ESTELA. She removes the chrome-colored hair dryer and we discover that ESTELA's hair is bright red.)

ESTELA (looking in hand mirror and primping). I like it. I like it a lot. Maybe I do got an attitude after all. *(Shimmies her hips as lights fade)*

SCENE SIX

RUDY *and* ALEX *are on the front lawn selling apples. They both look dejected.*

RUDY. You ever find money on the ground?

ALEX. Just pennies and nickels. *(Pause as he reflects)* One time I chased a piece of paper because it looked like a dollar. But it was just a coupon to have your rug shampooed.

RUDY. I found a dollar once.

ALEX. Really?

RUDY. Yeah. I spent it on a soda and a box of Cracker Jacks. And guess what I got for my Cracker Jack prize?

(ALEX shrugs his shoulders.)

RUDY. A little magnifying glass that I used to burn my *primo's* [53] forehead.

ALEX. No!

RUDY. He was a baby, too.

ALEX. You must have gotten in trouble.

RUDY. Trouble's not the word. He kept crying, even when I gave him a sip of my soda and let him pull my hair. My mom punished me by making me watch *telenovelas* for two whole weeks. Man, it was torture!

ALEX *(plucks a G.I. Joe from his pocket).* Your left, your left, your left *pata,* your left. Your right, your right, your right *pata,* your right. You think you might join the army?

RUDY. Nah, I don't like uniforms. I don't even like it when my *chones* match my T-shirts. Me, I just throw on anything.

ALEX. I can tell, homes.

---

53. *primo* (prē′mō), cousin

RUDY. Clothes are nothing. It's what's inside that counts.

ALEX. My cousin Tony's in the marines. He's pretty tough-looking. Check this out. When he takes off his shirt, he looks like rocks up and down his stomach.

RUDY. I want to be like that—tough.

ALEX. I'm hard as a rock.

RUDY. Look more like a fat boulder.

ALEX. Hey, *flaco sapo*,[54] you're always jumping on my case just because I put on a little weight. You'll see! Next year I'm going to play tackle on junior varsity.

RUDY. Yeah?

ALEX. I'll suit up. I'll put some black stuff under each eye.

RUDY. Shoe polish.

ALEX. Yeah, that stuff. *(Dreamily)* I'm going to have my own rooting section. They'll be going, "Alex! Alex! Alex!"

RUDY. Who's going to fill your rooting section? You hardly know anyone.

ALEX. What do you mean? In my own family I got three brothers and two sisters. Then there's Mom and Dad, *mis abuelitos, mis primos, mi niña,* and all the rest. We'll pack the stands.

RUDY. It'll be like a little Mexico.

ALEX. That's right.

(Boys pause as they munch on apples.)

RUDY. We've been out here three hours and not one sale.

ALEX. The economy is down, I guess.

(OLD MAN enters, mumbling to himself. He wanders around the stage before he stops in front of the apple display.)

OLD MAN. Plums?

RUDY. No, they're apples, sir. Five for a dollar. That's twenty cents each.

OLD MAN. You're good at math. What kind of apples are they?

ALEX. Rare antique apples.

OLD MAN *(repeating slowly).* Rare antique apples.

ALEX. Rare and old.

RUDY. Old as the hills.

OLD MAN. Ah, good in math and a phrasemaker. *(Examines apples)* Old as the hills, you say.

RUDY. They might be older than the hills.

ALEX. Old as the seas.

RUDY. The stars.

ALEX. The moon.

RUDY. Mars and Venus.

OLD MAN. And they haven't rotted yet?

RUDY. If you want to know, sir, they're Garden of Eden apples.

OLD MAN. You're pulling my leg!

ALEX. It's true, sir.

(OLD MAN looks curious.)

RUDY. The red variety is called Eve and the green variety is called Adam.

OLD MAN. You're kidding me.

ALEX. We're talking biblical fruit.

(With the mention of "biblical fruit," OLD MAN crosses himself.)

RUDY. That's what my grandmother told us anyway. *(Pause)* I bet your wife can make you some *empanadas*[55] in a jiffy.

OLD MAN *(quietly).* My wife is gone.

ALEX. Shopping?

———————
54. *flaco sapo* (flä′kō sä′pō), skinny chump
55. *empanadas* (äm pä nä′däs), fruit filled pastry, like a turnover.

RUDY. At the beauty parlor?

OLD MAN. Gone, gone.

(RUDY *and* ALEX *look at each other, as if to say, "How come you opened your big mouth?")*

OLD MAN. Either of you got a girlfriend?

RUDY *(eagerly).* You got someone in mind?

ALEX. I'm not picky. Anyone will do.

RUDY. Yeah, Alex is right. He's not picky. But I sort of have a girlfriend and she's pretty good-looking.

ALEX. *Mentiroso.*[56]

RUDY. You calling Pat ugly?

ALEX. No. You're just going out on a date, that's all. She ain't your girl-friend.

RUDY. She likes me. Doesn't that mean she's my girlfriend?

ALEX. No.

OLD MAN. Boys! Boys! Put a lid on it. *(Bites into an apple)* I'm seventy-six years old and, well, I haven't gone on a date since my wife passed away three years ago. I haven't done much, actually. To be frank, I'm just a boring guy.

RUDY. Don't put yourself down. You're really witty. Huh, Alex?

ALEX. Oh yeah.

RUDY. When we first saw you, I thought, man, this is a real funny *vato.*

OLD MAN. You did?

RUDY. We're Catholic. We wouldn't lie. I thought, man, he's a crackup.

OLD MAN. You two boys are OK. But I know I'm boring. I work, I sleep, I eat, I work again.

RUDY. That's more than us. We just eat and sleep.

ALEX. That's right. Just eat and sleep.

(OLD MAN *still looks sad.* RUDY *and* ALEX *huddle together for a brief moment.)*

RUDY. Besides selling apples, me and Alex give advice.

OLD MAN. Advice?

RUDY. Personal advice.

ALEX. Advice that would cost thousands on the open market.

RUDY *(in affected voice).* We're part-time romance specialists. On slow days we cut lawns and do flower beds.

ALEX. We hardly charge anything.

RUDY. We're today's youth. What's the problem, sir?

OLD MAN. This woman I met at bingo . . . Nah, you're too young to under-stand.

RUDY. Come on, sir. We're nearly fif-teen years old. In fact, I have a big date coming up. Older woman.

ALEX. Rudy, I admit, is a little bit older than me, but I've had more experi-ence.

RUDY. What do you mean? I've known you since you were, like, in Huggies. You didn't do anything different from me, except almost flunk kinder-garten because you couldn't figure out your colors.

ALEX. I knew my colors. I just couldn't tie my shoes. *(To* OLD MAN*)* Yes, I have had a lot more worldly experi-ence.

RUDY. Like what?

ALEX. Things.

RUDY. OK, what kind of things?

---

56. *mentiroso* (mān te rō′sō), liar

ALEX. Well, once I wore a tie.

RUDY. That's it? That's your big "thing"?

ALEX. I wore one to my cousin Bertha's *quinceañera.*

RUDY. A tie ain't nothing. I wore one before. I was the ring *vato* in my cousin's cousin's cousin's wedding.

OLD MAN. Put a lid on it, boys. Give me five each.

(ALEX *bags the apples and* RUDY *reflects on the* OLD MAN*'s loneliness.*)

RUDY (*volunteering advice*). Sir, I think you've got to get out.

OLD MAN. Get out?

RUDY. Yeah, you know, go to a movie or a concert or the park or . . . a restaurant.

OLD MAN. A restaurant?

RUDY. Yeah, treat yourself.

OLD MAN. Treat myself, you say? A restaurant. Hmmmm. Food for thought.

(OLD MAN *reflects on this and leaves stage.* ALEX *and* RUDY *sit quietly.* RUDY *bites into an apple.*)

RUDY. Alex, I don't know about girls. They're kind of like high math, hard to figure out.

ALEX. Yeah, I know what you mean. I remember this girl saying that she liked my smile and the next time I saw her, I smiled and she ran away.

RUDY. How come, bro?

ALEX. I had *chicharrones*[57] stuck in my teeth.

RUDY (*examines* ALEX*'s smile*). I think you got some now, homes.

(ALEX *shoves him away and they sit, dejected. Lights fade.*)

SCENE SEVEN

ights come up on restaurant. A WAITER *is setting a table.* WAITER *turns when he hears the sound of a guitar plaing.* JUAN *enters.*

JUAN. You won't be disappointed. I'll wow the crowd.

(JUAN *approaches an empty table and with a pretend microphone he asks, "What do you think, friend?" He responds for the invisible-friend, "Wow." Repeats this several times, all of the invisible couples saying, "Wow."*)

JUAN. Yeah, I'm going to wow the place.

WAITER. You don't have to please me. It's the boss. She expects you to bring in a crowd.

(JUAN *sits on a stool, places the guitar on his knee, and strums. He tunes the guitar. He eyes the salsa and chips on a table and begins to help himself. When* WAITER *returns with flowers for a table,* JUAN *returns quickly to his stool.*)

(RUDY *and* PATRICIA *walk into the restaurant.* RUDY *is awed by the elegance of the restaurant. With his back to his date, he takes out his wallet and counts his money. He puts the wallet back quickly when he sees the* WAITER *approaching.*)

WAITER (*looking up happily*). *Mademoiselle* and *monsieur.* Please take this seat by the window. (*Pulls chair out for* PATRICIA)

PATRICIA (*sniffs the flower on the table*). It's so romantic. So sophisticated, so charming, so . . . And look, a guitarist!

(RUDY *sees that it's his* UNCLE JUAN, *who waves at him.* RUDY *shakes his head at his uncle, as if to say, "Don't say anything."*)

---

57. *chicharrones* (chē chä rō′nas), fried pork rinds

PATRICIA. It's a discriminating restaurant.

RUDY. Do they discriminate against Latinos? If so, I ain't going to eat here. We'll go grub at Pollo Loco instead.

PATRICIA. No, Rudy. It's just a very fine restaurant. And look, cloth napkins. How fancy!

RUDY (*studies napkins*). Looks like a diaper.

PATRICIA. Rudy, you're so silly.

(JUAN *starts playing his guitar and singing.* RUDY *and* PATRICIA *listen.*)

PATRICIA. He's really talented.

RUDY. He's OK.

WAITER (*approaches with glasses of water*). Our special for the day is . . .

(*A "mooooo" sounds.*)

WAITER (*continuing*). . . . tender veal. We have spotted cow, brown cow, black-and-white cow, and—

(*The mooing sounds again.*)

WAITER. I'll be back to get your order. I have to see about something in the kitchen. (*Leaves, pulling meat cleaver from belt*)

PATRICIA. The food's really . . .

(*Moo again*)

PATRICIA. . . . fresh.

RUDY. Sounds like it's still alive. (*Notices her jewelry*) That's a cute cat pin.

PATRICIA. I got it when I was eight. That's when we got my cat.

RUDY. What's your cat's name?

PATRICIA. *Novio* Boy.

RUDY. *Novio* Boy? You mean, like "sweetheart boy"?

PATRICIA (*nods her head*). Lots of girl

cats find him adorable. You want to see a picture of him?

RUDY. Sure.

(PATRICIA *pulls a picture from her purse and shows it to him.*)

RUDY. And what happened to his ear? It's gone.

PATRICIA. He had a fight with another cat. He's small but he's valiant, kind of like you.

RUDY. I'm against fighting.

PATRICIA. That's great!

RUDY. Mostly because when I fight I get beat up.

(RUDY *sits and smiles.* WAITER *approaches.*)

WAITER. Have you two decided? The steaks are grade A choice, and the hamburger is fresh ground round, premium grade. Of course, you can have chicken. We can fix it up in some enchiladas, *caldo,*[58] or a taco.

RUDY. I'll pass on the *gallina.*[59]

PATRICIA (*picks up menu*). I'm gonna have the Texas burger with jalapeño cheese. Jumbo fries, a chocolate milkshake, a Caesar salad with garlic dressing. And a large homemade root beer.

(RUDY *grimaces at the prices on the menu.*)

RUDY (*muttering to himself*). Four dollars for fries?

PATRICIA. What are you having?

RUDY. I think I'm going to order just a little bit. (*To* WAITER) Crackers and a small diet soda with no ice. I'm wrestling this year and I have to watch my weight.

---

58. *caldo* (käl′dō), soup
59. *gallina* (gä yē′nä), hen

(WAITER *writes on his pad and leaves.*)

PATRICIA. Same here. I mean, I'm not wrestling, but I have to watch my weight.

RUDY. No way. You look great.

(PATRICIA *blushes. Pause.*)

PATRICIA. Guess what?

RUDY. You got your driver's permit?

PATRICIA. How did you know? My dad's going to let me start driving next month. Right now he lets me start up the car in the morning.

RUDY. I'm fourteen, and my mom lets me start up the dryer. (*Pause*) What's your mom like? She nice?

PATRICIA. Tall. Taller than my dad, just about an inch or so. She's pretty nice. But, you know, she's kind of overprotective. She thinks I'm at the library right now.

RUDY. She does?

PATRICIA. She doesn't like me seeing boys.

RUDY. Maybe if you told her I'm a freshman it would be all right. If she comes, I can jump in a high chair.

PATRICIA. Maybe, but probably not. She thinks boys are trouble.

RUDY. Am I trouble?

PATRICIA (*smiling*). 'Course not. As sweet as you are, how could you be trouble? I mean, you're nicer than most boys, and not stupid, either. (*Scoots her chair closer to* RUDY) I can see that there is something behind your eyes.

RUDY. You can?

PATRICIA. Sure. Your eyes . . . they tell me that you're . . . daring.

RUDY. Daring?

PATRICIA. Intelligent.

RUDY. Intelligent?

PATRICIA. Loyal.

RUDY. Loyal, too? You can see that in my eyes?

PATRICIA. It's all there.

RUDY. Can you see if I got *ojos mocosos*?[60]

PATRICIA. Rudy, you're silly.

(*As they talk, the* OLD MAN *from the yard sale enters. He looks about as* WAITER *leads him toward a table. He sees* RUDY *and stops.*)

WAITER (*leaves*). Take any seat, sir.

OLD MAN (*searching his memory*). Hey, you're that fella who sold me the apples, no?

(RUDY, *shocked, shakes hands with the* OLD MAN.)

RUDY. Yeah, that's me.

OLD MAN. You told me I should treat myself to nice things?

RUDY (*nervously*). Yeah, that's what I said.

OLD MAN (*bends down and whispers loudly to* RUDY). She's kind of cute. Do you think you can fix me up with her mom?

PATRICIA. Well, actually, my mom is married. (*Brightly*) But I'm sure that if she were single, she'd have her eyes on someone like you.

OLD MAN. That's good to know. Well, I'm going to have a seat and get a bite to eat. (*Loudly, to* JUAN) Say, young man, do you know that one that goes "Ay, ay, ay"?

(RUDY *grimaces.* OLD MAN *finds his seat.*)

PATRICIA. How do you know him?

RUDY. Well, he's one of my . . . clients.

---

60. *ojos mocosos* (ō′hōs mō kō′sōs), mucus in the eyes

OLD MAN (*very loudly*). Those were really good apples that you sold me. The Eve apples were really tasty. (*Mumbles and then falls silent.*)

(PATRICIA *gives a baffled look and then stands up when her beeper goes off.*)

PATRICIA. My beeper! It's my friend Alicia. Rudy, I'm going to make a call. Be back in a second.

RUDY. Sure.

(*When* PATRICIA *is out of earshot*, RUDY *speaks to* JUAN.)

RUDY. *Tío*, what are you doing here?

JUAN. It's my new job. What a cosmic coincidence!

RUDY. You're making me nervous.

JUAN. Hey, she's a good-looking girl. A little older.

RUDY. Yeah, older. You ever go out with an older woman, Unc?

JUAN. All the time. And even tall girls. I once went out with a girl with a two-foot vertical jump. Don't sweat it, Rudy. (*Dips into his pocket for crumpled dollar bills*) Here, dude, this might help out.

RUDY. Thanks, Unc.

(JUAN *steps forward, stage center.*)

JUAN (*to audience*). Yeah, I've had a few girlfriends hang on my arm. It must have been my Chicano magnetism. It sure wasn't my wallet. (*Brings out wallet; accordion plastic picture holder falls out*) Yeah, I've lost a lot of them. (*He picks up the folder, and looks at the photos as he reminisces.*) There was Teresa, Monica, Laura, Cha-Cha from Dinuba. Then there was Rachel, the violinist. Every time I complained that I didn't have any money, she

started pretending to play the violin. And, let's see, there's Veronica and Cindy and Estela and, *hijole*, I forgot all about Gaby, that go-go dancer who danced on TV. (*Wiggles his hips*) Then I went out with the twins, Jessica and Jennifer—that was fun, until we played tag-team wrestling and they beat me up. Then there was Lupe and Lupe's cousin, Smiley. (*Gives big smile; pause*) I guess I got around, and (*Looks behind one photo*) *mira*, I got ten dollars stuck behind Sara! I should have stuck with her, my good-luck girl.

(JUAN *returns to his stool when* PATRICIA *returns.*)

RUDY. I requested a song for you.

(JUAN *begins to sing, "Nothing in my wallet but a little crushed Lifesaver!"*)

RUDY. Uncle!—I mean, you! Something quiet.

(JUAN *begins to strum a softer, more romantic song.*)

(WAITER *returns with their order.* PATRICIA's *eyes widen and* RUDY *holds up one of his crackers.* WAITER *leaves after a "bon appétit."* PATRICIA *cuts the hamburger in two and offers a part to* RUDY, *who shakes his head.*)

PATRICIA. Don't be silly! Help yourself. Have some fries. Sounds weird, but I like my fries with mustard.

RUDY. Yeah? Me, too. (*Begins to eat* PATRICIA's *fries*) You ever put potato chips in your sandwich and then smash the sandwich?

PATRICIA. All the time. I like the way it sounds when the chips break up.

(*They eat.*)

RUDY (*clearing his throat*). I like your

hair. You know, my mom cuts hair for a living.

PATRICIA. Really?

(RUDY *pulls a notepad from his pocket and holds it in his lap to read it.*)

RUDY. Yeah, you have gorgeously mature and exciting hair. Your mouth is big, like a fashion model's mouth. Your eyelashes blow in the wind. You smell good.

(*Smiling,* RUDY *folds the notepad and puts it back into his pocket.* PATRICIA *smiles at these compliments. They eat silently.* ALEX's *face appears at the window wearing sunglasses.* ALEX *enters restaurant, slipping a dollar bill to the* WAITER.)

ALEX. A table near those two. (*Sits down, then notices the* OLD MAN, *who is looking at him curiously*)

OLD MAN. Say, you're the one who sold me the apples, no? (*Pointing to* RUDY) With your friend there, no?

(ALEX *hides behind menu, trying to ignore* OLD MAN.)

OLD MAN. Your friend has got a nice girl there . . . Her mom is married. No use in asking.

(PATRICIA *gets up and stands by* JUAN *as he strums the guitar very lightly. She snaps her fingers to the music.* RUDY, *wiping his mouth, excuses himself to go to* ALEX's *table.*)

RUDY (*whispering*). ¡Híjole! Pat is pigging out and I'm pecking on crackers like a parrot.

ALEX. And the old dude is here.

RUDY. He took our advice. ·

OLD MAN (*mumbling*). Yeah, you're nice boys. Good advice. Tasty apples! And the girl's mother is married. No use in asking.

(RUDY *and* ALEX *force a smile.*)

RUDY. And don't look, but Uncle's playing the guitar. It's his new job.

ALEX. Your uncle? Your *Tío* Juan-Juan?

(UNCLE *waves to* ALEX, *who returns his friendly wave.*)

ALEX. So how's it going?

RUDY. I don't know. I read from some notes that I wrote down.

ALEX. Forget the notes. Speak from your heart. What did you tell her?

RUDY. First I told her I liked her hair.

ALEX. Good.

RUDY. Then I said she has a big mouth, but a good one, a big mouth like a fashion model's.

ALEX. Give off that subject, homes. Talk about her personality. Girls like to hear about stuff like that.

RUDY (*looks around nervously, then addresses his friend*). Alex.

ALEX (*mockingly*). Rudy.

RUDY. Her mom doesn't know she's with me.

ALEX. So?

RUDY. So, maybe her mom might find out and hit me.

ALEX. That's why you have feet. Run if you see her. I'll keep an eye out. (*Reaches into his pocket*) Here, man. You can pay me back later.

(ALEX *stuffs a wad of money into* RUDY's *shirt pocket.* RUDY *smiles and gives his best friend a low five.*)

RUDY. You're the best, Alex.

ALEX. OK, get back in there. Turn on the charm. Don't worry about her mom. (*Pause*) But if her dad shows up, then you run. I got my bike outside.

(RUDY, *straightening the collar of his shirt, returns to the table;* PATRICIA *hurries to the table as well.*)

PATRICIA. Is he a friend of yours?

RUDY. Kind of. *(Pause)* Patricia, you got a . . . complex personality. I mean, you're not stuck-up. You're willing to go out with a boy who . . .

PATRICIA. What?

RUDY *(shyly).* Never mind.

PATRICIA. Come on, tell me.

RUDY. Who still has his G.I. Joes.

PATRICIA. You're cute! *(Pause)* You know, I saw you play baseball before.

(RUDY *perks up.*)

PATRICIA. You were at the playground.

RUDY. Was I any good?

PATRICIA. No, but I liked how you tried really hard.

RUDY. Well, I like baseball. It just feels good, standing in the box when the outfielders are playing in. You got to grip the bat like you mean it, kick at the dirt in the batting box, stare at the pitcher like you hate him, and do this. *(Spitting into palms)* And before, at home, you got to iron your jersey, put some black shine under your eyes, polish your mitt, and put on . . . *(becomes shy)*

PATRICIA. What?

RUDY. It's something private. *(Scribbles a note and hands it to* PATRICIA.*)*

PATRICIA. Oh, your athletic supporter.

RUDY. Last year I was wearing size Small, but I'm up to Medium now. *(Smiles proudly to himself)*

(RUDY'S MOTHER *and her friend* ESTELA *enter the restaurant. Each recognition that follows should be individually and sequentially highlighted. The* MOTHER *immediately sees* RUDY, *but he doesn't see her.* ESTELA *points at the young couple—*RUDY *and* PATRICIA*—but the* MOTHER *shushes* ESTELA. ALEX *sees* RUDY'S MOTHER; ALEX *gulps and hides behind a menu.* JUAN *raises a finger to his mouth. The two women take seats quietly and hide behind menus.*)

(WAITER *enters and takes away* RUDY's *and* PATRICIA's *plates and gives them a menu.*)

(RUDY *and* PATRICIA *look at each other.* RUDY *takes the menu and opens it up.*)

WAITER *(to his new customers).* I'll be with you in a moment.

RUDY. If you want, you can have dessert.

PATRICIA. No, I'm fine. That was good.

RUDY *(continuing romantically).* Pat, I like your hair.

PATRICIA. Thanks. I had it blow-dried.

RUDY *(pulls his notepad from his pocket and reads from it surreptitiously).* You exude cool vibrations that make me feel like a—*(Deep voice)* like a man. *(Back to regular voice)* You remind me of a crashing ocean, my mermaid. Or flowers in spring.

MOTHER. *¿Qué?* "My mermaid"?

(RUDY *looks around the restaurant; his* MOTHER *raises menu to her face.* RUDY *continues reading.*)

RUDY. You're the scent of spring—

MOTHER. Scent of spring!

RUDY *(looks around again).* Your hands are like doves—

ESTELA. *¡Qué romántico!*

RUDY *(looks in direction of the women).* Excuse me, Pat. (RUDY *gets up and looks behind the menu. He is shocked but quickly recovers. He starts to walk back to his table.)*

OLD MAN *(loudly whispers)*. Hey. *(RUDY stops near OLD MAN.)*

OLD MAN. Say, you know those women who just came in?

RUDY. Not really.

OLD MAN *(in loud whisper)*. The redhead is kind of cute. Go ask if she's married.

RUDY. I can't do that!

OLD MAN. What, you scared of work? I'll give you two dollars.

RUDY *(still feeling short of money, agrees. He goes up to ESTELA.)* That gentleman asked about you. *(ESTELA looks over at the OLD MAN and waves flirtatiously. RUDY returns to his table.)*

PATRICIA. Do you know them?

RUDY *(nervously)*. No, I never saw them before.

(JUAN strums dance music.)

PATRICIA. Let's dance, Rudy.

RUDY. Dance? No, I'm too full. Those crackers filled me up.

PATRICIA. Come on, *Novio* Boy. No one's around, except your friend.

(PATRICIA lifts RUDY from the chair and pulls him almost roughly. PATRICIA tries to dance closely but RUDY struggles to dance at arm's length, conscious of his MOTHER's watching. They dance until WAITER coughs for their attention and approaches.)

WAITER. Your bill, *monsieur*.

RUDY. Thank you. *(Gulps as he reads the bill. He digs into his pocket.)*

PATRICIA. We can split this.

RUDY. No, I got it. What's twenty-four dollars and fifty-four cents to me?

PATRICIA. Next time, it's my turn. Oh, wait! I'll pay the tip!

RUDY. OK.

PATRICIA. I have to be home by two o'clock. I had a lot of fun, Rudy.

RUDY. Me, too. *(Pause)* You don't mind if I'm younger?

PATRICIA. Of course not. *(Pause)* Listen, I'll teach you how to drive a car.

MOTHER. Drive a car!

PATRICIA *(looks toward the women)*. Are those women talking to us?

RUDY. Nah, they're just chattering.

PATRICIA. So—you want to learn? We can practice going back and forth in the driveway.

RUDY. *¡ Simón!* And I got my license, too.

PATRICIA. You do?

RUDY. Well, it's not a real license. It's a license on my bike that says RUDY. It hangs behind my seat.

PATRICIA *(laughs)*. You're a fun date. And a good dancer.

(PATRICIA gives RUDY a kiss on his cheek. She leaves. RUDY looks at his MOTHER and ESTELA angrily as they slowly lower the menus from their faces.)

RUDY. How come you're spying on me?

MOTHER. I'm not, *m'ijo!* Me and Estela came here to hear your uncle.

(JUAN strums guitar.)

MOTHER. I didn't know this is where you were taking your date.

RUDY. You're snooping! I know you are!

MOTHER. Cross my heart. I didn't know, really.

ESTELA *(to RUDY'S MOTHER)*. She's the girl whose hair you cut yesterday, *qué no?*

RUDY. You did her hair, Mom? She knows you?

MOTHER *(angry).* What, are you embarrassed? Ashamed of your mommy?

RUDY. No, it's just that . . . Mom, I can't get any privacy! You're here, Estela is here, and Alex, and Uncle! And even the guy we sold apples to. Everyone!

JUAN *(to* RUDY*).* Rudy, it's a cosmic thing that we gathered around you. We're watching out for you. *(To* MOTHER*)* But we got to give him a little space, *hermana.*

(Bug-eyed, they all stare at RUDY.*)*

RUDY. Well, you're doing too much watching.

MOTHER. She's a nice girl.

ESTELA. Pretty, *también.*

RUDY. You like her?

MOTHER. She's a good girl. But I don't want you driving a car with her. *(Pinching his cheek).* My little boy is growing up.

*(*ESTELA *eyes the* OLD MAN, *who has gotten up and joined them.)*

OLD MAN. I like your hair.

ESTELA. Thank you.

OLD MAN. And your smile.

ESTELA. That's sweet.

OLD MAN. And you possess an attitude that—

ESTELA *(angrily).* Why does everyone think I got an attitude?

OLD MAN. A nice attitude. *(Pause)* You married?

ESTELA *(flirting).* Sometimes.

*(*OLD MAN *smiles, then is at a loss as to how to continue.)*

OLD MAN *(whispering to* RUDY*).* What should I do next?

RUDY. Maybe you should take them on a walk or something. And don't forget to get her number.

OLD MAN. You gals care to go for a walk? And can I get your telephone number?

*(*OLD MAN, RUDY'S MOTHER, *and* ESTELA *leave the restaurant.* JUAN, RUDY, *and* ALEX *sit down at their table.)*

ALEX. *Mira,* she left a french fry. Here, *Novio* Boy. *(Feeds it to* RUDY*)*

RUDY. She wiped me out for the rest of ninth grade. But it beats doing nothing.

(At this JUAN *begins to play his earlier song about "nothing" from Scene Three.)*

RUDY. Thanks for helping out, Unc.

JUAN. No problema. You're my only nephew. About the money . . . You can pay me back later.

ALEX. But me first.

*(*JUAN *returns to his stool and starts strumming his guitar softly.)*

RUDY. I'm gonna have a yard sale, so I can earn back what I owe you and Mom and Uncle.

ALEX. What are you gonna sell?

RUDY. My G.I. Joes. And my baseball cards. And my basketball and my Ninja Turtle lunch box.

ALEX. Not your Ninja Turtle lunch box!

RUDY. This is a clearance sale! *¡La gran pulga!*[61] Out with it all!

ALEX. I'll help you out. I got some stuff underneath my bed. We'll have *una gran* swap meet right on the front lawn.

---

61. *¡La gran pulga!* (lä grän pül′gä), the big flea market

RUDY. You'll do that for me?

ALEX. *Simón,* bro. We ninth graders got to stick together.

RUDY. Like tortillas *y* frijoles.

ALEX. Guacamole *y* chips!

RUDY. *¡Huevos con chorizo!*[62]

ALEX. Soda *y* sunflower seeds!

(They shake hands elaborately.)

RUDY. You're the best, homes.

ALEX. Man, it's tough being a *Novio* Boy.

---

62 *huevos con chorizo* (wā bôs cōn chō rē′sō), eggs with sausage

Responding to the Play

1. Look back over the seven scenes in *Novio Boy* and pick your favorite. Describe in writing what you like about it and why.
2. Do the characters in the play seem realistic and well-rounded? Why or why not?
3. Which of the characters in the play would you go to for advice? Explain why.
4. If you were creating the set for this play, would it be elaborate or sparse? Choose a scene and describe the set for the class.
5. Think about a scene you especially liked. Draw the stage, scenery, sets, and props that would be essential to the scene.

About Spanish Pronunciations

Remember these tips when reading the Spanish words in *Novio Boy*:

a is pronounced /ä/ as in *father* *e* is pronounced as long *a* /ā/
i is pronounced as a long *e* /ē/ *o* is pronounced as in *low* /ō/
u is pronounced /ü/ as in *loot* *v* is pronounced *b*
j is pronounced *h* *h* is silent

CREATING AND PERFORMING

1. To develop an understanding of character, play the role of either El Gato or Mama Rosa answering these questions from the radio audience:

   "If I want someone to like me, what should I do?"
   "My friend and I had a fight, how can I make up?"
   "I want to earn money to buy Mom a gift. How can I do it?"

2. Rudy was given lots of suggestions about how to talk to Patricia. What do you think he has learned by the end of the play? Write four rules Rudy might come up with for breaking the ice. Read them to the class.

3. Think about how the characters listed below would stand, walk, and gesture. Choose one and demonstrate for the class.

Rudy	Alex	Patricia
Alicia	Rudy's Mother	Uncle Juan
El Gato	Mama Rosa	Estela

The Play as Literature: Diction

An author chooses to use certain words for many different reasons. *Diction*, the words the author uses, sets the tone for the work. Most literature contains diction that describes literally (*denotation*) while also offering emotional associations (*connotation*).

In writing *The Man in a Case*, Wendy Wasserstein accepted a unique challenge. She was asked to write a play based on a short story by the Russian author Anton Chekhov—a story set in Russia just before the turn of the nineteenth century. She was told she could change the story in any way she wanted. Wasserstein rose to the challenge. She crafted a play whose diction not only captures a time and place but two very distinct characters, while also presenting a story very much her own. (For more about Anton Chekhov, see p. 89.)

The Play as Theatre: Listening and Reacting

The interaction between actors is what holds a dramatic presentation together. An actor's life on stage is one of action and reaction. Being a good speaker goes without saying when one is performing, but being a good listener is just as important. By listening consciously, alertly, and creatively, the actor can react appropriately. And reaction is the key to a good performance. ·

When you act, be alert to any cues, verbal or physical, that another actor is giving. Your own vocal responses and movements should then offer an honest response to his or her words.

As you read *The Man in a Case*, be aware of how each actor in the play would react physically and verbally to the other's comments.

Warm Up!

Choose a partner and decide who will be "the speaker" and who will be "the listener." Partners look into one another's eyes. The speaker says something about the listener, such as "Your eyes sparkle with light," or "You have a dimple." Then the listener repeats what the speaker has just said, substituting the words *My* and *I* for *Your* and *You*. You must continue to look into one another's eyes throughout the warm up. Repeat the same phrase as many times as you can.

The Man in a Case

by Wendy Wasserstein
inspired by Anton Chekhov's story

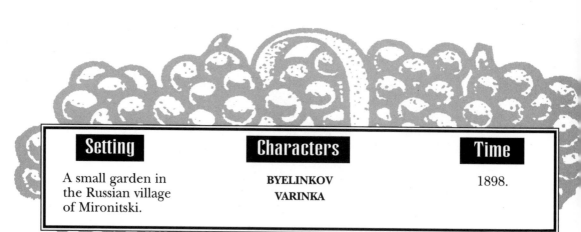

Setting	Characters	Time
A small garden in the Russian village of Mironitski.	BYELINKOV VARINKA	1898.

BYELINKOV *is pacing. Enter* VARINKA, *out of breath.*

BYELINKOV. You are ten minutes late.

VARINKA. The most amazing thing happened on my way over here. You know the woman who runs the grocery store down the road. She wears a black wig during the week, and a blond wig on Saturday nights. And she has the daughter who married an engineer in Moscow, who is doing very well, thank you, and is living, God bless them, in a three-room apartment. But he really is the most boring man in the world. All he talks about is his future and his station in life. Well, she heard we were to be married, and she gave me this basket of apricots to give to you.

BYELINKOV. That is a most amazing thing!

VARINKA. She said to me, "Varinka, you are marrying the most honorable man in the entire village. In this village he is the only man fit to speak with my son-in-law."

BYELINKOV. I don't care for apricots. They give me hives.

VARINKA. I can return them. I'm sure if I told her they give you hives, she would give me a basket of raisins or a cake.

BYELINKOV. I don't know this woman or her pompous[1] son-in-law. Why would she give me her cakes?

VARINKA. She adores you!

BYELINKOV. She is emotionally loose.

VARINKA. She adores you by reputation. Everyone adores you by reputation. I tell everyone I am to marry Byelinkov, the finest teacher in the county.

BYELINKOV. You tell them this?

VARINKA. If they don't tell me first.

BYELINKOV. Pride can be an imperfect virtue.

VARINKA. It isn't pride. It's the truth. You are a great man!

BYELINKOV. I am the master of Greek and Latin at a local school at the end of the village of Mironitski.

VARINKA (*kisses him*). And I am to be the master of Greek and Latin's wife!

BYELINKOV. Being married requires a great deal of responsibility. I hope I am able to provide you with all that a married man must properly provide a wife.

VARINKA. We will be very happy.

BYELINKOV. Happiness is for children. We are entering into a social contract,[2] an amicable agreement to provide us with a secure and satisfying future.

VARINKA. You are so sweet! You are the sweetest man in the world!

BYELINKOV. I'm a man set in his ways who saw a chance to provide himself with a small challenge.

VARINKA. Look at you! Look at you! Your sweet round spectacles, your dear collar always starched, always raised, your perfectly pressed pants always creasing at right angles perpendicular to the floor, and my most favorite part, the sweet little galoshes, rain or shine, just in case. My Byelinkov, never taken by surprise. Except by me.

BYELINKOV. You speak about me as if I were your pet.

VARINKA. You are my pet! My little school mouse.

BYELINKOV. A mouse?

VARINKA. My sweetest dancing bear with galoshes, my little stale babka.[3]

BYELINKOV. A stale babka?

VARINKA. I am not Pushkin.

BYELINKOV (*laughs*). That depends what you think of Pushkin.

VARINKA. You're smiling. I knew I could make you smile today.

BYELINKOV. I am a responsible man. Every day I have for breakfast black bread, fruit, hot tea, and every day I smile three times. I am halfway into my translation of the Aeneid from classical Greek hexameter into Russian alexandrines.[4] In twenty years I have never been late to school. I am a responsible man, but no dancing bear.

VARINKA. Dance with me.

BYELINKOV. Now? It is nearly four weeks before the wedding!

VARINKA. It's a beautiful afternoon. We are in your garden. The roses are in full bloom.

BYELINKOV. The roses have beetles.

---

1. pompous (păm'pəs), showing self-importance; arrogant
2. social contract, Byelinkov is referring to a marriage license.
3. babka (bäb'kä), a kind of Russian coffee cake. A stale babka would be one that is somewhat old.
4. the Aeneid from classical Greek hexameter/ Russian alexandrines, poetic rhythms used by Greek and Russian poets.

VARINKA. Dance with me!

BYELINKOV. You are a demanding woman.

VARINKA. You chose me. *(She begins to dance.)* And right. And left. And turn. And right. And left.

BYELINKOV. And turn. Give me your hand. *(He begins to dance with her.)* You dance like a school mouse. It's a beautiful afternoon! We are in my garden. The roses are in full bloom! And turn. And turn. *(He twirls her around.)*

VARINKA. I am the luckiest woman in the world! (BYELINKOV *stops dancing.*) Why are you stopping?

BYELINKOV. To place a lilac in your hair. Every year on this day I will place a lilac in your hair.

VARINKA. Will you remember?

BYELINKOV. I will write it down. *(He takes a notebook from his pocket and writes in it.)* Dear Byelinkov, don't forget the day a young lady, your bride, entered your garden, your peace, and danced on the roses. On that day every year you are to place a lilac in her hair.

VARINKA. I love you.

BYELINKOV. It is convenient we met.

VARINKA. I love you.

BYELINKOV. You are a girl.

VARINKA. I am thirty.

BYELINKOV. But you think like a girl. That is an attractive attribute.

VARINKA. Do you love me?

BYELINKOV. We've never spoken about housekeeping.

VARINKA. I am an excellent housekeeper. I kept house for my family on the farm in Gadyatchsky. I can make a beetroot soup with tomatoes and aubergines[5] which is so nice. Awfully, awfully nice.

BYELINKOV. You are fond of expletives.[6]

---

5. aubergine (ō′bər zhēn), another word for eggplant, a purplish or white oval vegetable
6. expletive (ek′splə tiv), a word that exclaims or simply serves to fill an empty space

VARINKA. My beet soup, sir, is excellent!

BYELINKOV. Please don't be cross. I, too, am an excellent housekeeper. I have a place for everything in the house. A shelf for each pot, a cubby for every spoon, a folder for favorite recipes. I have cooked for myself for twenty years. Though my beet soup is not outstanding, it is sufficient.

VARINKA. I'm sure it's very good.

BYELINKOV. No. It is awfully, awfully not. What I am outstanding in, however, what gives me greatest pleasure, is preserving those things which are left over. I wrap each tomato slice I haven't used in a wet cloth and place it in the coolest corner of the house. I have had my shoes for seven years because I wrap them in the galoshes you are so fond of. And every night before I go to sleep I wrap my bed in quilts and curtains so I never catch a draft.

VARINKA. You sleep with curtains around your bed?

BYELINKOV. I like to keep warm.

VARINKA. I will make you a new quilt.

BYELINKOV. No. No new quilt. That would be hazardous.

VARINKA. It is hazardous to sleep under curtains.

BYELINKOV. Varinka, I don't like change very much. If one works out the arithmetic, the final fraction of improvement is at best less than an eighth of value over the total damage caused by disruption. I never thought of marrying till I saw your eyes dancing among the familiar faces at the headmaster's tea. I assumed I would grow old, preserved like those which are left over, wrapped suitably in my case of curtains and quilts.

VARINKA. Byelinkov, I want us to have dinners with friends and summer country visits. I want people to say, "Have you spent time with Varinka and Byelinkov? He is so happy now that they are married. She is just what he needed."

BYELINKOV. You have already brought me some happiness. But I was never a sad man. Don't ever think I thought I was a sad man.

VARINKA. My sweetest darling, you can be whatever you want! If you are sad, they'll say she talks all the time, and he is soft-spoken and kind.

BYELINKOV. And if I am difficult?

VARINKA. Oh, they'll say he is difficult because he is highly intelligent. All great men are difficult. Look at Lermontov, Tchaikovsky, Peter the Great.

BYELINKOV. Ivan the Terrible.

VARINKA. Yes, him, too.

BYELINKOV. Why are you marrying me? I am none of these things.

VARINKA. To me you are.

BYELINKOV. You have imagined this. You have constructed an elaborate romance for yourself. Perhaps you are the great one. You are the one with the great imagination.

VARINKA. Byelinkov, I am a pretty girl of thirty. You're right. I am not a woman. I have not made myself into a woman because I do not deserve that honor. Until I came to this town to visit my brother, I lived on my family's farm. As the years passed, I became younger and younger for fear that I would never marry. And it wasn't that I wasn't pretty enough or sweet enough; it was just that no man ever looked at me and saw a wife. I was not the woman who would be there when he came home. Until I met you, I thought I would lie all my life and say I never married because I never met a man I loved. I will love you, Byelinkov. And I will help you to love me. We deserve the life everyone else has. We deserve not to be different.

BYELINKOV. Yes. We are the same as everyone else.

VARINKA. Tell me you love me.

BYELINKOV. I love you.

VARINKA (taking his hands). We will be very happy. I am very strong. (She pauses.) It is time for tea.

BYELINKOV. It is too early for tea. Tea is at half past the hour.

VARINKA. Do you have heavy cream? It will be awfully nice with apricots.

BYELINKOV. Heavy cream is too rich for teatime.

VARINKA. But today is special. Today you placed a lilac in my hair. Write in your note pad. Every year we will celebrate with apricots and heavy cream. I will go to my brother's house and get some.

BYELINKOV. But your brother's house is a mile from here.

VARINKA. Today it is much shorter. Today my brother gave me his bicycle to ride. I will be back very soon.

BYELINKOV. You rode to my house on a bicycle! Did anyone see you?

VARINKA. Of course. I had such fun. I told you I saw the grocery store lady with the son-in-law who is doing very well, thank you, in Moscow, and the headmaster's wife.

BYELINKOV. You saw the headmaster's wife!

VARINKA. She smiled at me.

BYELINKOV. Did she laugh or smile?

VARINKA. She laughed a little. She said, "My dear, you are very progressive to ride a bicycle." She said, "You and your fiancé Byelinkov must ride together some time. I wonder if he'll take off his galoshes when he rides a bicycle."

BYELINKOV. She said that?

VARINKA. She adores you. We had a good giggle.

BYELINKOV. A woman can be arrested for riding a bicycle. That is not progressive, it is a premeditated revolutionary act. Your brother must be awfully careful on behalf of your behavior. He has been careless—oh, so careless—in giving you the bicycle.

VARINKA. Dearest Byelinkov, you are wrapping yourself under curtains and quilts! I made friends on the bicycle.

BYELINKOV. You saw more than the headmaster's wife and the idiot grocery store woman?

VARINKA. She is not an idiot.

BYELINKOV. She is a potato-vending sausage-armed fool!

VARINKA. Shhh! My school mouse. Shhh!

BYELINKOV. What other friends did you make on this bicycle?

VARINKA. I saw students from my brother's classes. They waved and shouted, "Anthropos in love! Anthropos in love!"

BYELINKOV. Where is that bicycle?

VARINKA. I left it outside the gate. Where are you going?

BYELINKOV (muttering as he exits). Anthropos in love. Anthropos in love.

VARINKA. They were cheering me on. (She calls after him.) Careful, you'll trample the roses.

BYELINKOV (returning with the bicycle). Anthropos is Greek singular for man. Anthropos in love translates as the Greek and Latin master in love. Of course they cheered you. Their instructor, who teaches them the discipline and contained beauty of the classics, is in love with a sprite on a bicycle. It is a good giggle, isn't it? A very good giggle! I am returning this bicycle to your brother.

VARINKA. But it is teatime.

BYELINKOV. Today we will not have tea.

VARINKA. But you will have to walk back a mile.

BYELINKOV. But I have my galoshes on. (He gets on the bicycle.) Varinka, we deserve not to be different. (He begins to pedal. The bicycle doesn't move.)

VARINKA. Put the kickstand up.

BYELINKOV. I beg your pardon.

VARINKA (giggling). Byelinkov, to make the bicycle move, you must put the kickstand up. (BYELINKOV puts it up and awkwardly falls off the bicycle as it moves forward. VARINKA laughs.) Ha, ha, ha! My little school mouse. You look so funny! You are the sweetest, dearest man in the world.

BYELINKOV (after a pause). Please help me up. I'm afraid my galosh is caught.

VARINKA (trying not to laugh). Your galosh is caught! (She explodes with laughter again.) Oh, you are so funny! I do love you so. (She helps BYELINKOV up.) You were right, my pet, as always. We don't need heavy cream for tea. The fraction of improvement isn't worth the damage caused by the disruption.

BYELINKOV. Varinka, it is still too early for tea. I must complete two stanzas of my translation before late afternoon. That is my regular schedule.

VARINKA. Then I will watch while you work.

BYELINKOV. No, you had a good giggle. That is enough.

VARINKA. Then while you work, I will work, too. I will make a list of guests for our wedding.

BYELINKOV. I can only concentrate when I am alone in my house. Please take your bicycle home to your brother.

VARINKA. But I don't want to leave you. You look so sad.

BYELINKOV. I never was a sad man. Don't ever think I was a sad man.

VARINKA. Byelinkov, it's a beautiful day. We are in your garden. The roses are in bloom.

BYELINKOV. Allow me to help you onto your bicycle. *(He takes* VARINKA*'s hand as she gets on the bike.)*

VARINKA. You are such a gentleman. We will be very happy.

BYELINKOV. You are very strong. Good day, Varinka. *(*VARINKA *pedals off.* BYELINKOV, *alone in the garden, takes out his pad and rips up the note about the lilac, strews it over the garden, then carefully picks up each piece of paper and places them all in a small envelope as lights fade to black.)*

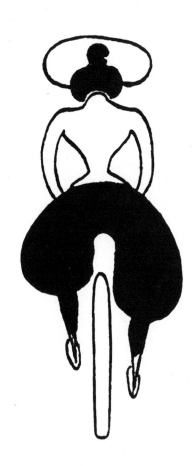

Chekhov's *The Man in a Case* by Wendy Wasserstein

The Man in a Case

Responding to the Play

1. Did you identify more with Byelinkov or Varinka? Why?
2. Reread Byelinkov and Varinka's first three exchanges. What do their words tell you about them as individuals and as a couple?
3. Discuss the importance of Byelinkov's galoshes and Varinka's bicycle to them and to one another.
4. Explain the significance of Byelinkov's actions in the final stage direction of the play, beginning *"Byelinkov, alone in the garden,...."*
5. If you were playing Byelinkov listening to Varinka saying the lines on page 87 that begin *"They were cheering me on...,"* how would you react? Write a short statement.

More About Anton Chekhov

Though this play is based on his short story, Anton Chekhov (1860-1904) is best known for his own plays, such as *Uncle Vanya* and *The Cherry Orchard*. Chekhov's most famous plays are serious dramas, but he labeled many of them "comedies," highlighting the irony in his plot lines and the warm humanity of his characters.

Creating and Performing

1. Chekhov's story ends with Byelinkov going to his bed and dying. Wasserstein's ending takes place in the garden. Write your own ending to the play.
2. Try a short mime routine: You are trying to ride a bicycle for the first time in your life, when your shoe gets caught on the pedal.
3. With a partner, practice the exchange between Byelinkov and Varinka from the top of column 2, page 87, to the end of the play.

Before Reading

Variations on the Death of Trotsky

The Play as Literature: Comic Irony

While it is true that Russian revolutionary Leon Trotsky was murdered in 1940, little else about him as revealed in *Variations on the Death of Trotsky* could have happened. Playwright David Ives uses *irony,* the contrasting of what appears to be with what really is, to set this off-beat play spinning. The comedy comes in when his characters respond to dire events with unexpectedly matter-of fact attitudes.

All the while Trotsky grumbles and wisecracks on stage, there is an axe buried in his skull. He remains alive and robust until the moment he realizes he is, all kidding aside, a dead man. (For more about Trotsky, see page 99.)

As you read the play, be on the lookout for ironic situations.

The Play as Theatre: Burlesque

Burlesque is a kind of comedy based on exaggeration. There are two forms of burlesque: the *mock epic*, in which a trivial subject is treated very seriously, and the *travesty*, in which a serious subject is treated quite frivolously. Burlesque goes to great lengths to make fun of its subject—using mockery, impersonations, jokes, and asides to the audience. Actors who attempt burlesque must take care not to over-play the seriousness or silliness of the form.

Comic timing is an important element in burlesque. Waiting for just the right moment to insert a "zinger," counting a beat before reacting to another's line, or looking to the audience for help in the middle of an exchange are just a few tricks an actor might use.

Surely nothing could be more serious than death and revolution. And no man in history was more serious about his cause than Leon Trotsky. Trotsky, therefore, is a perfect foil for this travesty.

WARM UP!

Say these two lines in a variety of intonations and voices:

You're pretty funny, aren't you?   *Now, that's a good idea.*

Write a sentence that could be read in a variety of ways.

Variations on the Death of Trotsky

on the
Death of
Trotsky

by David Ives

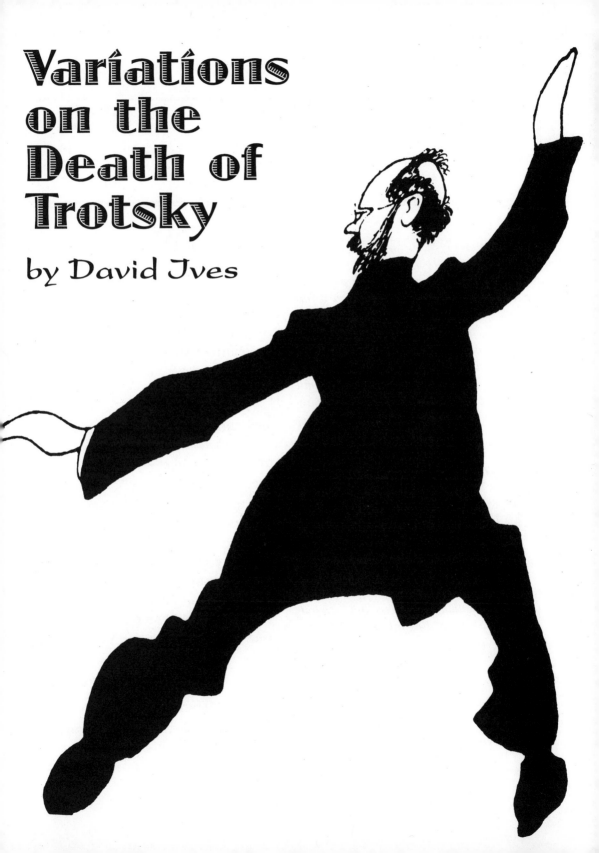

Setting	Characters	Time
a study in Coyoacan, Mexico	LEON TROTSKY MRS. TROTSKY RAMON MERCADER	August 21, 1940

TROTSKY's[1] *study in Coyoacan, Mexico. A desk, covered with books and papers. A mirror hanging on the wall. A doorway, left, louvered* [2] *windows upstage, through which we can glimpse lush tropical fronds and greenery. A large wall calendar announces that today is August 21, 1940. Lights up on* TROTSKY *sitting at his desk, writing furiously. He has bushy hair and a goatee, small glasses, a dark suit. The handle of a mountain-climber's axe is sticking out of the back of his head.*

Variation One

TROTSKY *(as he writes).* "The proletariat[3] is right. The proletariat must always be right. And the revolution of the proletariat against oppression must go on . . . forever!"

*(*MRS. TROTSKY *enters, grandmotherly and sweet, in an ankle-length dress and high-button shoes. She is holding a large book.)*

MRS. TROTSKY. Leon.

TROTSKY. "And forever and forever . . . !"

MRS. TROTSKY. Leon, I was just reading the encyclopedia.

TROTSKY. The heading?

MRS. TROTSKY. "Trotsky, Leon."

TROTSKY. Good. It's about me.

MRS. TROTSKY. Listen to this. *(Reads)* "On August 20th, 1940, a Spanish Communist named Ramon Mercader smashed a mountain-climber's axe into Trotsky's skull in Coyoacan, a suburb of Mexico City. Trotsky died the next day."

TROTSKY. What is the year of that encyclopedia?

MRS. TROTSKY *(checks the spine).* 1999. *(Or whatever year it happens to be now)*

TROTSKY. Strange.

MRS. TROTSKY. Yes.

TROTSKY. But interesting. I am Trotsky.

MRS. TROTSKY. Yes, dear.

TROTSKY. And this is our house in Coyoacan.

MRS. TROTSKY. Yes.

TROTSKY. And we have a Spanish gardener named Ramon—?

MRS. TROTSKY. Mercader. Yes.

---

1. Trotsky (trät'skē), Leon (1879–1940) Russian Communist
2. louvered (lü'vèrd) having shutters with horizontal boards
3. proletariat (prō le tèr'ē ət), the laboring class, especially industrial workers

TROTSKY. Hmm . . . There aren't any *other* Trotskys living in Coyoacan, are there?

MRS. TROTSKY. I don't think so. Not under that name.

TROTSKY. What is the date today?

MRS. TROTSKY *(looks at the calendar)*. August 21st, 1940.

TROTSKY. Then I'm safe! That article says it happened on the twentieth, which means it would've happened yesterday.

MRS. TROTSKY. But Leon . . .

TROTSKY. And I'd be dead today, with a mountain-climber's axe in my skull!

MRS. TROTSKY. Um—Leon . . .

TROTSKY. Will the capitalist[4] press never get things right? *(He resumes writing.)*

MRS. TROTSKY. But Leon, isn't that the handle of a mountain-climber's axe, sticking out of your skull?

TROTSKY *(looks into the mirror)*. It certainly does look like one . . . And you know, Ramon was in here yesterday, telling me about his mountain-climbing trip. And now that I think of it, he was carrying a mountain-climber's axe. I can't remember if he had it when he left the room . . . *(TROTSKY considers all this.)* Did Ramon report to work today? *(TROTSKY dies, falling face forward onto his desk.)*

(A bell rings.)

Variation Two

(TROTSKY resumes writing.)

TROTSKY. "No one is safe. Force must be used. And the revolution of the proletariat against oppression must go on forever and forever . . ."

MRS. TROTSKY. Leon . . .

TROTSKY. "And forever!"

MRS. TROTSKY. Leon, I was just reading the encyclopedia.

TROTSKY. Is it the *Britannica*?

MRS. TROTSKY. Listen to this.

TROTSKY *(to audience)*. The universe as viewed by the victors.

MRS. TROTSKY. "On August 20th, 1940, a Spanish Communist named Ramon Mercader smashed a mountain-climber's axe into Trotsky's skull in Coyoacan, a suburb of Mexico City. Trotsky died the next day."

TROTSKY *(impatient)*. Yes? And?

MRS. TROTSKY. I *think* that there's a mountain-climber's axe in your own skull right now.

TROTSKY. I knew *that*! When I was shaving this morning, I noticed a handle sticking out of the back of my head. For a moment I thought it was an ice pick, so at first I was worried.

MRS. TROTSKY. No, it's not an ice pick.

TROTSKY. Don't even say the word! You know my recurring nightmare.

MRS. TROTSKY. Yes, dear.

TROTSKY. About the ice pick that buries itself in my skull.

MRS. TROTSKY. Yes, dear.

TROTSKY. That is why I have forbidden any of the servants to allow ice picks into the house.

MRS. TROTSKY. But Leon—

---

4. capitalist (kap'it al ist), person who believes in private ownership and has money invested in business; often a person of wealth

TROTSKY. No one may be seen with an ice pick in this house. *Especially* not Spanish Communists.

MRS. TROTSKY. But Leon—

TROTSKY. We'll do without ice. We'll drink our liquor neat and our Coca-Cola warm. Who cares if this *is* Coyoacan in August? Hmm. Not a bad song title, that. "Coyoacan in August." *(Writes it down)* Or we'll get ice, but we just won't pick at it. Ice will be allowed into the house in blocks, but may not be picked or chipped under any circumstances— at least, not with ice picks. Ice-cube trays will also be allowed, if they've been invented yet. I'll bet this article doesn't say anything about an *ice-cube tray* in my skull, does it?

MRS. TROTSKY. No . . .

TROTSKY. Does it?

MRS. TROTSKY. No.

TROTSKY. HA! I've outsmarted destiny![5] *(To audience)* Which is only a capitalist explanation for the status quo![6]

MRS. TROTSKY. Leon . . .

TROTSKY. Also—look at this. *(Opens a desk drawer and takes out a skull)* Do you know what this is?

MRS. TROTSKY. No.

TROTSKY. It's a skull.

MRS. TROTSKY. Well I knew that, but—

TROTSKY. I bought this skull. I own this skull. So what does that make this?

(Pause)

MRS. TROTSKY AND TROTSKY *(together).* Trotsky's skull.

TROTSKY. If some Spanish-Communist-posing-as-a-gardener wants to bury

anything in my skull, be it a *(he is about to say "ice pick")* you-know-what or anything else—this will be here as a decoy. He'll see this skull, recognize it as my skull, bury something in it, and he'll go his way and I'll go mine. Is that ingenious?

MRS. TROTSKY. Up to a point.

TROTSKY. Fifty more years of Trotsky!

MRS. TROTSKY. I have some very bad news for you, Leon. *(Shows him the entry in the encyclopedia)*

TROTSKY. A mountain-climber's axe . . .? Ingenious! (TROTSKY *dies.*)

(Bell)

Variation Three

TROTSKY. Funny. I always thought it was an ice pick.

MRS. TROTSKY. A mountain-climber's axe! A mountain-climber's axe! CAN'T I GET THAT THROUGH YOUR SKULL?

(TROTSKY *dies.*)

(Bell)

Variation Four

(TROTSKY *begins to pace.*)

TROTSKY. This is very bad news. This is serious.

MRS. TROTSKY. What is serious, Leon?

TROTSKY. I have a mountain-climber's axe buried in my skull!

MRS. TROTSKY. Smashed, actually. It says

---

5. destiny (des′tin ē), fate; a predetermined force of events
6. *status quo* (stat′əs kwō), the existing state of affairs

Mercader "smashed" the axe into your skull, not "buried"—

TROTSKY. All right, all right. What am I going to do?

MRS. TROTSKY. Maybe a hat would cover the handle. You know. One of those cute little Alpine hats, with a point and a feather . . .? *(Sees the look on his face, and stops.)*

TROTSKY. The encyclopedia says that I die today?

MRS. TROTSKY. The twenty-first. That's today.

TROTSKY. Does it say what time?

MRS. TROTSKY. No.

TROTSKY. So much for the usefulness of that encyclopedia. All right, then, I have until midnight at the latest.

MRS. TROTSKY. What should I tell Cook about supper?

TROTSKY. Well, she can forget the soup course. (TROTSKY *falls to the floor and dies.)*

MRS. TROTSKY. *Nyet,*[7] *nyet, nyet!*

(Bell)

Variation Five

TROTSKY. But this man is a gardener.

MRS. TROTSKY. Yes.

TROTSKY. At least he's been *posing* as a gardener.

MRS. TROTSKY. Yes.

TROTSKY. Doesn't that make him a member of the proletariat?

MRS. TROTSKY. I'd say so.

TROTSKY. Then what's he doing smashing a mountain-climber's axe into my skull?

MRS. TROTSKY. I don't know. Have you been oppressing him?

TROTSKY. Why would Ramon have done this to me? *(He holds up the skull, Hamlet-like.)*

MRS. TROTSKY. Maybe he's a literalist.

TROTSKY. A what?

MRS. TROTSKY. A literalist. Maybe Ramon ran into Manuel yesterday. You know—Manuel? The head gardener?

TROTSKY. I know who Manuel is.

MRS. TROTSKY. I know you know who Manuel is.

TROTSKY *(Ralph Kramden*[8] *).* One of these days, Mrs. Trotsky . . . Bang! Zoom!

MRS. TROTSKY. Maybe Ramon asked him, "Will Mr. Trotsky have time to look at the nasturtiums[9] today?" And maybe Manuel said, "I don't know— axe Mr. Trotsky." HA HA HA HA HA Ha!

TROTSKY. Very funny.

MRS. TROTSKY. Or maybe he was just hot-to-trotsky.

TROTSKY. Oh very, very funny.

MRS. TROTSKY. Or maybe he just wanted to pick your brain! HOO HOO HEE HEE HAA HAA!

TROTSKY. Stop it! Stop it! *(He dies.)*

---

7. *nyet* (nyet), *Russian.* no
8. Ralph Kramden, a character in the early TV show *The Honeymooners.* He would often say these words to his wife, Alice, in frustration and annoyance.
9. nasturtium (nas tėr′shem), a brightly colored yellow, red, and orange flower with round, lime green petals

MRS. TROTSKY. HA HA HA HA HA HA!
(Bell)

Variation Six

TROTSKY. Call Ramon in here.

MRS. TROTSKY. Ramon!

TROTSKY. You'd better get him quickly. I have a mountain-climber's axe in my skull.

MRS. TROTSKY. Ramon! Come quickly!

(RAMON enters: sombrero, serape, huaraches,[10] *and guitar.)*

TROTSKY. Good morning, Ramon.

RAMON. Good morning, señor. *(They shake hands.)*

TROTSKY. Have a seat, please. *(To* MRS. TROTSKY*)* You see? We have very good

employer-employee relations here. *(To* RAMON*)* Ramon, did you bury this mountain-climber's axe in my skull?

RAMON. I did not bury it, señor. I smashed it into your skull.

TROTSKY. Excuse me?

RAMON. You see? You can still see the handle.

MRS. TROTSKY. It's true, Leon. The axe is not entirely out of sight.

RAMON. So we cannot say "buried," we can only say "smashed," or perhaps "jammed"—

TROTSKY. All right, all right. But why did you do this?

---

10. sombrero, serape, huaraches, Mexican wearing apparel; a large straw hat, a multicolored shawl, and leather sandals.

RAMON. I think I read about it in an encyclopedia.

TROTSKY (to audience). The power of the printed word!

RAMON. I wanted to use an ice pick, but there weren't any around the house.

TROTSKY. But why? Do you realize who I am? Do you realize that you smashed this axe into the skull of a major historical figure? I helped run the Russian Revolution! I fought Stalin! I was a major political theorist! Why did you do this? Was it political disaffection? Anti-counter-revolutionary backlash?

RAMON. Actually—it was love, señor.

MRS. TROTSKY. It's true, Leon. (She and RAMON join hands.) I'm only sorry you had to find out about it this way.

TROTSKY. No.

MRS. TROTSKY. Yes.

TROTSKY. No.

RAMON. Sí!

TROTSKY. Oh God! What a fool I've been! (He dies.)

(Bell)

Variation Seven

TROTSKY. Why did you really do this, Ramon?

RAMON. You will never know, Señor Trotsky.

TROTSKY. This is a nightmare!

RAMON. But luckily for you—your night will soon be over.

(TROTSKY dies.)

(Bell)

Variation Eight

TROTSKY. All right, Ramon. Thank you. You may go.

(RAMON starts out. Stops.)

RAMON. Señor Trotsky—?

TROTSKY. Yes?

RAMON. Do you think you will have time to look at the nasturtiums today? They are really very beautiful.

TROTSKY. I don't think so, Ramon. But I'll try.

RAMON. Thank you, señor. *Hasta la vista.* Or should I say, *buenas noches.* (Exits)

TROTSKY. Well. All right then. The twenty-first of August, 1940. The day I'm going to die. Interesting. And to think that I've gone over so many twenty-firsts of August in my life, like a man walking over his own grave . . .

MRS. TROTSKY. It's been wonderful being married to you, Leon.

TROTSKY. Thank you, Mrs. Trotsky.

MRS. TROTSKY. Though it was a burden at times, being married to a major historical figure.

TROTSKY. I'm sorry I was away from home so often, tending the revolution.

MRS. TROTSKY. I understand.

TROTSKY. And I'm sorry I couldn't have been more in touch with my feelings.

MRS. TROTSKY (gentle protest). No . . . please . . .

TROTSKY. And that I often had such trouble expressing my emotions.

MRS. TROTSKY. Oh, I haven't been everything I should have been.

TROSTKY. Well, it's a little late for regrets, with a mountain-climber's axe buried in one's skull.

MRS. TROTSKY. Smashed, actually.

TROTSKY. So it wasn't old age, or cancer, or even the ice pick that I feared for years. It was an axe wielded by a Spanish Communist posing as a gardener.

MRS. TROTSKY. You really couldn't have guessed that, Leon.

TROTSKY. So even an assassin can make the flowers grow. The gardener was false, and yet the garden that he tended was real. How was I to know he was my killer when I passed him every day? How was I to know that the man tending the nasturtiums would keep me from seeing what the weather will be like tomorrow? How was I to know I'd never get to see *Casablanca*, which wouldn't be made until 1942 and which I would have despised anyway? How was I to know I'd never get to know about the bomb, or the eighty thousand dead at Hiroshima? Or rock and roll, or Gorbachev, or the state of Israel? How was I supposed to know I'd be erased from the history books of my own land . . . ?

MRS. TROTSKY. But reinstated, at least partially, someday.

TROTSKY. Sometime, for everyone, there's a room that you go into, and it's the room that you never leave. Or else you go out of a room and it's the last room that you'll ever leave. *(He looks around.)* This is my last room.

MRS. TROTSKY. But you aren't even here, Leon.

TROTSKY. This desk, these books, that calendar . . .

MRS. TROTSKY. You're not even here, my love.

TROTSKY. The sunshine coming through the blinds . . .

MRS. TROTSKY. That was yesterday. You're in a hospital, unconscious.

TROTSKY. The flowers in the garden. You, standing there . . .

MRS. TROTSKY. This is yesterday you're seeing.

TROTSKY. What does that entry say? Would you read it again?

MRS. TROTSKY. "On August 20th, 1940, a Spanish Communist named Ramon Mercader smashed a mountain-climber's axe into Trotsky's skull in Coyoacan, a suburb of Mexico City. Trotsky died the next day."

TROTSKY. It gives you a little hope about the world, doesn't it? That a man could have a mountain-climber's axe smashed into his skull, and yet live on for one whole day . . . ? Maybe I'll go look at the nasturtiums.

(TROTSKY dies. The garden outside the louvered window begins to glow.)

The Lights Fade

Variations on the Death of Trotsky

Responding to the Play

1. Pick your favorite variation. Explain what you like about it.
2. Think about the various uses of comic irony in the play. Discuss with classmates the ones you found most amusing.
3. Think of a popular song that could be Trotsky's theme. Share with the class why this song suits Trotsky.
4. Compare Trotsky's character in Variation One to Trotsky's character in Variation Eight.
5. Who would a Variation Nine include? How would it begin and end?

More About Leon Trotsky and the Russian Revolution

The Russian Revolution was a series of strikes, rebellions, and uprisings that lasted from before 1900, through World War I, and on into the 1920s. Born of many causes, it was fueled by the indifference of Russian rulers to the poor living conditions of the workers (the proletariat). Around 1916 Russian ruler Tzar Nicholas II created the Duma, an elected group of lawmakers, who were to advise him. Before long, he terminated the Duma, and by 1917 his overthrow was inevitable.

During this time, a number of revolutionary factions fought to support the proletariat. The leading faction, led by V. I. Lenin, with Leon Trotsky as second in command, was the Bolsheviks. Trotsky was imprisoned by the tzar in 1905 and 1907 and later expelled from Russia. He spent 10 years in Europe spreading the Bolshevik cause, even coming to the United States. When Lenin died in 1924, Stalin became dictator and expelled Trotsky. Trotsky and his wife settled in Coyoacan, Mexico. The rest, as they say, is history.

CREATING AND PERFORMING

1. Read your favorite variation again. Show the class how you would move and gesture as you read the first four lines of all parts.
2. Look again at the puns and plays on words in variations Three and Five. Make up one more along the same line.
3. Look back at question 5 above. Write Variation Nine and read it to the class.

Before Reading

A Conversation with My Dogs

The Play as Literature: Tone

In the same way an artist's brushstrokes give a painting depth and texture, an author's tone shapes and colors a piece of writing. The *tone* of a work reveals the way an author feels about a subject—his or her attitude concerning the issues being presented.

A writer treating a subject such as divorce will probably use a well-balanced, reasoning tone. This tells the reader that the subject is serious. A writer who wishes to present a quirky world in which dogs engage in lighthearted bantering, however, will strike a different tone altogether—a tone that alerts us to the funny business at hand. As you read the play, be aware of the author's tone.

The Play as Theatre: Physical Acting

Some plays require much more physical acting than others. In the play you are about to read, two of the characters are dogs, which requires the actors to assume very stylized and physical acting. This physicality will convey as much to the audience about the characters' lives as dogs as do the words they speak. Be aware of the following when trying to create a character—human or dog.

Posture A character's posture broadcasts vast information about mood, attitude, age, intentions, and so on. A sad person's head hangs; the shoulders droop. A happy person moves with spring in his or her step. A happy dog moves in a single bound.

Gesture It helps to develop a distinct gesture that sums up the character's personality. Acting the part of a dog requires the realization that those are paws at the end of your arms—and they can scratch, dig, and shake.

Expression An actor's face should show a character's greatest joy as well as the slightest irritation. Man or dog, when angry, the eyes widen; when guilty, the head lowers.

Warm Up!

Write one word that describes what you see as the physical essence of the items below. Pick one and think about how you would portray it.

lamp   telephone   ant   pencil   beagle   cloud

A Conversation with My Dogs

Merrill Markoe

Setting	Characters	Time
A living room	**ME** **BOB** **STAN**	The Present

*I*t is late afternoon. Seated at my desk, I call for my dogs to join me in my office. They do.

ME. The reason I've summoned you here today is I really think we should talk about something.

BOB. What's that?

ME. Well, please don't take this the wrong way, but I get the feeling you guys think you *have* to follow me *everywhere* and I just want you both to know that you don't.

STAN. Where would you get a feeling like that?

ME. I get it from the fact that the both of you follow me *everywhere* all day long. Like for instance, this morning. We were all together in the bedroom? Why do you both look blank? Doesn't this ring a bell at all? I was on the bed reading the paper . . .

BOB. Where was I?

ME. On the floor sleeping.

BOB. On the floor sleepi . . .? Oh, yes. Right, I remember that. Go on.

ME. So, there came a point where I had to get up and go into the next room to get a Kleenex. And you both woke up out of a deep sleep to go with me.

STAN. Yes. So? What's the problem?

BOB. We *like* to watch you get Kleenex. We happen to think it's something you do very well.

ME. The point I'm trying to make is why do you both have to get up out of a deep sleep to go with me? You sit there staring at me, all excited, like you think something really good is going to happen. I feel a lot of pressure to be more entertaining.

BOB. Would it help if we stood?

STAN. I think what the lady is saying is that where Kleenex retrieval is concerned, she'd just as soon we not make the trip.

BOB. Is that true?

ME. Yes. It is.

BOB *(deeply hurt).* Oh, man.

STAN. Don't let her get to you, buddy.

BOB. I know I shouldn't. But it all comes as such a shock.

ME. I think you may be taking this wrong. It's not that I don't like your company. It's just that I see no reason for you both to follow me every time I get up.

BOB. What if just one of us goes?

STAN. And I don't suppose that "one of us" would be *you?*

ME. *Neither* of you needs to go.

BOB. Okay. Fine. No problem. Get your damn Kleenex alone from now on.

ME. Good.

BOB. I'm just curious. What's your position on pens?

ME. Pens?

BOB. Yes. How many of us can wake up out of a deep sleep to watch you look for a pen?

ME. Why would *either* of you want to wake up out of a deep sleep to follow me around while I'm looking for a pen?

STAN. Is she serious?

BOB. I can't tell. She has such a weird sense of humor.

ME. Let's just level with each other, okay? The *real* reason you both follow me every place I go is that you secretly believe there might be food involved. Isn't that true? Isn't that the real reason for the show of enthusiasm?

STAN. Very nice talk.

BOB. The woman has got some mouth on her.

ME. You mean you *deny* that every time you follow me out of the room it's actually because you think we're stopping for snacks?

BOB. Absolutely false. That is a bald-faced lie. We do it for the life experience. Period.

STAN. And sometimes I think it might work into a game of ball.

BOB. But we certainly don't expect anything.

STAN. We're *way* past expecting anything of you. We wouldn't want you to overexert yourself in any way. You have to rest and save up all your strength for all that Kleenex fetching.

BOB. Plus we know it doesn't concern you in the least that we're both *starving to death.*

STAN. We consume on the average about a third of the calories eaten daily by the typical wasted South American street dog.

ME. *One* bowl of food a day is what the *vet* said I should give you. No more.

BOB. One bowl of food is a joke. It's an hors d'oeuvre.[1] It does nothing but whet my appetite.

ME. Last summer, before I cut your food down, you were the size and shape of a hassock.[2]

BOB. Who is she talking to?

STAN. You, pal. You looked like a bean-bag chair, buddy.

BOB. But it was not from overeating. In summer, I retain fluids, that's all. I was in very good shape.

STAN. For a hippo. I saw you play ball back then. Nice energy. For a dead guy.

BOB. Don't talk to me about energy. Who singlehandedly ate his way through the back fence. Not just once but on *four separate occasions?*

ME. So *you're* the one who did that?

BOB. One who did what?

---

1. *hors d'oeuvre* (ôr derv′), a small appetizer eaten to whet the appetite for dinner
2. hassock (has′ək), a padded cushion on legs that serves as a foot rest. Some hassocks are large and round.

ME. Ate through the back fence.

BOB. Is there something wrong with the back fence? I have no idea what happened. Whoever said that is a liar.

STAN. The fact remains that we are starving all day long and you continually torture us by eating right in front of us.

BOB. Very nice manners, by the way.

ME. You have the nerve to discuss my manners? Who drinks out of the toilet and then comes up and kisses me on the face?

BOB. That would be Stan.

ME. No. That would be *you.* And while we're on the subject of manners, who keeps trying to crawl *into* the refrigerator? Who always has *mud* on their tongue?

STAN. Well, that would be Bob.

ME. Okay. But the point I'm trying to make is that where manners are concerned, let's just say that you don't catch me trying to stick my head in *your* dinner.

BOB. Well, that may be more a function of menu than anything else.

ME. Which brings me right back to my original point. The two of you do not have to wake up and offer me fake camaraderie[3] now that you understand that *once* a day is all you're ever going to be fed. Period. Nonnegotiable. For the rest of your natural lives. And if I want to play ball, I'll *say so.* End of sentence.

STAN. Well, I see that the nature of these talks has completely broken down.

BOB. I gotta tell you, it hurts.

ME. There's no reason to have hurt feelings.

STAN. Fine. Whatever you say.

BOB. I just don't give a damn anymore. I'm beyond that, quite frankly. Get your own Kleenex, for all I care.

STAN. I feel the same way. Let her go get all the Kleenex and pens she wants. I couldn't care less.

ME. Excellent. Well, I hope we understand each other now.

BOB. We do. Why'd you get up? Where are you going?

ME. Into the next room.

STAN. Oh. Mm hmm. I see. And why is that?

ME. To get my purse.

STAN. Hey, fatso, out of my way.

BOB. Watch out. I was first.

STAN. *I* was first.

BOB. We're getting her purse, I go first. *I'm starving.*

STAN. You don't listen at all, do you. Going for *pens* means food. She said she's getting her *purse.* That means *ball.*

---

3. camaraderie (kăm ä rad′er ē′), friendliness; loyalty among friends

A Conversation with My Dogs

Responding to the Play

1. In order to understand the characters better, write a short biography for each one.
2. With a partner, create a program for this play. Be sure to draw a cover.
3. How would you describe the tone of this play? Give examples to support your opinion.
4. Think of ways you would portray Bob and Stan physically. Write a list of their movements during a specific interchange.
5. Write a monologue in which Bob complains about his treatment by Me.

About Merrill Markoe and Her Dogs

Merrill Markoe won four Emmy Awards during her years as head writer for the television show *Late Night with David Letterman*. She created "Stupid Pet Tricks" for the show and edited the book *Late Night with David Letterman: The Book*. She has written and performed in original specials for cable television. Markoe lives in California with her dog, Lewis, and her stepdog, Beau.

For more about her adventures with Stan and Bob, you might want to read *What the Dogs Have Taught Me and Other Amazing Things I've Learned*, published in 1992 by Viking Penguin, New York, or *The Day My Dogs Became Guys*, published by Viking Penguin in 1999.

Creating and Performing

1. Get together in groups of threes and choose a character from the play to portray. All members should help those who play the dogs create a dog persona—including appropriate physical movements and voice modulation.
2. You probably noticed that this play has no stage directions. Add some that you feel are appropriate. Choose one page of the play, and write the stage directions for all the characters.
3. Look back at the list you created for question 4 above. Show the class one or two of the movements you would perform.

He Who Says Yes and He Who Says No

The Play as Literature: Theme

The central idea of a literary work is called its *theme*. The theme may be boldly stated or softly implied, and it makes each play unique.

Bertolt Brecht believed that his ideas, or themes, were the most important part of his plays, so he developed a form of "epic theater" to highlight them. Brecht's "epic" plays feature a series of episodes, or scenes. Each scene is crafted to present an idea.

In the play you are about to read, the theme in the first part *(He Who Says Yes)* is different than the theme in the second part *(He Who Says No)*. As you read, compare and contrast these two themes. (See p. 117 for more about Brechtian theatre.)

The Play as Theatre: The Chorus

Have you ever sung in a chorus? If so, you have some idea of how a chorus in a drama functions. In the theatre, a chorus always speaks as one. No particular voice is heard above the others. Often employed by Greek dramatists in the early 400s B.C., the chorus comments on what is happening on stage. It questions, urges, supposes, translates, and summarizes. It could be called the busybody of the production. Often, the chorus helps keep things moving—making just the right comment at just the right time.

Noh mask of a young girl

In this play, Brecht draws upon a classical theatre form, the Noh Theatre of Japan. In Noh, an eight-man chorus sits at the side of the stage, narrating the background and story of the play. Sometimes the chorus describes a character's thoughts and emotions. It may even sing a character's lines.

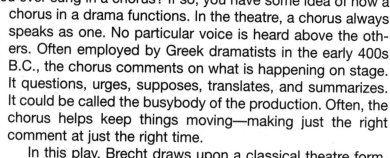

Warm Up!

Get together with three other students. Choose either the first or second paragraph of this page to read together. Discuss how you would stand and move during the reading. Will your reading be dramatic, matter-of-fact, instructional, or comic? Will you read quickly or slowly? Jot down your ideas. Be prepared to read your paragraph aloud.

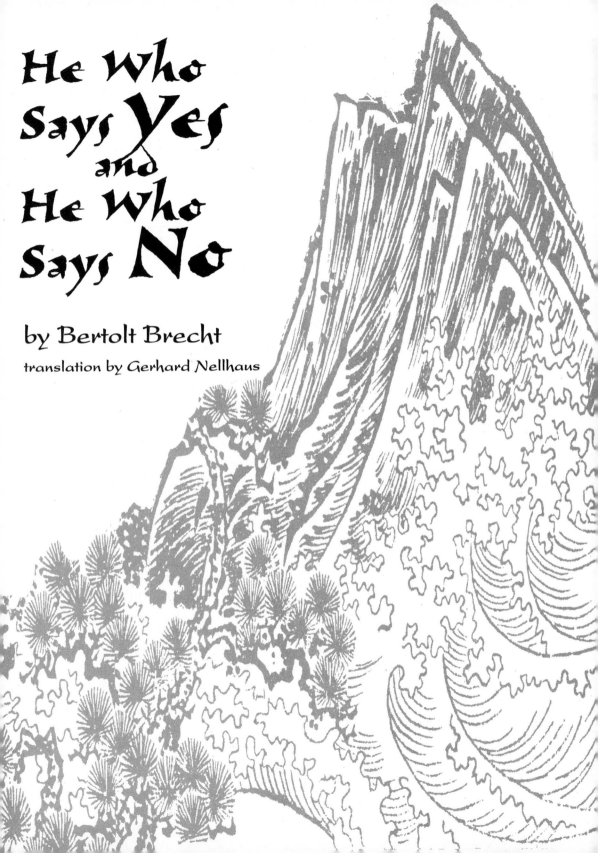

He Who Says Yes and He Who Says No

by Bertolt Brecht

translation by Gerhard Nellhaus

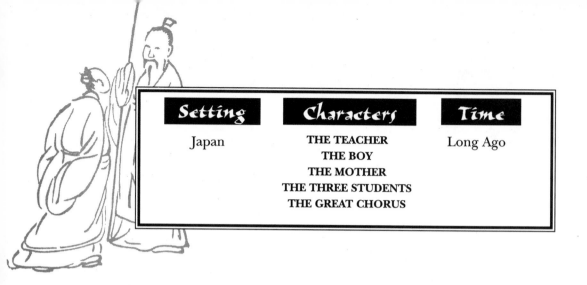

Setting	Characters	Time
Japan	THE TEACHER THE BOY THE MOTHER THE THREE STUDENTS THE GREAT CHORUS	Long Ago

He Who Says Yes
1

GREAT CHORUS.

Above all learn when to say Yes.
Many say Yes without understanding.
Many are not asked, and many
Say Yes to falsehoods. Therefore:
Above all learn when to say Yes.

(THE TEACHER is now in Room 1, THE MOTHER *and* BOY *in Room 2.)*

TEACHER. I am the teacher. I teach school in the city and I have a student whose father is dead. He has only his mother to take care of him. I've come to say goodbye to them now because I am about to start on a trip over the mountains. An epidemic[1] has broken out among us, and in the city beyond the mountains live some famous doctors. *(He knocks at the door.)* May I come in?

BOY *(stepping from Room 2 into Room 1).* Who is it? Oh, the teacher; teacher's come to visit us!

TEACHER. Why haven't you been to school for so long?

BOY. I couldn't come because Mother was sick.

TEACHER. I didn't know that your mother, too, was ill. Please tell her I'm here.

BOY *(calling into Room 2).* Mother, Teacher is here.

MOTHER *(sitting in Room 2).* Ask him to come in, please.

BOY. Please come in.

(They enter Room 2.)

TEACHER. I haven't been here for a long time. Your son tells me that you, too, have caught the sickness. Are you feeling any better now?

MOTHER. No, unfortunately I'm not getting any better; nobody here knows how to treat this disease.

TEACHER. A way must be found. That's why I came to say goodbye: tomorrow I'm starting out on a trip over

---

1. epidemic (ep/ə dem/ik), an outbreak of disease that affects many people

the mountains to get medicine and advice. For in the city beyond the mountains live the famous doctors.

MOTHER. A relief expedition[2] over the mountains! Yes, indeed, I've heard that the famous doctors live there, but I've also heard that the trip is dangerous. Were you thinking of taking my boy with you?

TEACHER. That's no trip for a child!

MOTHER. I agree. I hope you will return safely.

TEACHER. I have to go now. Goodbye. Get well. (TEACHER goes to Room 1.)

BOY (follows THE TEACHER into Room 1). I want to say something.

(MOTHER listens at the door.)

TEACHER. What do you want to say?

BOY. I want to go over the mountains with you.

TEACHER.
As I've already told your mother
The trip is hard and dangerous.
You won't be able to come along.
Besides: How can you want to leave
    your mother
When she is so ill?
Stay here. It's really impossible
For you to come along.

BOY.
Just because Mother is sick, I want
To come with you.
I must get her
Medicine and advice
From the famous doctors in the city
    beyond the mountains.

TEACHER. I must talk this over with your mother. (He returns to Room 2. BOY lis-

tens at the door.) As you see, I've come back. Your son has asked to come with us. I told him he couldn't leave you while you are ill; and also that it is a hard and dangerous trip. It was out of the question for him to come along, I said. But he said he had to come with us to the city beyond the mountains to get medicine and advice for you.

MOTHER. I heard what he said. I know the boy means well and would like to make the dangerous trip with you. Come in, Son. (THE BOY enters Room 2.)
Ever since
Your father left us
I've had no one
But you at my side.
You were never longer
Out of my mind and out of my sight
Than it took
To prepare your meals
To fix your clothes and
To earn a living.

BOY. What you say is true. But still you can't get me to change my mind.

BOY, MOTHER, TEACHER. I am (he is) going to make the dangerous trip
To get for your (my, her) illness
Medicine and advice
In the city beyond the mountains.

GREAT CHORUS.
You saw that no argument
Could move him.
Then the teacher and the mother said

_____
2. expedition (ek'spə dish'ən) a journey undertaken for a specific purpose

In one voice:

TEACHER and MOTHER.

Many say Yes to falsehoods
But he says Yes not to illness
But that illness be healed.

GREAT CHORUS. Now the mother said:

MOTHER.

I have no more strength.
If it has to be
Go with the teacher.
But hurry, hurry,
Return to me soon.

He Who Says Yes
II

GREAT CHORUS.

The people have started
On the trip over the mountains,
Among them the teacher
And the boy.
The boy was not equal to the strain:
He overworked his heart
In their hurry to return.
At dawn at the foot of the mountains
He could hardly
Drag himself on.

(Into Room 1 enters THE TEACHER, THE THREE STUDENTS *and finally* THE BOY *with a jug.)*

TEACHER. We climbed rapidly. There is the first hut. Let's rest there a while.

THREE STUDENTS. We'll do that.

(They step on the raised platform in Room 2. THE BOY *holds* THE TEACHER *back.)*

BOY. I want to say something.

TEACHER. What do you want to say?

BOY. I don't feel well.

TEACHER. Not another word. Whoever undertakes a trip such as this must not say such things. Perhaps you're just tired, not being used to climbing. Stop and rest a while. *(He steps on the platform.)*

THREE STUDENTS. It seems that the boy is tired from climbing. Let's ask the teacher.

GREAT CHORUS. Yes, do.

THREE STUDENTS *(to* THE TEACHER*).* We hear that the boy is tired from climbing. What's the matter with him? Are you worried about him?

TEACHER. He said he didn't feel well, but he really is all right. He is tired from climbing.

THREE STUDENTS. Then you aren't worried about him? *(Long pause, then* THE STUDENTS *among one another.)*

Do you hear? The teacher said
The boy is only tired from climbing.
But doesn't he look strange?
Right after the hut comes the narrow
    pass.
Only clutching the cliff
With both hands
Can you pass.
Let's hope he's not sick.
For if he cannot go on, we must
Leave him here.

(They call down to Room 1, forming a megaphone with their hands.)

Are you sick? He doesn't answer.
Let's ask the teacher again. *(To* THE TEACHER*)* When we asked you before about the boy you said he was only

tired from climbing, but now he looks so strange. He even sat down.

TEACHER. I see that he has fallen ill. Try to carry him over the narrow pass.

THREE STUDENTS. We'll try. *(THE THREE STUDENTS try to carry THE BOY over the narrow pass. This must be constructed so that THE THREE STUDENTS can pass, one by one, but not carrying THE BOY.)* We can't carry him over and we can't stay with him. In any event, we must move on, for a whole city is waiting for the medicine we are to bring back. We say it with dread but if he cannot go on we will have to leave him here in the mountains.

TEACHER. Yes, maybe you'll have to. How can I oppose you? But I think it only right that we should ask the sick boy if we should turn around for his sake. I feel a deep sorrow for this human being. I'll go and break his fate to him gently.

THREE STUDENTS. Please do. *(They face each other.)*

THREE STUDENTS and GREAT CHORUS.

We'll ask him (They asked him)
   whether he demands (demanded)
That we (they) turn around now for
   his sake.
But even if he demands (demanded) it,
We will (they would) not turn back,
But leave him here and go on.

TEACHER *(has gone to THE BOY in Room 1)*. Listen closely. Since you are sick and cannot go on we must leave you here. But it is only right to ask the one who is sick if we should turn around for his sake. But custom demands also that the sick person

answer: You shall not turn back.

BOY. I understand.

TEACHER. Do you demand that we turn back for your sake?

BOY. No, you shall not turn back!

TEACHER. Then you agree to stay behind?

BOY. I must think this over. *(Pause of reflection)* Yes, I agree.

TEACHER *(calls from Room 1 into Room 2)*. He answered as necessity demanded.

GREAT CHORUS and THREE STUDENTS

(The latter are going down to Room 1.)
He said yes. Go on! *(THREE STUDENTS stand still.)*

TEACHER.

Go on now, don't stop.
For you've decided to move on.

(THE THREE STUDENTS stand still.)

BOY. I want to say something: I ask you not to let me lie here but to throw me into the valley, for I'm afraid to die alone.

THREE STUDENTS. We cannot do that.

BOY. Why not? I demand it.

TEACHER.

You have decided to move on and to
   leave him here.
It is easy to decide his fate.
But hard to carry it out.
Are you ready to throw him into the
   valley?

THREE STUDENTS. Yes. *(THE THREE STUDENTS carry THE BOY to the platform in Room 2.)*

Lean your head on our arms.
Don't strain yourself
We'll carry you carefully.

(*The* THREE STUDENTS *stand in front of* THE BOY, *hiding him, on the furthest edge of the platform.*)

BOY (*not visible*).

I knew that on this trip
I might lose my life.
The thought of my mother
Tempted me to go.
Take my jug
Fill it with the medicine
And on your return
Give it to my mother.

GREAT CHORUS.

Then the friends took the jug
And bewailed the hard ways of the
    world
And its bitter necessities,
And threw the boy down.
Shoulder on shoulder they pressed
    together
At the edge of the abyss[3]
And closing their eyes they hurled
    him down,
No one guiltier than his neighbor.
And they threw clumps of earth
And flat stones
After him.

He Who Says No
1

GREAT CHORUS.

Above all learn when to say Yes
Many say Yes without understanding.
Many are not asked, and many
Say Yes to falsehoods. Therefore:
Above all learn when to say Yes.

(THE TEACHER *is now in Room 1,* THE MOTHER *and* THE BOY *in Room 2.*)

TEACHER. I am the teacher. I teach school in the city and I have a student whose father is dead. He has only his mother to take care of him. I've come to say goodbye to them now, because I'm about to start a trip over the mountains. (*He knocks at the door.*) May I come in?

BOY (*stepping from Room 2 into Room 1*). Who is it? Oh, the teacher; the teacher's come to visit us!

TEACHER. Why haven't you been to school for so long?

BOY. I couldn't come because Mother was sick.

TEACHER. I didn't know that. Please tell her I am here.

BOY (*calling into Room 2*). Mother, Teacher is here.

MOTHER (*sitting in Room 2*). Ask him to come in please.

BOY. Please come in.

(*They enter Room 2.*)

TEACHER. I haven't been here for a long time. Your son tells me you've been sick. Are you feeling any better now?

MOTHER. No need to worry about my illness. It left no bad effects.

TEACHER. Glad to hear it. I came to say goodbye to you because I'm going on a research trip over the mountains soon. For in the city beyond the mountains live the famous teachers.

MOTHER. A research trip over the mountains! Yes, indeed, I've heard

---

3. abyss (ə bis′) a very deep pit or hole

that the famous teachers live there, but I've also heard that the trip is dangerous. Were you thinking of taking my boy with you?

TEACHER. That's no trip for a child!

MOTHER. I agree. I hope you will return safely.

TEACHER. I have to go now. Goodbye. Get well. (TEACHER goes to Room 1.)

BOY (follows the TEACHER into Room 1). I want to say something.

(MOTHER listens at the door.)

TEACHER. What do you want to say?

BOY. I want to go over the mountains with you.

TEACHER.
As I've already told your mother
The trip is hard and dangerous.
You won't be able to come along.
Besides: How can you want to leave your mother
When she is ill?
Stay here. It's really impossible
For you to come along.

BOY.
Just because Mother is sick, I want
To come with you;
I must get her
Medicine and advice
From the famous doctors in the city
beyond the mountains.

TEACHER. But would you agree to everything that might happen to you on the trip?

BOY. Yes.

TEACHER. I must talk this over with your mother. (He returns to Room 2. BOY listens at the door.) As you see, I've come

back. Your son has asked to come with us. I told him he couldn't leave you while you are still ill; and also that it is a hard and dangerous trip. It was out of the question for him to come along, I said. But he said he had to come with us to the city beyond the mountains to get medicine and advice for you.

MOTHER. I heard what he said. I know the boy means well and would like to make the dangerous trip. Come in, Son. (THE BOY enters Room 2.)
Ever since
Your father left us
I've had no one
But you at my side.
You were never longer
Out of my mind and out of my sight
Than it took
To prepare your meals,
To fix your clothes and
To earn a living.

BOY. What you say is true. But still you can't get me to change my mind.

BOY, MOTHER, TEACHER.
I am going (He is going) to make the dangerous trip
To get for your (my, her) illness
Medicine and advice
In the city beyond the mountains.

GREAT CHORUS.
You saw that no argument
Could move him.
Then the teacher and the mother said
In one voice:

TEACHER and MOTHER.
Many say Yes to falsehoods

But he says Yes not to illness
But that illness be healed.

GREAT CHORUS.

Now the mother said:

MOTHER.

I have no more strength.
If it has to be
Go with the teacher.
But hurry, hurry
Return to me soon.

He Who Says No II

GREAT CHORUS.

The people have started
On the trip over the mountains
Among them the teacher
And the boy.
The boy was not equal to the strain:
He overworked his heart
In their hurry to return.
At dawn at the foot of the mountains
He could hardly
Drag himself on.

(Into Room 1 enter THE TEACHER, THREE STUDENTS, *and finally* THE BOY *with a jug.)*

TEACHER. We climbed rapidly. There is the first hut. Let's rest there a while.

THREE STUDENTS. We'll do that.

(They step on the raised platform in Room 2. THE BOY holds THE TEACHER back.)

BOY. I want to say something.

TEACHER. What do you want to say?

BOY. I don't feel well.

TEACHER. Not another word. Whoever undertakes a trip such as this must not say such things. Perhaps you're just tired, not being used to climbing. Stop and rest a while. *(He steps on the platform in Room 2.)*

THREE STUDENTS. It seems that the boy is tired from climbing. Let's ask the teacher.

GREAT CHORUS. Yes, do.

THREE STUDENTS *(to* THE TEACHER*).* We hear that the boy is tired from climbing. What's the matter with him? Are you worried about him?

TEACHER. He said he didn't feel well, but he really is all right. He is tired from climbing.

THREE STUDENTS. Then you aren't worried about him? *(Long pause, then the students among one another.)*

Do you hear? The teacher said
The boy is only tired from climbing.
But doesn't he look strange?
Right after the hut comes the narrow
    pass.
Only clutching the cliff
With both hands
Can you pass.
We can't carry anyone.
Should we follow the great custom
And hurl him into the valley?

(They call down to Room 1, forming a megaphone with their hands.)

Are you sick from climbing?

BOY.

No!
See, I'm still standing up.
Wouldn't I sit down

If I were sick? *(Pause. The* BOY *sits down.)*

THREE STUDENTS. We'll tell the teacher. Sir, when we asked you before about the boy you said he was only tired from climbing, but now he looks so strange. He even sat down. We say it with dread, but since ancient times a great custom has ruled here: He who can go no further is hurled into the valley!

TEACHER. What? You want to throw this child into the valley?

THREE STUDENTS. Yes!

TEACHER. As you say. This is a great custom existing since ancient times. How can I oppose it? But doesn't the great custom also demand that we should ask the sick one if we should turn around for his sake? I feel a deep sorrow for this human being. I'll go and gently tell him of the great custom.

THREE STUDENTS. Please do. *(They face each other.)*

THREE STUDENTS and GREAT CHORUS.

We'll ask him (They asked him)
  whether he demands (demanded)
That we turn around now for his
  sake.
But even if he demands (demanded)
  it,
We will (they would) not turn back
But hurl him into the valley.

TEACHER *(has gone down to* THE BOY *in Room 1).* Listen closely. Since ancient times a law has ruled that he who falls ill on such a trip must be hurled into the valley. Death is instant. But the custom also demands that we should ask the sick one if we should

turn back for his sake. And the custom demands that the sick person answer: You shall not turn back. If I could take your place, how gladly I would die.

BOY. I understand.

TEACHER. Do you ask that we turn back for your sake? Or do you agree that we throw you into the valley as the great custom demands?

BOY. No! I do not agree.

TEACHER *(calling from Room 1 to Room 2).* Come down here! He did not answer as the custom demands. He who says A, must also say B. When you were asked before whether you would agree to everything that might happen to you on this trip, you said yes.

BOY. The answer that I gave was false. But your question was even more false. He who says A, does not have to say B. He can also realize that A was false. I wanted to get medicine for my mother. But now that I am sick myself, it's no longer possible. And I want to turn back immediately now that things have changed. So I ask you to turn back and to bring me home. Surely, your research can wait. If there's something to learn over there, as I hope there is, then it can only be that in a situation such as ours now, we should turn around. And as for the great ancient custom, I see no sense to it. Rather, I need a great new custom, one we must introduce here and now: the custom to give each new situation new thought.

THREE STUDENTS *(to* THE TEACHER*).* What are we to do? What the boy says is sensible, even if it's not heroic.

TEACHER. I leave it up to you to decide what to do now. But I must tell you: People will hurl laughter and disgrace at you if you turn back.

THREE STUDENTS. Isn't it a disgrace that he speaks for himself?

TEACHER. No, I see no disgrace in that.

THREE STUDENTS. Then we'll turn back and no laughter and no abuse shall keep us from doing the sensible thing; and no ancient custom shall keep us from agreeing to a valid thought.

Lean your head on our arms.

Don't strain yourself
We'll carry you carefully.

GREAT CHORUS.

So the friends took the friend
And established a new custom
And a new law
And they brought the boy back.
Side by side they walked pressed
    together
Against the abuse,
Against the laughter, with open eyes,
No one more cowardly than his
    neighbor.

He Who Says Yes and He Who Says No

Responding to the Play

1. Do you think this play has a lesson for your life? Why or why not?
2. Think about the theme of the play. To what did the boy say yes? To what did he say no?
3. Make a simple diagram of the set for this play. Include both rooms and the platform.
4. Compare and contrast the role of the chorus to the role of the three students.
5. Suppose you were to costume this play. Would you use traditional Japanese kimono, contemporary clothing, or something else all together? Explain your reasoning.

More About Brechtian Theatre

Bertolt Brecht wanted audiences to learn as they were being entertained. He didn't want them to become so emotionally involved in the action that they would lose sight of the play's underlying ideas. So he developed a series of techniques he called the "alienation effect."

Brecht used several tactics to produce his alienation effect. Sometimes he had actors hold up printed signs for the audience to read. Sometimes characters turned and spoke or sang directly to the audience. Sometimes he employed distracting noises or aimed bright lights directly into the eyes of the audience. All these distractions were designed to remind the audience that they were watching a play that they could think about, comment on, and learn from.

Creating and Performing

1. Look back at page 111, in which the three students attempt to carry the boy over a narrow pass. Say the lines as you would say them normally, then say them as you would while carrying someone.
2. Write a third ending to the play titled, "He Who Says Perhaps." Include the boy, the teacher, the chorus, and the three students.
3. Draw a simple sketch of the costumes that each of the characters in the play would wear.

Before Reading

I NEVER SAW ANOTHER BUTTERFLY

The Play as Literature: Dramatic Monologue

A *monologue* is any fairly lengthy speech that a single character addresses to the audience. In a dramatic monologue, the character speaks at a critical moment in the play. The monologue reveals something about the speaker or fills in important circumstances that have occurred beyond the knowledge of the audience.

In the play you are about to read, the main character, Raja Englanderova (ra′ya in glan drō′va), steps back and forth in time and in and out of the action to reveal to the audience events that happen outside the immediate action of the play. As you read, think about how her monologues help give the play depth and fullness.

The Play as Theatre: Sound

Dramatic presentations often must rely on sound production that goes beyond the voices of the actors. Sound equipment is used in the theatre to make the actors' voices louder, to provide special effects (such as a ringing phone or a train engine), or to supply music that sets the mood for the play. In professional theatres, sound is enhanced by microphones, amplifiers, and speakers. Engineers sit at a sound control board to oversee all of these devices, as well as tapes, CDs, and records that might be used in the production. Amateur and school productions are often limited in the sound production equipment they have. Sometimes a few microphones, a tape recorder, and creative thinking must do the trick.

Sound effects are indicated in a script in italic type enclosed in parentheses. Keep track of the types of sounds called for in the play.

WARM UP!

Get together with a partner and come up with various ways you might collect the following sounds for a production:

a) names being announced   **d)** children playing
b) a train pulling into a station   **e)** dogs barking
c) bells ringing   **f)** orchestral music

I
NEVER SAW
ANOTHER
BUTTERFLY

by Celeste Raspanti

SETTING	CHARACTERS	TIME
Terezin, Czechoslovakia	RAJA ENGLANDEROVA FATHER MOTHER VERA, her aunt PAVEL, her brother ERIKA, a neighbor IRENA SYNKOVA, a teacher RENKA, Irena's assistant IRCA, Pavel's fiancée HONZA, a friend of Raja RABBI at Terezin CHILD I CHILD II CHILD III CHILD IV CHILDREN of Terezin LOUDSPEAKER, a voice The YOUTH of Terezin	1940's

An open stage. Projection screen. The stage is set with various levels and steps. As the house dims and the music comes up, butterflies are projected over the entire stage area. The music grows in intensity until a train whistle in the distance drowns it out. As the train sound increases, the butterflies disappear. As the train sound fades, lights come up on RAJA, *who stands downstage facing the audience. She is carrying a school bag and a bundle whose outer covering is a black shawl.*

RAJA. My name is Raja. I was born in Prague. I am a Jew—and I survived Terezin. *(She sets down her belongings, sits down and removes her scarf, looking out over the audience.)*

LOUDSPEAKER. Zuzana Winterova, 11 years old—perished at Auschwitz, October 4, 1944. Gabriela Freiova, 10 years old—perished at Auschwitz, May 18, 1944. Frantisek Brozan, 14 years old—perished at Auschwitz, December 15, 1943. Eva Bulova, 15 years old—perished at Auschwitz, October 4, 1944. Liana Franklova, 13 years old—perished at Auschwitz, October 19, 1944. Alfred Weisskopf, 16 years old—perished at Auschwitz, December 18, 1944. Honza—Honza Kosek, $16\frac{1}{2}$ years old—perished at Auschwitz, January 21, 1945 . . .

RAJA *(stands to face in the direction of the voice; she walks slowly downstage and speaks).* My name—is Raja. I was born in Prague. Father, Mother, Pavel, Irca—Irena, Honza—they are all gone, and I am alone. But that is not important. Only one thing is important—that I am a Jew, and that I survived. Terezin was a fortress built by Emperor Joseph II of Austria for his mother Maria Teresa. About sixty kilometers from Prague, it slept quietly in its green valley under blue skies until . . .

LOUDSPEAKER *(an arrogant, military voice, interrupting).* <u>March 5, 1939</u>. German Wehrmacht enters Prague. *(Martial music under the following announcements)* <u>December 1, 1939</u>. Jewish children excluded from state elementary schools. <u>June 14, 1940</u>. Auschwitz concentration camp set up. <u>September 27, 1941</u>. Reinhard Heydrich orders mass deportation of Jews and establishes Terezin as a Jewish ghetto. <u>October 16, 1941</u>. *(Train sounds start and accelerate.)* First transports leave Prague for Terezin. *(Train sounds)* Among them were children . . .

(Train noises die down as light flashes on in upstage area. IRENA SYNKOVA, *one of the first inhabitants of Terezin, stands in the light with her back to the audience. She is holding a sheaf of odd-sized papers. She is a strong woman; one knows this by her voice and by the way she evokes strength in others. She has taken responsibility for the children in the camp, organized them into groups, planned lessons in a makeshift school for them. She is obsessed with their survival, and the survival in them of what is best.* RENKA, *a young woman who assists* IRENA *with the*

school and the care of the children, speaks from the darkness.)

RENKA. Irena, Irena Synkova—it's Renka. . . .

IRENA. Here—in the back. *(She approaches the outer rim of the dark circle that circumscribes[1] the classroom. She extends her hand to* RENKA.*)* Have the children arrived?

RENKA *(coming into the light, followed by a small group of children).* Yes, nearly four hundred—more than the earlier transport. *(She turns to the children who are now surrounding her, speaking warmly and kindly.)* Come, come along—we'll go with the others.

IRENA. Later, when the workers return—and the older children, we'll find places for them in the barracks—each one must have a place.

RENKA. And tomorrow, when another trainload arrives?

IRENA. We'll find a place for them—in the barracks and—*(With determination)* —here in the school. They must start living again. *(To the children huddled around* RENKA*)* School—yes, you will go to school again. . . . But go along now with Renka . . . to the bathhouse and then supper. . . . I promise . . .

RENKA. Come. *(She leads the group off. They seem to walk more quickly now.)*

*(*RAJA, *who has been watching from the distance, steps out of the area and takes her place in line with the children.* IRENA *has returned to folding and arranging papers when she notices the child.)*

---

1. circumscribe (sər′kəm skrīb′), to define or mark off

IRENA. You must go along now to the bath house, dear. (*RAJA remains tense, staring. There is a shrill, siren-like sound. She sits on the ground clutching her bag to her, following the children with her eyes.*)

RAJA. They told Papa, "Come along now to the bathhouse . . . you must take a shower so that we don't get any sickness in the camp." They told him to leave his clothes in the yard on the ground in front of him. They told him to put his shoes next to his clothes so he could find them again . . . but they took him to the gas . . . he never got his shoes . . .

IRENA (*walking to her*). Don't be afraid. (*She sees that RAJA is staring after the children.*) This is a real bathhouse. You can have soap and take a shower.

RAJA (*pulling away, frightened*). They took him to the bathhouse—he never got his shoes . . .

IRENA (*finally understanding*). That was Auschwitz. Here you are with friends. What is your name? (*RAJA shakes her head and pulls away.*) I am Irena Synkova. I'm a teacher here in Terezin. You'll come to school with us, won't you? (*RAJA turns and drops to the floor, covering her face with her hands. IRENA kneels at a distance from her, talking very quietly.*) You are from Prague? I once taught in Prague. It's a beautiful city. When I first came to Prague, I was about your age. I remember how frightened I was. But after I made some friends, I was happy to live there. Now you are not alone, and you must not be afraid either. (*She reaches for her gently. At the* first touch, the child recoils, but does not move away. She allows IRENA to remove her scarf and to take the sack from her clenched fist. She watches IRENA's face.*) Now that you know my name, you must tell me yours. How can we be friends? I won't know what to call you.

RAJA. My number is tattooed here. (*Still watching her, RAJA stretches out her arm and shows a number tattooed on her arm. IRENA, touched by this, caresses her arm gently and smoothes her hair. She begins to look through the pack and finds an identification tag.*)

IRENA (*reading the tag*). Raja Englanderova. (*RAJA watches silently as IRENA carefully replaces the tattered clothes, the box, etc. in her pack. IRENA rises.*) Come, Raja, Raja Englanderova. Let me tell you about our school. (*When the child does not respond, IRENA walks to the side and kneels to sort the papers she had with her. She is very much aware that RAJA is watching her.*) There's so much to do here in school. You will be coming here, tomorrow, perhaps. There are many children here. We have few books—but we have many songs: every day if you wish, you may paint and draw; here, see, each of the children has drawn a spring picture. Would you like to paint? I'll find some paper for you, then tomorrow—you may begin. (*RAJA has been watching IRENA from a kneeling position. She rises slowly and walks up behind IRENA, who is busily sorting and folding papers.*) See, we save all the paper we can find: forms, wrapping paper—

and some of the children brought their own. And when there's enough, the children draw and paint. Would you like to choose a piece—of your own, Raja? (*She turns and very gently touches the child's hair, her cheek, her arm.* RAJA *does not move.*)

RAJA (*At a level with* IRENA's *shoulder, she timidly imitates her action as if she were trying to convince herself that this gentle person is real and not a lie; with her hand on* IRENA's *arm,* RAJA *finally speaks.*) My . . . name . . . is . . . Raja. . . . (*She leans her head wearily on* IRENA's *shoulder.* IRENA *embraces her gently. Music.*)

(*Getting up slowly,* RAJA *turns from her past and returns to the lighted area downstage.*)

RAJA. Slowly I began to heal, I and hundreds of children who passed through Irena Synkova's school. It was months before I could say anything but *My name is Raja.* I said it over and over to hear the sound of my voice—perhaps just to make sure I still knew my name—Raja. It was an achievement for me. Irena knew it. She gave me paper and paint and I wrote my name in stiff, crippled characters: Raja, Raja, Raja! It helped me to be sure I was still alive. One day, I suddenly wrote another name: *Irena.* Then I knew I was healed. I could paint and draw and speak again. I could tell Irena the things I was remembering. I was no longer afraid to remember. . . .

RAJA *turns to observe the scene upstage coming to life as the lights come up. She sees her* MOTHER *readying the* table for the Sabbath. *When her* MOTHER *calls,* RAJA *enters and takes her place in the scene.*

MOTHER (*as she enters carrying the candles, speaking over her shoulder*). Raja, cover the bread—and close the door to the kitchen; the candles will go out. . . .

RAJA (*entering the scene from the darkness*). Papa's coming up the street—Aunt Vera is with him. I can see them from the back window.

MOTHER (*sharply*). Raja, you must not open the back shutters. I've told you that . . . do you hear?

(PAVEL *enters.*)

PAVEL. She'll get us all in trouble!

MOTHER. She'll be careful. (*Calling*) Raja, come, it's time to light the Sabbath.

RAJA. Without Papa? He's coming. . . .

MOTHER. Then he will be here. Come away from the window, now.

(MOTHER *turns, relieved, as* FATHER *and* AUNT VERA *enter.*)

MOTHER. Papa, at last!

FATHER (*with false ease*). All right, Mama, all right. I'm late, but . . .

RAJA (*running to him*). I saw you from the window, so you weren't really late, Papa.

FATHER (*kissing her and looking around at the others with a knowing look*). Of course not—as long as I am in sight, I'm not late. Besides—I was delayed by your Aunt Vera.

AUNT VERA. I knew I would be blamed for it all. (*To her sister*) It's true this time, Anna. I kept him waiting . . . you'll understand.

I Never Saw Another Butterfly by Celeste Raspanti   **123**

MOTHER (*smiling, but exasperated*). Of course, you would protect him. . . . *(There is a kind of communication going on between the adults in the room, but an intended carelessness in their voices.)*

FATHER *(who has removed his coat, stepping into the center with an affectionate but tired embrace for* MOTHER*)*. Now, Anna, I'm here.

(MOTHER *begins to light the candles, and suddenly the room is filled with the sounds of low-flying planes. They are dangerously close and the family cringes, following the sound of each plane as it flies over the roof.* PAVEL *runs to the window to look.* MOTHER *quickly draws him back.)*

MOTHER. Pavel, come away from the window. We must keep the shutters closed . . . you know that.

PAVEL. Nazis. So close you can see the damned swastikas on the wings.

MOTHER. Pavel! The Sabbath!

PAVEL. Sabbath Eve—and the Nazis about to join us!

VERA. Pavel, if you . . . if we are not careful . . .

RAJA *(attentive)*. They're gone now. . . .

FATHER *(intently, to his son)*. Be careful—we must all be careful. Tonight, the planes; tomorrow, tanks . . .

MOTHER. Tomorrow? Josef, what do you mean?

FATHER. Mama, Pavel—all of you. . . . *(Almost in tears)* Mama, today—today, I lost my place. . . .

MOTHER. Josef, it can't be true. . . .

FATHER. We all knew it had to come!

MOTHER. But you were promised!

FATHER. Promises! What do they mean?

I must report to work at Litomerice—they are building a station . . .

RAJA. But, Papa, you're not a carpenter. You're a teacher.

VERA. Hush, Raja! Let your father explain. . . .

FATHER. I must learn manual labor. Imagine—all of us at the school—all of us.

PAVEL *(contemptuously[2])*. Building a station!

FATHER. Today they came to the school. We were given one hour to clear away—books, papers, everything. One hour after all those years!

MOTHER. And the school?

VERA. Anna, wait, there is still more.

FATHER. Mama, it may be that—(PAVEL *stares at his father.*) —that we will have to move—again. . . . *(Helplessly)* It may be that . . . we must do so. The landlord is German—and we are . . .

PAVEL *(angry)*. Jews!

VERA. Pavel . . . try to have patience. . . .

FATHER. We . . . are . . . Jews. . . . They are relocating the boundaries—twelve blocks on either side—and we must all of us move into the area of the old ghetto.

MOTHER *(unbelieving)*. So . . . once again.

RAJA. But, Papa, they promised!

MOTHER. How soon?

FATHER. Tomorrow.

VERA. By sundown, Sabbath sundown, Anna.

———————
2. contemptuously (kən temp′chü wəs lē), showing a lack of respect or extreme dislike

PAVEL. They give us the Sabbath to get ready—it saves a working day! What did you tell him, Papa?

FATHER. What should I have told him? *(Hopefully)* Some say it is the last order.

PAVEL. Someone always says this will be the last order but every month the ghetto grows smaller.

FATHER. What should I tell him? What does a Jew tell his German landlord?

PAVEL. They can't expect us to . . .

MOTHER *(trying to understand the whole impact of the orders)*. And Vera?

FATHER. The women, too . . . they were released to work in the streets.

VERA. All unmarried women must report to work in the streets . . . with the men.

PAVEL *(realizing the import of this)*. Irca!

FATHER. Irca, too. . . . *(Then gently, to MOTHER)* Mama, you must give up the school. Jews are no longer allowed to teach. . . .

PAVEL. Irca? Where is she?

FATHER. They were turned out in the streets—with the rest.

PAVEL. But we thought the Council[3] was going to appeal? Why does the Council sit waiting while the whole Nazi army walks in?

FATHER. There have been . . . meetings.

PAVEL. Talk!

FATHER. There are—considerations. . . . *(He is beginning to show his anger.)* So, you will attack, shout slogans, you—and your friends—*(Derisively[4])* —be brave!

PAVEL. Better than hiding behind our prayer shawls! *(FATHER rises, affronted, and stands staring at PAVEL.)*

MOTHER. Pavel, you go too far.

PAVEL. At least shouting lets the Nazis know we're alive.

FATHER. You go too far . . . too far. . . . *(He is limp with controlling his anger. He sits wearily and then turns to speak directly to PAVEL.)* You think we don't know—last night, your joke, at the Regional Theatre . . .

MOTHER *(looking at her son)*. The Regional Theatre? Pavel, you know Jews are not allowed to . . .

PAVEL. A little joke on the guards. *(Cautiously, to his father)*. What do you know? *(With uneasy bravado)* So we stoned out the lights in the street and attacked them from ambush near the theatre arcade. . . . They never knew what happened to them. . . .

FATHER. A joke! Not so amusing this morning. Hanus was taken, his number called before the rest.

PAVEL. Why Hanus?

MOTHER. Josef, you are not telling us all.

FATHER. A guard knows one of the Council. He said he recognized his son among the "pranksters."

PAVEL. But Hanus wasn't there. He didn't even know about it.

MOTHER. Pavel! It might have been you—and Papa. . . .

---

3. Council (koun′səl), group of Jews in the Prague ghetto elected by their peers to represent them. The Council had no real power.
4. derisively (di rī′siv lē), showing scorn

FATHER. The guard said he recognized him. There is no quarreling with a Nazi Guard!

PAVEL. And the rest of the Council? They didn't intervene? No one protested?

FATHER (*almost ashamed*). Hanus is on the train now. . . .

PAVEL. Without a word! What cowards!

FATHER (*near weeping with hurt anger*). Pavel!

PAVEL. No wonder the star is yellow!

FATHER (*striking him across the mouth*). You go too far . . . too far. (*He turns, ashamed.*)

PAVEL (*ashamed, but angry*). Papa, I'm . . . sorry, but . . .

FATHER. But you do not understand . . . you cannot!

PAVEL. I understand. I have this to remind me! (*Gestures to the star on his jacket*)

MOTHER (*finally losing her composure*). What is this talk? The star cannot destroy us—but I will tell you what can. . . . (*She turns on the boy roughly.*)

VERA. Anna . . . the boy doesn't know what he is saying.

MOTHER. I will tell you what can kill us. To starve! No white bread, meat, eggs, cheese, fish, poultry—fruit, jam . . .

VERA. Anna, please . . .

MOTHER. None of it—for a Jew! This will destroy us—to be denied the necessities of life . . .

PAVEL. I know, Mama . . .

MOTHER. And for your father . . . no tobacco, cigars, cigarettes, no beer—all the little pleasures taken away. . . .

PAVEL. I know that, Mama . . .

MOTHER. And the big ones, too: the school, the synagogue—this will destroy us. . . .

PAVEL. Mama, for God's sake!

MOTHER (*reaching a point of exhaustion*). No. I am not yet finished with being a Jew. It means for all of us separation—and the fear of separation—planes today; tanks tomorrow; and always, the guards, the Nazis! You and your foolish bravado! . . . (*Breaking with her own weariness and fear*) And we may all be lost . . . all—lost.

PAVEL. I know, Mama. I see what's going on, but to just endure. It seems so . . .

FATHER. Weak? To you, it's weak. But think—the Nazis want us to work for them! If we must work, we must eat. There's that chance for life.

PAVEL. I don't call this living!

MOTHER (*recovering*). But while we live, we stay together, and perhaps later . . .

FATHER. Yes . . . if they bid us work, then we will eat, and we may survive—together—this war. It cannot last much longer. . . .

PAVEL (*giving in to his father's optimism*). All right, Papa.

FATHER. All right, all right. So no more shouting and no more jokes on Nazi guards! In a few months we will be back in our flat. Huber has promised to keep the furniture for us—he does not wish us harm. It will be here when we come back.

PAVEL (wearily). Yes, Papa.

FATHER. And you and Irca will be married, as we planned, you will see . . . I promise . . .

PAVEL (laughing wryly). Promises!

FATHER. You will see. (Cheerfully) Come now, Mama, the lights.

(MOTHER assumes her place at the table and begins to light the Sabbath candles. As she does, lights dim. Searchlights flash through the windows and light up the faces of the group. They become tense, but MOTHER continues the ceremony.)

MOTHER. Blessed art thou, O Lord our God, King of the Universe, who has hallowed us by . . .

PAVEL (listening to the outside noises that have begun to arise). The tanks . . . and guards. They're in the street.

MOTHER. . . . His commandments and commanded us to . . .

PAVEL. They are starting to cordon off the street.

FATHER (resignedly). They'll be here soon.

MOTHER (continuing through the remarks) . . . . to kindle the Sabbath lights. (The room is bright with searchlights. The outside is alive with the sounds of tanks, marching feet. Lights and sound reach their highest intensity as all candles are lit. Blackout. In the darkness, mother puts out each candle slowly.)

RAJA walks out of the group as the candles go out one by one. She reaches the downstage area and turns to see the last candle extinguished. She turns again to the audience.

RAJA. The first transports for Terezin left Prague the next day. We waited our turn and hoped. . . . Families moved in together. We moved in with Irca's family, and then we moved again. Each week another decree shrank our ghetto—and our lives. Even then we couldn't really believe it all. It was incredible. Our friends lined the street and watched us leave—five thousand Jews. . . . Erika Schlager called to me. . . . (RAJA turns to face upstage again.)

(ERIKA appears in the dim lights upstage.)

ERIKA (calling out to RAJA across the darkness). Raja, Raja, where are you going? Come with me to the cinema!

RAJA (facing her across the darkness). I can't, Erika. We have to go to the Municipal Building.

ERIKA. But why?

RAJA. I don't know.

ERIKA. Didn't they say why?

RAJA. They say we have to go. (Lights out on ERIKA. RAJA turns from her.) I ran ahead to join my mother. That was the day we left home. . . .

(A glaring light flashes on upstage to reveal RAJA's family and several children huddled together, bewildered.)

LOUDSPEAKER (the voice metallic and full of authority). Jews—Achtung![5] Step quickly. Men left! Women and children right! Keep moving. Schnell![6] Schnell!

(The voice accelerates as the group of women and children separate themselves from the men and older boys. This group moves downstage where IRENA is now standing.)

---

5. Achtung (ăk tung′), German. attention
6. schnell (shnel), German. hurry

IRENA (gathering the children around her). Don't be afraid. We're only going on the train. (The following dialogue is almost simultaneous—excited, afraid, wondering.)

CHILD I. Where's Father? What happened to Father?

IRENA. You'll see him again at the camp. Quiet now. We must wait.

CHILD II. It's been so long. I'm thirsty.

CHILD III. I'm hungry! Please, is there bread?

IRENA. Wait . . . wait . . . just a little while, and we'll have plenty of food.

CHILD I. When will we be there? Will Father be there?

IRENA (smiling encouragingly). Patience!

CHILD III. Where are we going now? What are they doing in the room there?

IRENA. We'll see. We must wait our turn.

CHILD I. Are we going to work? They told us we would work—together.

CHILD II. They told me to remember this number—always.

IRENA. Yes, you must remember. At roll call, they will ask your number. You must remember, and answer promptly.

CHILD III. They laughed and told us we were marked, like pigs. They said—it will never go away.

IRENA (calming them). Quiet, now. Don't be afraid! Remember, you are not alone. Whatever you see or hear, whatever is done, remember, we are together—and then you will not be afraid! (She walks them into a lighted area set with steps and stools, her "class-room.") Come, sit close together.

The children take places on the steps and stools, facing away from each other. They hold drawing and writing materials. They are still as the light comes up on the group and move only when they speak. RAJA observes them from the distance and then, as if in a dream, she walks through the scene, standing over each child for a moment. Finally she returns to the edge of the lighted area and speaks.

RAJA. I was one of them—the children of Terezin, one who saw everything, the barbed wire fence, the rats, the lice, one who knew hunger, dirt and smells, one who heard trains arrive and leave, screaming sirens, and the tread of heavy feet in the dark. I sat in Irena Synkova's classroom to write and paint the story of those days. (She takes her place in the group.)

(During the following, while the poems are being recited, various paintings from the book I Never Saw Another Butterfly may be projected on a screen.)

RAJA.

I never saw another butterfly. . . .
The last, the very last,
　　so richly, brightly, dazzling yellow.
Perhaps if the sun's tears sing
　　against a white stone . . .
Such, such a yellow
Is carried lightly 'way up high.
It went away I'm sure because it
　　wished to kiss the world goodbye.
For seven weeks I've lived in here,
Penned up inside this ghetto,
But I have found my people here.

The dandelions call to me,
And the white chestnut candles in the court.
Only I never saw another butterfly.
That butterfly was the last one.
Butterflies don't live here in the ghetto.

CHILD II. It is weeks since I came to this ghetto. I did not know that such a thing could happen to me. When I go home, I'm going to eat only white bread. . . .

CHILD III. When I go home, I'm going to make my bed every day, clean. . . .

CHILD IV. When I go home, I'm going to drink hot chocolate in the winter, lots of it. . . .

CHILD I. When I go home, I'm going to have pretty white curtains—rugs, too.

CHILD II. I'm going to play ball in the courtyard when I go home and shout if I want to. . . .

CHILD III. I'm going to sit very quiet and read story books as long as I want to when I go home—all night maybe. . . .

CHILD IV. I'm going to play the piano when I go home and everyone will sing and we

won't care how noisy we are. . . .

RAJA. When I go home . . . (*She walks away from the group and faces the audience as she speaks her poem.*)

I've lived here in the ghetto more than a year,
In Terezin, in the black town now,
And when I remember my old home so dear,
I can love it more than I did, some- how.
Ah, home, home,
Why did they ever tear me away?
Here the weak die easy as a feather.
And when they die, they die forever.
I'd like to go back home again,

Detail from a pasted collage by Dita Valentikova, born 1933, found at Terezin

I Never Saw Another Butterfly by Celeste Raspanti   **129**

It makes me think of sweet spring
  flowers.

Before, when I used to live at home,

It never seemed so dear and fair.

CHILD I (*interrupting* RAJA *as she speaks her last line*). Everything here is so strange—different from anywhere else in the world.

CHILD II. People walk on the street, not just on the sidewalk. But there are so many of us here that we wouldn't fit on the sidewalk. Cars do not drive here, though, so nothing can run over us.

CHILD III. We sleep in bunks, and everywhere lots of people are packed in.

CHILD IV. Mothers and fathers don't live together and children live away from them in homes, or whatever you call it.

CHILD I (*wistfully*). When you hear the word *home,* you imagine something quite nice. Well, here it's all quite different. . . .

CHILD III.

The buildings now are fuller,

Body smelling close to body,

The garrets scream with light for
  long, long hours.

CHILD IV.

This evening I walked along the
  street of death.

On one wagon, they were taking the
  dead away.

CHILD III. I haven't seen my mother for so long—I don't even know if she has arrived. Irena says that somewhere, she is looking for me; if I stay here, and keep well, she will find me.

I wonder where she is . . . and Father . . . and Grandpa. He told me to wait for him at the station, but they wouldn't let me. I think, maybe, he never came at all.

CHILD II. I have never been away from home before, not even over the holidays because I have no aunt or uncle to visit in the country. So this is my first trip away from my parents. It's so strange. . . . I've learned here to appreciate ordinary things that, if we had them when we were still free, we didn't notice them at all. Like riding a bus or a train, or walking freely along a road, to the water, say. Or to go to buy ice cream. Such an ordinary thing is out of our reach. . . .

CHILD III.

In Terezin in the so-called park

A queer old granddad sits

Somewhere in the so-called park.

He wears a beard down to his lap

And on his head a little cap.

Hard crusts he crumbles in his gums,

He's only got one single tooth.

Instead of soft rolls, lentil soup.

Poor old greybeard.

CHILD I. May I call you "grandfather"? You have no little girl and I have no grandpa.

RAJA. Tuesday, March 16, 1943. Today I went to see my uncle in the Sudeten barracks, and there I saw them throw potato peelings and people threw themselves on the little piles and fought for them.

CHILD II. Tuesday, April 6, 1943. Tomorrow the SS men are coming and no children can go out on the street. Daddy won't know this and I'll die of hunger by evening. . . . Wednesday, April 7, 1943. I missed Daddy yesterday, but I didn't cry. The other children couldn't see their parents either. . . .

CHILD III. We aren't allowed to go out of the barracks. We can't go out in the streets without a pass and children don't get a pass. They say this can last a week or even months . . . like a bird in a cage . . .

RAJA. Last night I had a beautiful dream. I was home; I saw our flat and our street. Now I am disappointed and out of sorts, because I awoke in the bunk instead of my own bed. This isn't a home any more, it's a hospital. Everyone avoids us; half the children are sick in bed . . . the number of the sick goes up every day. Rooms full of patients, and the doctor does not know what to do.

CHILD III. Typhoid raged through Terezin. The hospitals and infirmaries are crowded. They cleared out a whole house and made a typhoid ward of it. Everywhere you see the sign: *Achtung, Tyfus!* At every water faucet and pump, *Don't forget to wash your hands.* But anyway, the water hardly ever runs.

CHILD I. I caught six fleas and three bedbugs today. Isn't that a fine hunt? I don't need a gun and right away I have supper. A rat slept in my shoe. Walter, our Hausaltester,[7] killed it. Now I'm going to pitch a tent for the night with Eva.

RAJA. It's terrible here now. There is a great deal of tension among the older children. They are going to send transports to the new ghetto—into the unknown. And fifteen hundred children will arrive tonight. They are from Poland. We are making toys, little bags, and nets for them.

CHILD III. They came yesterday. No one was allowed near them. But we managed to get some news from the barracks. None of the children can speak Czech. We don't even know if they are Jewish children or Polish or what. You can see them a little from the fortress wall, and they went in the morning to the reception center.

CHILD I. They look awful. You can't guess how old they are. They all have old faces and tiny bodies. They are all barelegged and only a very few have shoes. They returned from the reception center with their heads shaved. They have lice. They all have such frightened eyes.

RAJA.

The poor thing stands there vainly.
Vainly he strains his voice.
Perhaps he'll die. Then can you say
How beautiful is the world today?

CHILD II. We got used to standing in line at 7 o'clock in the morning, at 12 noon and again at 7 o'clock in the evening. We stood in a long line with a plate in our hand, and they gave us a little warmed-up water with a salty or coffee flavor. Or else they gave us a few potatoes. We got used

---

7. *Hausaltester* (hô sôl′tes tər), person who takes care of a household

to sleeping without a bed, to saluting every uniform, to not walking on the sidewalks and then again to walk on the sidewalks. We got used to undeserved slaps, blows, and executions. We got used to seeing people die in their own excrement, to seeing piled-up coffins full of corpses, to seeing the sick amidst dirt and filth and to seeing the helpless doctors. We got used to it that, from time to time, one thousand unhappy souls would come here and that, from time to time, another thousand unhappy souls would go away. . . . *(Distant train noises)*

CHILD I. Sunday, September 5, 1943. This was the day, but it's all over now. They are already in the train. From our room Pavla, Helena, Olila, and Popinka are going.

CHILD III. Everyone gave Olila something, she is such a poor thing. At six this evening they reported for the transport. Each one somewhere else. The parting was hard.

RAJA. Monday, September 6, 1943. I got up at six to see Zdenka. When I came up to the barracks the last people were just going through the back gates and getting on the train. Everything was boarded up all around so no one could get to them and so they could not run away. I jumped over, ran up to the last people going through the gates. I saw the train pulling away and in one of the cars Zdenka was riding. *(Train noises up and out)*

(RAJA looks up from her reading when she hears the train. She sees lights come up on another acting area and she recognizes the scene. She rises and takes her role in that memory. When she speaks there is an adult bitterness in her voice.)

RAJA. Where did Zdenka go?

IRENA. The transport—to the East . . .

RAJA. Why?

IRENA. To work . . . resettlement . . . to . . .

RAJA *(interrupting)*. Auschwitz.

IRENA. Auschwitz?

RAJA *(turning away and sitting wearily, with an old sigh)*. She will not come back. Jiri told us. And he knows. You die if you go to Auschwitz.

IRENA. Raja . . .

RAJA. It is true. I know. You die, and the ovens and the chimneys—when you die, you burn to ashes . . .

IRENA. We do not *know* this is true.

RAJA. I know. And you know, too. And you think because we are children that we do not know. . . .

IRENA *(slowly realizing RAJA's awareness)*. What have you heard? Where?

RAJA. Jiri told us; he came from Warsaw. You die if you go to Auschwitz. And no one returns. Every day—the trains go—and no one returns. Jiri was there. He escaped. He told us. How is it that *you* do not know?

IRENA *(quietly)*. I've heard the same talk—we all have. It can't be true. Think, Raja, such things can't be true.

RAJA. But it is—he told us—we are going to die.

IRENA. Raja—wait—you are only afraid . . . wait . . .

RAJA (pleading with her, really frightened). Irena—I want to go home—I hate this place—and everything. . . .

IRENA. Everything? . . .

RAJA. Yes, what's the use of anything if we are going to die? Zdenka—last night we shared our bread and sang together—and now she is gone.

IRENA. I know. . . . (These lines are almost simultaneous.)

RAJA. And Eva and Mariam and Marianna . . .

IRENA. I miss them, too. . . .

RAJA. Gabriela and Zuzana . . .

IRENA. I know . . . I know. . . .

RAJA. We'd promised—we'd keep together—that next year in Prague—we'd go to school—together. Now there is nothing left.

IRENA. They were your friends. You loved them. Do not forget how you worked together—in this very room—and the poems, and the songs. Eva, Zuzana and Gabriela—their pictures, see . . .

RAJA (snatching them away). No. They will burn them, too! (She tries to rip them.)

IRENA (retrieving the pictures and holding RAJA's arms). Raja, listen to me. You are no longer a child—this minute, you are no longer a child—and so I tell you. . . . (She gently forces RAJA to sit down and, holding her hands, continues.) I have a child—she is nine years old—she was torn away from my arms and thrown from the train by an angered guard. I tried to throw myself after her—but I was dragged back into the car. I wanted to die

until I came to Terezin and found thousands of children waiting for me—and then I knew I must not die. . . . Do you understand? (RAJA has listened, stunned but calmed. She turns away.) You are no longer a child—and so I tell you. I have a child and she lives whenever I comfort another child or dry her tears. (RAJA turns away in despair. IRENA stands waiting helplessly but tenderly. IRENA opens her arms and RAJA, in a gesture that recalls their first meeting, puts her head on IRENA's shoulder and weeps. She rises with a new-found strength and walks downstage as the lights go down on the scene.)

Lights come up on RAJA, who is sitting DL. She is an older child, the RAJA of the liberation. She addresses the audience.

RAJA. Fear—this is half the story of Terezin—its beginning, but not its end. I was a child there, I knew that word. I became a woman there because I learned another word from Irca and Pavel, from Father and Mother, from Irena Synkova. I learned the word "courage" and found the determination to live—to believe in life. . . .

(Lights come up on IRCA and PAVEL.)

IRCA. I believe in life . . . I and Pavel. (She goes to PAVEL and takes his hand.) Pavel, I am coming with you. I settled everything myself, and I have a number in your transport.

PAVEL. Your mother and father need you. Go back to the barracks.

IRCA. Pavel, you are closer to me than

parents. I must come with you! *(PAVEL, taking her hand, walks toward the edge of the circle of light and calls quietly.)*

PAVEL. Rabbi, we want . . . Could you marry us, Rabbi?

(The RABBI appears at the edge of the lighted area.)

RABBI. I can. Have you . . . a wedding ring?

PAVEL. Yes.

RABBI. How much time?

PAVEL. An hour at most.

RABBI. That will be enough. Tell me your Hebrew names . . . and we must call your parents and some friends.

(Slowly a few people [this group includes the members of PAVEL's family] enter as if to a great ceremony. A ritual canopy is brought in and held over the young couple. With as much of the ritual as possible, simple and touching in a makeshift way, a traditional Jewish wedding is performed. The group surrounds the couple as the RABBI addresses them.)

RABBI. Dearly Beloved, in the Bible we read three words, the meaning of which we have never understood as well as today. They are: *Lekh, red, vealila*—go, lower yourself, and you will rise. We too have sunk very low but risen very high, because we did not let our sad fate overwhelm us; we have not lost hope that right will finally be victorious over injustice, friendship over hostility, love over hatred, peace over war. If these terrible times had not come, you two young people might not have met and loved and decided to share your lives. And so you may say—good may

arise out of evil. *(The RABBI blesses them and intones the Psalm. As the Psalm continues, members of the group come to the young couple with their greetings.)*

Happy those who live in your house
   and praise you all day long;
Happy the pilgrims inspired by you
   with courage to make the journey.
As they walk through the Valley of
   Sorrow, they make it a place of
   springs. . . .
Yahweh Sabaoth, hear my prayer,
Listen, God of Jacob;
God our shield, now look on us
   and be kind to your anointed.
For God is battlement and shield
   conferring grace and glory;
Adonoi withholds nothing good
   from those who walk without
   blame.
As they walk through the Valley of
   Sorrow, they make it a place of
   springs. . . .

(He blesses the cup of wine.)

Blessed art Thou, O Lord our God,
King of the universe, who hast created the fruit of the vine.

(He gives the cup to PAVEL, who drinks. PAVEL then gives it to IRCA. After she drinks she returns the cup to AUNT VERA, who is standing by. MOTHER takes off her wedding ring and gives it to PAVEL with a quiet gesture of affection. He places the ring on IRCA's forefinger. He repeats after the RABBI:)

PAVEL. Thou art consecrated[8] to me with this ring as my wife, according

---

8. consecrated (kăn′sə krāt′id), dedicated to a sacred purpose

to the faith of Moses and Israel. *(The wedding couple and the* RABBI *exchange positions. The* RABBI *then pronounces the priestly benediction.[9])*

RABBI. May the Lord bless you and protect you; may the Lord show you favor and be gracious to you. May the Lord turn in loving kindness to you and grant you peace. Amen.

(The tallis[10] is removed. AUNT VERA *steps forward and presents* PAVEL *with a glass and a kerchief. He wraps the kerchief around the glass, places it on the floor and steps on it. "The breaking of the glass" is intended to temper the joy of the occasion by reminding those present of the destruction of the Temple in Jerusalem and of other calamities that befell the Jewish people. At the moment* PAVEL *breaks the glass, the sound of an approaching train is heard. One by one the crowd exit.)*

RAJA *(who has been watching from a distance, now turning to the audience).* One by one the transports came. Mother, Father, Aunt Vera—they went. Pavel and Irca—they went. Everyone I knew and loved in Prague. There was no one who could remember me before I had come here as a child of twelve . . . but there were many left standing at the train as the transports started up, the cars crowded, boarded, sealed. . . . *(Sound of train departing is heard.* RAJA *follows the sound as it leaves. As her eyes move across the stage she sees* HONZA. *He turns to her.)*

RAJA. And we turned and found each other. . . .

HONZA *(staring after the train).* Jiri—they said they wouldn't take him. He was a plumber, an electrician—so clever—they said they wouldn't take him. . . .

RAJA. Everyone goes. . . . Jiri? Was he your friend?

HONZA *(turning).* He was my brother. . . .

RAJA. You're Honza Kosek. I heard about you. My name is Raja—Raja Englanderova. My brother . . . Pavel . . . and Irca . . .

HONZA. I know . . . they just got married, and now . . . what's the good of that?

RAJA *(turning away, a little angry).* They're still together.

HONZA. What's the good of that!

RAJA. Together they'll not be afraid. That's the good!

HONZA *(embarrassed).* You are afraid.

RAJA. What if I am? You're laughing at me . . . you think I'm a coward. . . .

HONZA. I'm laughing at you because you're a girl, and don't know the first thing about—about anything.

RAJA. Well . . . it's all easy for you. I've heard how you get by the guards—it's easy for a boy.

HONZA. Maybe. *(He touches her shoulder almost tenderly and turns her around to face him.)* My father was beaten and left for dead before my eyes. I saw it. I couldn't move, I was so afraid. But I didn't run. I never understood it—until my father dying told me, "You're a good boy, Honza: you are afraid, but you are not a coward."

---

9. benediction (ben ə dik′shən), the giving of a blessing
10. tallis (tal′is), shawl worn over the head and shoulders by Jewish men during prayers

RAJA *(ashamed).* I'm sorry. . . . *(Reluctantly)* Well, it's late. . . . I have to go. . . .

HONZA. Where're you going?

RAJA. Number twenty-five. . . . Where do you live?

HONZA. House Number two—on the other side, near the wall.

RAJA *(eager to talk).* There're thirty girls—in our group—most of us from Prague. . . . Irena . . . she's in charge of the whole compound—she lives with us.

HONZA. We live alone; we elect our own leader—and we have meetings—secret ones.

RAJA. Don't you have one of the older men there?

HONZA. What for? We're all old enough—we work in the fields. . . .

RAJA. So do we—some of us. I do. I'm old enough.

HONZA. We take care of everything ourselves. I'm the leader now—I was elected. So I'm in charge.

RAJA. Don't you go to school—at night, after work?

HONZA. We do—sometimes. Sometimes we have meetings—the leaders from the boys' homes—and we talk and plan. . . .

RAJA. What?

HONZA. Oh, like someone gets an idea about something and we talk about it—or someone does something we don't like and we tell him to quit it or else. A lot of things. We're working on something right now.

RAJA. For the boys' home?

HONZA. Well, not just for the boys—we're going to have a newspaper and report the news in camp.

RAJA. Have you got a printing press?

HONZA. No—we don't need that. It's not that kind of a paper. We make copies of the news and hang them around in the barracks. It's my idea. . . .

RAJA. Will you put one in the girls' home?

HONZA. I suppose we could—I never thought about it.

RAJA. I'd copy it over—I could do that.

HONZA. I'd have to talk about it with the rest. I suppose it's a good idea. . . . Well, I guess I've got to go now—we're going to have a meeting about the paper. *(He walks away, and then turns, shrugging a shoulder at her.)* You can come if you want to. *(She hesitates, and then runs to him.)*

Lights go down as RAJA *walks downstage, speaking to the audience.*

RAJA. And so VEDEM was born—and lived for three years, and helped us live. We waited to read the copy posted in our barracks, and later when, for safety, it was read aloud, no one was missing. It was an invisible line of communication between the houses so that even across the dark yards and crowded barracks, the youth of Terezin grew up together.

HONZA *(calling from the darkness to* RAJA, *who has just finished speaking).* Raja? *(Lights up on his area when she enters)*

RAJA. Yes? I can only stay a few minutes. Is this week's VEDEM ready?

HONZA. Here it is. . . .

RAJA. I'll take it and get started. (She turns.)

HONZA. Wait. . . . I was thinking. . . . We've talked about it at the meeting . . . we could run some of the poems from the girls' house— when there's room.

RAJA. Good. Irena will be glad of that. She said it might happen. The smaller girls got all excited!

HONZA. There won't be room for too many. . . .

RAJA. I'll tell her. (She turns to leave, almost reluctantly.) I'll see you. . . .

HONZA. Wait. . . . I saw you in the field today. Of course I couldn't say anything.

RAJA. I know. I saw you—across the road.

HONZA. Maybe we could plan a way to meet there—in case . . . there are messages . . . or anything.

RAJA. It wouldn't be safe! The guards are everywhere.

HONZA. We meet here . . . at night.

RAJA. The guards think we're inside the barracks.

HONZA. I'm not afraid . . . are you?

RAJA. No . . . yes, I guess I am. They'd beat you.

HONZA. It wouldn't be the first time. I always get up again. . . .

RAJA. Some day . . .

HONZA. Some day, maybe, I won't, I suppose. What difference does it make?

RAJA. Don't talk like that. I'll go if you do. (Starts to leave)

HONZA. Wait . . . wait. I'm only teasing.

RAJA. It would be lonesome without you. I mean, the boys need you, and the paper. Irena says you're the only one she can trust to bury the drawings and the poems.

HONZA. Others would do that. . . .

RAJA. It would be hard . . . I mean . . . these months we've been good friends. . . . I'd miss you, too. (She walks over to his side.)

HONZA (after a silence; taking her hand). I meant to say that first.

RAJA I know. (They walk together in silence, hand in hand, to the edge of the lighted area.) Good night. . . .

HONZA Good night. (They separate and run to other lighted areas. Turning away, they speak to each other across the darkness.) Raja, Raja!

RAJA. Yes. . . .

HONZA. I have some flowers for you.

RAJA. Honza, if you get caught . . .

HONZA. You know the square in front of the tower . . .

RAJA. The prisoners aren't allowed there. . . .

HONZA. I know, but they can't stop us from looking at it. Look, from here . . . see the flowers near the corner—and the butterflies? . . .

RAJA. I see them. . . .

HONZA. Well, I'm giving them to you, and every time you pass . . .

RAJA. I'll say—they're mine. Honza gave them to me—all the flowers— and all the butterflies. Thank you, oh, thank you. . . . (They turn into another lighted area.) Honza, Irena gave me a book of poetry—I left it for you at the end of the field near the shed. I want you to read one special poem. . . .

HONZA. I found it—and read it—and left one for you . . . look for it. *(They hold hands and run together into another area.)* Raja, look. . . .

RAJA *(holding a small package).* What is it?

HONZA. Open it—careful—it's very expensive.

RAJA. It must be—since you crawled through the barracks to bring it. Why didn't you leave it in the shed?

HONZA. It can't be left—not around here.

RAJA *(opening package slowly, pulling out a sausage).* Honza, a sausage—you're wonderful—and sausage, I haven't— but where did you get it?

HONZA. I liberated it. . . .

RAJA. Liberated it? Honza . . .

HONZA. Actually, I took it.

RAJA *(biting one end, then handing him the other).* Stole it. No wonder it tastes so good—you're so brave! *(They hold hands and run together to another area.)*

HONZA *(haltingly).* I won't be here—for a few days . . .

RAJA. Why? Where are you going?

HONZA. Don't take any chances—coming to meet me, I mean.

RAJA *(frightened).* Honza, what is it?

HONZA. Nothing. A special detail to build something outside the fortifications. They're picking the strongest—I'll be chosen.

RAJA. But—what if something happens?

HONZA. There'll be a chance for extra food. *(Smiles)* Maybe another sausage.

RAJA. I don't care about the sausage. . . . Honza, I'm afraid!

HONZA. Don't worry . . . they want the job done—it's some kind of walled courtyard . . . nothing much can happen. . . . Well, I have to go.

RAJA *(reluctantly, almost angrily).* Good-bye then. . . . *(They walk together to the edge of the lighted area.* HONZA *walks into the darkness.)* Good-bye. I'll be waiting . . . waiting. . . . Please come back. *(She sits with her head in hands.)*

*(*IRENA *calls from a lighted area a distance away.)*

IRENA. Raja, Raja, it's all right. A message came through.

RAJA *(growing tense).* What is it? Tell me. Tell me.

IRENA. The boys are back . . . all of them!

RAJA *(coming to her).* I've been holding my breath for two days . . . waiting . . . waiting . . . I couldn't think of anything else but Honza!

IRENA. What would you have done if he had not come back? If weeks and months had passed?

RAJA. Waited . . . and held my breath . . . for tomorrow . . . then waited again.

IRENA. Waiting days are long days, Raja. You would learn to stop thinking of tomorrow and to keep alive today. That's the secret of waiting—remember that—to keep alive today.

RAJA. Part of me would always be waiting.

IRENA. Then you would do what we all learn to do to make waiting bearable.

RAJA. I don't know how. . . I'm afraid. . . .

IRENA. Afraid of tomorrow? Then think of today—now. Can you live until tonight?

RAJA (*puzzled*). Yes. . . .

IRENA (*intensely*). And tomorrow morning . . . do you think you can live till noon?

RAJA. Yes. . . .

IRENA. And at noon, in the heat and the hunger, the stench and the weariness . . . can you live until tonight?

RAJA. Yes, yes. . . .

IRENA. Then you will survive. Each day you find some reason . . .

RAJA (*aware of Irena's meaning*). As you have done.

IRENA. Yes. Somehow—one of us is sure to survive. One of us must teach the children how to sing again, to write on paper with a pencil, to do sums and draw pictures. So we survive each today. . . . (*Lights down on scene.*)

RAJA (*walking to the edge of the stage*). The singing, the reading, the learning— the poetry and the drawings—this was part of our survival. In spite of the SS Guards and the orders against teaching, Irena kept school in the children's barracks. An older boy was always on guard and at sight of the SS men he whistled, and teaching turned into children's games. Games were permitted, but learning was a crime—for Jews. (*She sits down. Lights come up on another area where the CHILDREN are dancing and singing in mime.*)

We had books. Each of us had brought at least one book with him. Professional musicians, actors, and singers brought their repertoire with them. Irena brought *Ludvik*, the children's opera, with her and she did it with the children. (*The music of* Ludvik *comes up. Over the music,* RAJA'*s voice.*) In Terezin *Ludvik* was one of the things one had to see. Thousands heard its melodies, hundreds of children experienced in the rehearsals and performances the strongest impressions of their short lives. . . . (*She turns to watch the children as they pantomime the opera with suitable makeshift costumes and gestures.*)

The story was an old one—the legend of the birds of Cheb and the villain, Ludvik the Carpenter, who hated them because of their song. (*In the pantomime* HONZA *enters as a villain and begins to build cages.*) He built boxes and cages for the birds and trapped them one by one until Cheb lay sad and silent without song. But Pepicek, the smallest child in the village, gathered the children together and marched singing into the woods, freeing the birds and routing the wicked Ludvik. (*In the pantomime a group of children chase* HONZA *about the stage.*)

The lesson? Alone, we are helpless. Together we are not afraid of Ludvik—or of anyone. (*The* CHILDREN *sing. The following words can be put to almost any folk song.*)

CHILDREN.

Ludvik, the Carpenter, warning we

I Never Saw Another Butterfly by Celeste Raspanti   **139**

bring you.

Children of Cheb come to claim stolen song.

Close both your ears while our merry songs sing you:

Marching together we'll drive you along.

Out of our village we'll run you and rout you,

Freeing our birds from your cages and bars.

Children together we don't fear to flout you,

Standing together the victory is ours.

(They sing. Bells ring. LUDVIK *comes into the scene and the* CHILDREN *sing loudly. They begin to chase him and he runs off. The refrain of the song keeps returning and dies away as* LUDVIK *disappears. The final notes wind down to silence.)*

RAJA *(as she turns, smiling in remembrance, from the scene).* Ludvik—with the rehearsals, the performances—was our hope. We could not let it die.

The transports carried away children to die—new children took the empty places but *Ludvik* stayed, and the children found strength and courage in playing their parts in it. *(She listens to the last strains of music in the distance. She looks out over the audience quickly as if she recognizes someone in the group.)*

I know a game. I'll bet that lady with the little girl over there will turn around. Or maybe that gentleman. . . . I hum a motif from *Ludvik,* and no matter where they are, they hear it. That would not work with anyone else. . . . *(She hums a motif, and waits. Then as from a great distance, she hears the melody repeated.)* You can try it anywhere in the world. Just hum a motif from our opera, and you will find them. They are sure to come—the few who remember Terezin. *(Train sounds come up. Over the loudspeaker,* RAJA *hears the names of the children.)*

LOUDSPEAKER. Eve Heska, 14 years

Watercolor by Helena Schanzerova, born in Prague in 1933, died May 18, 1944, in Auschwitz

old—perished at Auschwitz. Ela Hellerova, 13 years old—perished at Auschwitz. Hanus Hachenburg, 14 years old; Petr Fischl, 15 years old; Marika Friedmanova, 12 years old; Frantisek Bass, 14 years old—perished at Auschwitz. Bedrich Hoffman, 12 years old; Josef Pollak, 14 years old; Dita Valentikova, 13 years old; Nina Ledererova, 14 years old—perished at Auschwitz. Eva Steinova, 13 years old; Hana Lissauova, 15 years old—perished at Auschwitz. Honza Kosek . . . *(Train sounds up)*

ights come up on RAJA, *seated. She seems wounded and stunned by the names she hears. When she hears* HONZA's *name, she runs to the edge of the lighted area, searching the darkness.* HONZA *can be heard, but not seen.*

RAJA. Honza?

HONZA. Raja . . . don't—don't turn or move.

RAJA *(trying to locate the voice).* Honza, where are you?

HONZA. Don't move. Here, on the other side of the wall—don't move, don't—just listen. I have a number in this transport.

RAJA. No! *(She searches the darkness for him, moving on hands and knees.)*

HONZA. Please—don't turn, don't move. . . . I have a number and . . . I must report . . .

RAJA. No!

HONZA. But the news is good. . . .

RAJA. What do you mean?

HONZA. The war is coming to an end. . . .

RAJA. Honza . . . no!

HONZA. Things are going bad for the Nazis—something will happen before long. . . . Raja, please, listen. . . .

RAJA. Honza . . . where are you? I'm coming with you.

HONZA. You can't . . . it's too late. You must wait here.

RAJA (quieter, but intensely). I cannot. . . . Where are you?

HONZA. No . . . you must wait . . . for me.

RAJA (angrily). Honza, I cannot live waiting. . . . Please, please, where are you, where are you? (Pleading with him.)

HONZA (tenderly). I am with you—wherever you are. . . . Listen, Raja. . . .

RAJA (vanquished). I'm listening. (She stares unseeing into the darkness.)

HONZA. I have something. I never told you—about the poem. I wrote one too, for the contest, remember?

RAJA (dazedly). You never handed it in . . .

HONZA. It was supposed to be about a memory, only it's about you . . .

RAJA. You never told me . . .

HONZA. I'll leave it here, under the post near the corner. Read it some time . . . but . . . don't laugh . . . you laughed once at the other poem, remember?

RAJA. I remember.

HONZA. When you read this . . .

RAJA. I won't laugh . . . I won't. I promise. . . . Honza. . . . (She starts to move toward the darkness.)

HONZA. Don't, don't, don't come out here. The guards. . . . Just stay there, stay there, and wait. Good-bye. . . .

(He leaves.)

RAJA. Honza . . . Honza? . . . Good-bye. . . .

(She walks to the edge of the area and finds the sheet of paper. She reads, and HONZA's voice is heard reading with her.)

Memory, come tell a fairy tale

About my girl who's lost and gone,
Tell, tell about the golden grail[11]
And bid the swallow, bring her back to me.

Fly close to her and ask her soft and low
If she thinks of me sometimes with love,
If she is well? Ask too before you go
If I am still her dearest, precious dove.
And hurry back, don't lose your way.
So I can think of other things.

(RAJA stops reading and HONZA's voice continues.)

HONZA. But you were too lovely, perhaps, to stay.

I loved you once. Good-bye, my love.

RAJA (folding the paper very slowly, carefully). Good-bye. It was the motto of Terezin. It should have been written over the entrance instead of the lie that greeted newcomers: "Work makes us free." It was good-bye, not work, that made us free. It was the only thing we knew would never change. Good-bye . . . good-bye . . . good-bye. It freed us all. What was there to fear when you had said good-bye to everyone you ever loved?

Lights come up on IRENA, ready for transport. She puts a shabby jacket over her shoulders and sits down with a stub of a pencil to write a note. Her voice is heard as she writes.

IRENA. Raja, Raja Englanderova, you

11. grail (grāl), object of a long and difficult search

know by now that my number—102866—was called; when you come to school today you will see that I have gone. You will have questions, and I will answer them before you ask. Once I saw an old Bible picture. Satan was about to pierce a saint through with his lance. The saint was sitting comfortably there, as if it had nothing to do with him. I used to think that the medieval painters were incapable of presenting feelings like fear, astonishment, or pain—so it looked as if the saints had shown no interest in their own martyrdom. Now I understand the saints better: What could they do? *(She rises and goes to the side where she enacts the following.)*

I have wrapped up the last of the pictures and poems in my shawl. See that these are buried with the rest—somewhere. And remember what they mean to all of us. I have nothing else to give you but this—what you and all the children have made of Terezin—the fields, the flowers—and all the butterflies. . . . Good-bye. . . .

(She, IRENA SYNKOVA, *places the rolled package tenderly near the letter. She leaves with a last look. The light stays up on this last remembrance of Terezin, then slowly dims to black.)*

(RAJA steps out of the darkness into the light. The sack she left at the beginning is there.)

RAJA. Irena Synkova—perished at Auschwitz, January 28, 1945. . . . And I have survived. Mother, Father, Pavel, Irca, Zdenka—Honza. Irena, too, in the end, perished at Auschwitz and I, Raja Englanderova, after the liberation returned to Prague—alone, alone.

A dim light comes up on a group standing upstage huddled in the background. As the lights grow brighter, they turn, each addressing RAJA *in a quiet voice as if from a great distance. Music under the montage of voices. On the projection screen, paintings, pictures . . .*

CHILD II.
For seven weeks I've lived in here,
Penned up inside this ghetto,
But I have found my people here. . . .

IRENA. Now you are not alone. And you must not be afraid.

FATHER. We will return. You will see, somehow, we will return. . . .

CHILD I. I missed Daddy, yesterday, but I didn't give in to my sadness. . . .

CHILD II. Some Polish children are coming. We are making toys and little bags and nets for them. . . .

CHILD III. I went to look for Zdenka. She cried and laughed at the same time, she was so happy to see someone before she left. . . .

IRCA. *I* believe in life—I and Pavel . . .

IRENA. Now you are not alone. You must not be afraid. . . .

RABBI. Yes, yes, I will marry you, if you wish to go together. . . .

HONZA. I never understood, until my father, dying, told me: "You are a good boy, Honza. You are afraid, but you are not a coward. . . ."

IRENA. Somehow one of us is sure to survive. One of us will teach the children how to sing again, to write on paper with a pencil, to do sums and to draw—

CHILD I.

He doesn't know the world at all

Who stays in his nest and doesn't go out.

He doesn't know what birds know best,

Nor what I want to sing about,

That the world is full of loveliness.

(Music: Snatches of chorus from Ludvik*)*

HONZA. Raja . . . I am with you—*wherever* you are . . .

RABBI. As they walk through the Valley of Sorrow, they make it a place of springs.

IRENA. I have nothing else to give you but this . . . the fields, the flowers, and all the butterflies. . . . *(As the voices grow in intensity,* RAJA *turns to view the people who have called to her from the past. She speaks to each.)*

RAJA. Mother, Father, Pavel, Irca, I hear you. Honza, I hear and I remember. . . . Irena Synkova, I taught the children. *(She picks up the sack and adjusts her coat. She pushes up the sleeve of the coat and looks at a number on her arm, then determinedly, pulls down her sleeve. She faces the audience again.)*

My name is Raja—I am a Jew; I survived Terezin—*not* alone, and *not* afraid. *(She walks slowly across the stage. Music, creating the determined, strengthened mood of her liberation. Suddenly, butterflies are projected on the screen in the back, on the floor of the stage, everywhere. The whole stage is bright with color, moving with butterflies, as* RAJA *walks off, leaving the butterflies alive before the audience. Lights dim to black as music rises.)*

THE END

I NEVER SAW ANOTHER BUTTERFLY

Responding to the Play

1. As a young girl in the camp, Raja asks, "What's the use of anything if we are going to die?" Based on your reading of the play, what is the answer to her question?
2. How does the fact that Raja goes back and forth between the past and the present help shape the play?
3. What is the significance of the poem on pp. 128–129 to this play?
4. As the play opens and closes, the stage directions call for butterflies to be projected over the entire stage. If a projector were not available, how could the butterflies be represented?
5. Draw a picture of your impression of the children's lives at Terezin.

More About Raja and Terezin

After Nazi Germany invaded Czechoslovakia in 1939, the town of Terezin, near Prague, was converted into a ghetto and concentration camp for Jews. One of the goals of the Nazis was to "concentrate" the Jewish population in controlled locations, thus the term "concentration camp." From 1942 to 1945, Terezin became a stopping-off place for many thousands on their way to the gas chambers of Auschwitz or Mauthausen. That number included 15,000 children.

The Nazis used Terezin for propaganda purposes, making films of the children performing in plays before sending them to their deaths. When Terezin was liberated in 1945, only about one hundred children were still alive. One child, Raja Englanderova, returned to Prague. This play is a re-creation of her story from documentary materials.

Today the children's art is displayed in a museum in Terezin.

CREATING AND PERFORMING

1. With a group of four, perform for the class the Ludvik the Carpenter song on pages 139–140.
2. Make a list of the sound effects called for in the play. With a partner, decide how you would produce these sounds for the play.
3. Choose a monologue from the play to work on. Memorize it and practice it in front of a mirror.

Painted Rain

The Play as Literature: Mood

Remember the first time you rode a roller coaster? How about the time your favorite pet got sick? How did you feel? Your emotions during those experiences created an atmosphere around you that was vivid and real. We call this atmosphere *mood*.

If you were to write about that roller coaster ride today, your story would probably crackle with a mood of excitement and anticipation. Your sick pet story would be different—describing feelings of dread or loss. The mood would be heavy and dark.

As you read *Painted Rain*, be aware of the mood of intense longing Janet Allard creates using simple stage directions and a cast of three.

The Play as Theatre: Props

In a play, as in life, characters are defined by the things they say and do, the way they look, and the property they own. Often, a character's properties, or props, are used to make symbolic statements about that character. For example, a man who fiddles with his umbrella is nervous. If his umbrella is ragged, he is probably poor. If his hat is silly, he is probably a comic figure.

Props also help establish the setting and mood of a play. Important props generally are mentioned in a script, but directors and designers often call for additional pieces. In most productions, the director and scene designer make a list of props needed, and then the prop crew obtains them. Some props have to be built or painted, but most are borrowed, rented, or purchased. A prop crew organizes and cares for large properties. Smaller props might be assigned to the actors, who must care for and keep track of them.

Warm Up!

Play the "prop game." Each student brings to class an item belonging to someone else. Collect the items in a bag and take turns pulling one object at a time from the bag. (If you pick your own, throw it back.) You must try to identify the gender, age, and occupation of the person to whom it belongs. Explain how you came to your conclusion.

Painted Rain

by Janet Allard

Setting	Characters	Time
A foster Home in Hawaii	TEDDY DUSTIN BARBARA	1989

Scene One

The lights rise to reveal the bedroom of two foster children. There are two beds situated to the side of a rather large window, which is separated into squares of glass by a thin wooden frame. There are a few personal items, a couple of odd-looking pictures, and painting tools scattered about DUSTIN's side of the room. TEDDY's side is mostly bare. As the lights rise to a dim, early morning, we find DUSTIN, a boy of sixteen, lying in bed asleep. Behind the bed, and barely visible, are a wheelchair, a pair of long leg braces, and a pair of crutches. TEDDY, a boy of about eleven, is sitting on his bed singing a simple, childlike song, or humming and playing absentmindedly with his bed sheets. He quiets down and pauses, then looks over at DUSTIN.

TEDDY (*softly*). Dustin? (*Pause*) Hey, Dustin? (*TEDDY gets up, wanders over to DUSTIN's bed, and stands looking down on him.*) Dustin, are you awake?

(DUSTIN *remains still, and there is silence. TEDDY stands looking down on him for another minute, then begins his singing again. He walks softly back to the area between the two beds and sits in the middle of the floor. Leaning over, TEDDY reaches under* his bed and pulls out a large bag filled with many interesting items he's collected over the years. One by one he pulls these things out and places them on the floor. As he does this, he begins talking. The sound of rain hitting against the windowpane can be heard softly in the background.)

TEDDY. Look, Dustin, it's raining. (DUSTIN *remains asleep.*) Not very hard, though. I guess whoever's making the rain doesn't want to wake you up. (*He looks over at* DUSTIN.) Dustin? (*Pause*) Dustin? You awake yet?

DUSTIN (*groggily*). Yeah.

TEDDY. Want to go out and play?

DUSTIN. I want to go back to sleep. It's two o'clock in the morning.

TEDDY.
No, it's not. It's three.

DUSTIN.
Who the hell cares? Just shut up and go to sleep.

TEDDY (*softly*). I care. (TEDDY *goes back to the floor and, singing softly, puts his stuff back in his bag. He comes across a pair of dark glasses, which he examines with interest, then puts on. He puts his stuff back under the bed, keeping the* *glasses on. He starts feeling around in front of him as if he were blind. He gets up and walks forward, still pretending he's blind, and runs into the furniture.)* Dustin? *(No response)* Dustin, I'm blind. *(Still pretending,* TEDDY *walks over to* DUSTIN'*s bed and looks down on him.)* Dustin, I can't see. *(After getting no response,* TEDDY *reaches down and touches* DUSTIN'*s face.* DUSTIN *bolts to a sitting position.)*

DUSTIN. What are you doing?

TEDDY. I'm blind, Dustin.

DUSTIN. Would you take off those stupid dark glasses and quit playing around?

TEDDY. No. Dustin, come play with me. You could lead me around.

DUSTIN. I don't want to. I want to sleep.

TEDDY. Then I guess I'm just going to run into things, huh? *(*TEDDY *starts walking around, hits* DUSTIN'*s bed, and falls on top of him.)*

DUSTIN. Hey, cut it out! Get off of me!

TEDDY. That's what happens when nobody leads blind people around.

DUSTIN. You're not blind, stupid. Now, let me sleep.

TEDDY. But, Dustin . . .

DUSTIN. Teddy, I mean it! *(*TEDDY *goes back over to his bed and lies down on his back. Keeping the dark glasses on, he feels in the air, still pretending he's blind.* TEDDY *begins singing softly again and slowly raises his voice.* DUSTIN *turns over and looks at* TEDDY.*)* I can't even go back to sleep now.

TEDDY. Why not?

DUSTIN. Because I'm mad, that's why.

TEDDY. I didn't do anything. I only wanted you to lead me around.

DUSTIN *(Pays little attention to* TEDDY. *He sits up, brings the wheelchair around from behind his bed, and drags himself into it with his arms as* TEDDY *is saying his line. As soon as* DUSTIN *is in his chair, the lights brighten.)* Well, I'm not going to.

TEDDY. Then I'll lead you around. Now that you're up, we can play.

DUSTIN. No. Now that I'm up, I can paint.

TEDDY. Dustin, you're my brother. You're supposed to play with me.

DUSTIN. I am not your brother.

TEDDY. Well, we're almost brothers.

DUSTIN. You can't almost be brothers with someone.

TEDDY. Yes, you can. We've lived together for a long time, and that makes us almost brothers.

DUSTIN. It hasn't been more than a year.

TEDDY. That's a long time.

DUSTIN. That's relative.

TEDDY. Barbara says that I could think of you as my brother if I wanted.

DUSTIN. Well, don't.

TEDDY. Why not?

DUSTIN. Just don't.

TEDDY. She says that I could think of you as my brother as long as I know that if you get adopted, you can belong to someone else too.

DUSTIN. Yeah, well, I'm not going to get adopted.

TEDDY. Okay. I won't either. *(*TEDDY *turns away and begins singing again.*

DUSTIN *pulls out his paints and starts painting.* TEDDY's *singing gets louder and louder until* DUSTIN *interrupts.)*

DUSTIN. Will you shut up!

TEDDY. Yeah, I think I will. (DUSTIN *goes back to painting, ignoring* TEDDY.) I didn't have anything to sing anyway. I'm running out of songs. Help me pick one, Dustin.

DUSTIN. How would I know what you want to sing?

TEDDY. I don't know. You could help me make one up.

DUSTIN. Teddy—

TEDDY. We could sing a song about painting if you want.

DUSTIN. Shut up! I'm trying to work.

TEDDY. A true artist could paint with me talking. But that's okay. We'll make the room very quiet so you can concentrate. *(Both of them are silent. Then they look over at each other at the same time.)*

DUSTIN. Teddy!

TEDDY. Shhh! You're trying to concentrate. (DUSTIN *throws a pillow at* TEDDY.) Okay, okay, you win! *(Silence. Then* TEDDY *looks over at the painting.)* What are you painting?

DUSTIN. Come over here and take a look.

TEDDY. No.

DUSTIN. If you took off those stupid dark glasses, you could see it from there.

TEDDY. I want you to tell me about it.

DUSTIN. Teddy, paintings are meant to be looked at, not told about.

TEDDY. Who says?

DUSTIN. Everybody says. That's just the way it is.

TEDDY. Aw, com'on, Dustin. Any artist could show their painting. It takes a really good one to describe it.

DUSTIN. Where did you hear that one?

TEDDY. I made it up. It's just that I've never heard anyone describe a painting before.

DUSTIN. Well, I'm not going to describe it.

TEDDY. Then I'm going back to sleep.

DUSTIN. Good.

TEDDY. Why is that good?

DUSTIN. Because it's three o'clock in the morning.

TEDDY. No, it's not. I bet it's almost four.

(Lights fade to black.)

Scene Two

TEDDY *bends over backward from his bed, reaches under it, and pulls out a bottle of orange juice. He then flips over onto the floor and opens the lid.* DUSTIN *keeps painting.*

TEDDY. Hey, Dustin?

DUSTIN. What?

TEDDY. Want some orange juice?

DUSTIN. Where did you get that?

TEDDY. Under the bed.

DUSTIN. You can't keep orange juice under the bed, stupid. It'll spoil.

TEDDY. I'm going to drink it before it spoils, so I can keep it wherever I want. *(He takes a long sip, then offers it to* DUSTIN, *who turns away.)*

DUSTIN. At least drink it out of a glass.

TEDDY. Why?

DUSTIN. Because everybody drinks out of glasses.

TEDDY. Well, I don't. Maybe everyone else should drink like I do.

DUSTIN (absentmindedly). Maybe.

TEDDY. Adults always say you should drink out of glasses and paint the sky blue and the trees green. Why?

DUSTIN. What are you asking me for? I'm not an adult.

TEDDY. If everyone else jumped off a cliff, would you do it too?

DUSTIN. Of course I wouldn't. Would you?

TEDDY. Maybe I would, but it would be a DIFFERENT cliff.

DUSTIN. Teddy, just leave me alone for a while.

TEDDY (moves over to DUSTIN). Dustin, why is it all sort of blue?

DUSTIN. Why is what blue?

TEDDY. Your painting.

DUSTIN. I don't know. It just is.

TEDDY. What time is it?

DUSTIN. Time?

TEDDY. In the painting.

DUSTIN (as if he's picking a time at random). It's two o'clock in the morning.

TEDDY. And it's BLUE?

DUSTIN. Yeah. What's wrong with blue?

TEDDY. Never mind, you don't care.

DUSTIN. You're right.

TEDDY. It's just that it's yellow at two o'clock in the morning.

DUSTIN. The sun's not up yet. It's blue.

TEDDY. If you wanted to do it right, you'd paint it yellow. That's the color it is at that time.

DUSTIN. I told you it doesn't matter. Besides, yellow wouldn't look right anyway.

TEDDY. How about red?

DUSTIN. Red?

TEDDY. Yeah, a big red splash.

DUSTIN. It would look out of place.

TEDDY. Not if you were the red splash.

DUSTIN. Teddy, you can't be a red splash.

TEDDY. I can be whatever I want to. Maybe you couldn't pretend you're one. But I could.

DUSTIN. That's stupid, Teddy.

TEDDY. Splash.

DUSTIN. What?

TEDDY. From now on I want you to call me Red Splash.

DUSTIN. Teddy—

TEDDY. Splash.

DUSTIN. You're being stupid, Theodore.

TEDDY. Teddy!

DUSTIN. I thought you wanted me to call you Splash.

TEDDY. I changed my mind. I don't like it.

DUSTIN. Good. (TEDDY gets up, moves over to the window, and stands looking out. DUSTIN begins to look over at TEDDY and take an interest in what he's doing.) You like what you see out there, Teddy?

TEDDY. Yeah, you can just look straight out into the trees and grass. At home I used to just look out the window and watch the rain.

DUSTIN. Did it rain a lot?

TEDDY. Yeah, all the time. I used to sit with my face right up against the glass and try and see if I could find one raindrop and follow it all the way until it hit the ground.

DUSTIN. Could you?

TEDDY. Naw, they always moved too fast. It works with snow, though. Snow just kinda floats.

DUSTIN. You like snow, Teddy?

TEDDY (nods). I like rain better. Raindrops are more fun to watch. Did you ever watch 'em?

DUSTIN. I guess I must've.

TEDDY. Do you like rain?

DUSTIN. It's okay.

TEDDY. Do you like it to go out in?

DUSTIN. I did when I was a little kid.

TEDDY. Not that it matters, but I just thought I'd tell you that I would have followed you out into the rain, Dustin.

DUSTIN. What are you talking about?

TEDDY. About that one time when you were really mad at me and I went out into the rain and you didn't follow me. Remember that time?

DUSTIN. No, not really.

TEDDY. Dustin?

DUSTIN. What?

TEDDY. Never mind. (Pause) Dustin?

DUSTIN. What?

TEDDY. Would you follow me out into the pouring rain?

DUSTIN. It's not pouring, Teddy.

TEDDY. If it was. (DUSTIN doesn't answer.) We could jump out through the window if you wanted.

DUSTIN. What?

TEDDY. If we go out through the window, then you're out in the rain right away. We'd have more time to play. We wouldn't have to walk down the hall and go through lots of doors.

DUSTIN. That's stupid.

TEDDY. No, it's not. I could help you through the window.

DUSTIN. I don't think so. You're being childish.

TEDDY. ChildLIKE. It would be fun. Come on.

DUSTIN. Teddy, I'm busy.

TEDDY. You could stop painting and we could go out and climb trees and play in the mud. We could just splash around in the puddles if you wanted.

DUSTIN. Naw, I don't feel like it.

TEDDY. Why not?

DUSTIN. I'm not in the mood to splash around.

TEDDY. You would be when we got out there. You could probably make bigger splashes than I could.

DUSTIN (motioning to his wheelchair). Not in this thing.

TEDDY. Dustin.

DUSTIN. Forget it, Teddy. It's hardly raining anymore. It wouldn't be much fun. (He goes back to painting.)

TEDDY. I guess. Rain is always more fun when it's coming down hard. (DUSTIN looks away, frustrated by TEDDY's childlike way of thinking. There is a sound of a doorbell.) It's probably Barbara.

DUSTIN. Barbara?

TEDDY. Yeah, she was going to stop by to talk to us sometime.

DUSTIN. When?

TEDDY. I thought you didn't care about time.

DUSTIN. Teddy—just go let her in.

TEDDY. Why can't you?

DUSTIN. Because I'm PAINTING.

TEDDY. OKAY!

(TEDDY *exits.* DUSTIN *waits until he's gone, then wheels to the corner of the room, where his braces are resting. He picks them up, wheels back to the bed, and leans down, shoving the braces under the bed.* DUSTIN *returns to painting.* TEDDY *bounds into the room, jumps on the bed, then collapses, and lies down on his back with his hands behind his head.* BARBARA *enters. She is a social worker in her early thirties. She is overweight and relatively pretty.*)

BARBARA. Hi, guys!

TEDDY. Barbie! What a surprise. Look, Dustin, Barbara stopped by to see us.

DUSTIN. I can see her, Teddy.

BARBARA. How do you think I look?

DUSTIN. Fine.

BARBARA. I lost a few pounds last week.

TEDDY. It looks like you found them again this week.

BARBARA (*laughs*). What's that supposed to mean?

TEDDY. It means that I DIDN'T lose any weight last week, and I'm still skinnier than you.

BARBARA. Aw, come on. I'm not that fat.

TEDDY. Well, you have something to bug us about, so we have to bug you about something too.

BARBARA. The only reason you say I'm overweight is because other than a couple pounds, you can't find anything wrong with me.

TEDDY. Oh, yeah?

BARBARA. Yeah! You can't even see straight with those dark glasses on. So I shouldn't even listen to you.

TEDDY. I don't have to see straight. I can tell you're fat anyway.

BARBARA. How?

TEDDY. You sound fat.

BARBARA. Why don't you take them off, Teddy?

TEDDY. 'Cause I like them on.

BARBARA. Come on now. This game was fun for a little while, but it's time to take off the glasses.

TEDDY. I can't. I'm blind.

BARBARA. You are not blind, honey.

TEDDY. I am too.

BARBARA. Two weeks ago you were pretending you were deaf.

TEDDY. So what?

BARBARA. So you can't keep pretending there's something wrong with you.

TEDDY. There's nothing wrong with me. I'm just blind, that's all.

DUSTIN. Cut it out, Teddy.

TEDDY. Why?

DUSTIN. 'Cause Barbara's not here to play games with you.

TEDDY. Yeah, she's here to bug me about being blind.

BARBARA. We do have some things we should talk about, Ted.

TEDDY. I just want to play right now.

DUSTIN. Didn't you hear her? She said she wants to talk to you.

TEDDY. I want you to come.

DUSTIN. No. We just can't go outside and play and leave Barbara here.

TEDDY (*walks to the doorframe and looks at* DUSTIN). Are you coming or not?

DUSTIN. No. Now, come back here and sit down. (TEDDY *exits.*) Teddy! (DUSTIN *jerks his wheelchair toward the door and looks as if he's going to go after him. He stops himself, slowly turns back, and begins painting again.*)

BARBARA. That's all right. Let him go. I wanted to talk to you a little too.

DUSTIN. Anything special, or you just want to talk about whatever comes to mind?

BARBARA. How about Teddy?

DUSTIN. He's been acting real weird lately.

BARBARA (*making both beds*). Weird? How?

DUSTIN. I mean, he's been acting like he's a little kid. I can't even carry on a conversation with him.

BARBARA. Could you ever?

DUSTIN (*laughs*). He also asked me to go out and play with him when it was raining really hard. I mean, it just came out of nowhere. All of a sudden he wanted me to go climb trees in the rain.

BARBARA. Did you go play with him?

DUSTIN. I'm too old to play his stupid little games.

BARBARA. Is that all?

DUSTIN. Well, the wheelchair doesn't help any. And I really wanted to paint. I mean, look at this. (*He holds up his painting for* BARBARA.) It's a lot more fun to create something like this than to try and climb a tree in a wheelchair.

BARBARA. What about using your braces?

DUSTIN. You think I could climb a tree with THEM on?

BARBARA. No. But I do think you could walk with them on.

DUSTIN. I guess so.

BARBARA. Speaking of walking, your teacher called me today. She said you've been going to therapy late.

DUSTIN. I've been busy.

BARBARA. Try to make it on time next week, all right?

DUSTIN. Fine.

BARBARA. Does Teddy ever help you walk?

DUSTIN. No. He used to watch me a lot, but now it's like I don't even have an impairment. He completely ignores it and asked me to climb out the window and splash in the puddles. (*They both look out the window.*)

BARBARA. How does it feel to watch him play outside when you're in here?

DUSTIN. The same way it feels for him to sit there and watch me paint.

BARBARA. What do you mean?

DUSTIN. Do you feel bad 'cause you're not playing right now? (BARBARA *shakes her head no.*) Neither do I.

BARBARA. Things would just be a lot easier if you could walk.

DUSTIN. You mean I would get adopted into a real home faster.

BARBARA. That's not what I said.

DUSTIN. Well, look at Teddy. He can walk and he's still here with me.

BARBARA. Has Teddy talked to you about leaving?

DUSTIN (*defensively*). No, why?

BARBARA. We've been working out an arrangement for a couple to adopt him.

DUSTIN. It'll probably fall through.

BARBARA. I don't think so. They're stopping by to see him again next week. It looks like this time it's really going to work out.

DUSTIN. Does he know that?

BARBARA. I told him.

DUSTIN. And he's still pretending he's blind.

BARBARA. Yeah, that's the problem. He has to be ready next week. He can't be running around refusing to take off a pair of dark glasses.

DUSTIN. Ya know, he asked me to describe my painting to him today.

BARBARA. Did you?

(TEDDY *enters, having heard* DUSTIN's *last line, and bounces onto the bed.*)

DUSTIN. No. I mean, how do you describe a painting?

TEDDY. You did too describe it. It's all kinda blue. I think it's pretty.

DUSTIN. You can't see it.

TEDDY. I already know what it looks like.

BARBARA. You can't really know what it's like if you don't see it.

TEDDY. And you can't really know what it FEELS like if you DO see it.

BARBARA. Honey, the whole idea of a painting is that they're to look at. You can't get the effect of a painting by just hearing about it.

DUSTIN. See, I told you.

TEDDY. Nobody asked you. (TEDDY *reaches under the bed for his orange juice and feels the braces.*)

DUSTIN (*forcefully*). Your orange juice isn't under there, Teddy.

BARBARA (*turning to* TEDDY). You keep juice under your bed?

TEDDY. Let me guess. YOU don't, right?

DUSTIN (*forcefully*). I put it back in the fridge.

TEDDY. Thanks.

BARBARA. Ted, the couple you met is going to drop by to visit with you sometime next week, okay?

TEDDY. Me and Dustin don't need any visitors. We do just fine by ourselves.

BARBARA. They want to see you and show you your new home.

TEDDY. I can't see them. I'm blind.

DUSTIN. How did I know he was gonna say that?

BARBARA. Ted, you're not, and you have to stop playing this silly game.

TEDDY. How do you know I'm not?

DUSTIN. Teddy, stop.

TEDDY. I'm not doing anything wrong.

BARBARA. No one said you were, sweetie.

TEDDY. Then quit bugging me!

BARBARA. Pretending you can't see is not going to prevent you from being adopted.

TEDDY. I didn't say it was. Leave me alone.

DUSTIN. I told you it was hopeless.

BARBARA. Okay. Well, Dustin what do you say we show Teddy how to cooperate and get you to do some walking now?

DUSTIN. Why?

BARBARA. Just for a bit of extra practice.

DUSTIN. I left my braces at school.

BARBARA. They're not going to do you any good there. Get them home so you can practice.

DUSTIN. I wouldn't have time. I have to finish my art project.

BARBARA. Walk first, paint later.

TEDDY. Play first, walk later, and don't worry about painting.

BARBARA. Whatever, just get it straightened out, all right, Dustin?

TEDDY. And then he'll be well-rounded just like you.

BARBARA (playfully). All right, that's enough. I'll see you guys tomorrow.

DUSTIN. Okay.

TEDDY (sarcastically). We'll all be looking forward to it.

BARBARA. Good. Then maybe I'll give you the cookies I have in my bag. (BARBARA swings her bag tauntingly over her shoulder, gives the boys a smile, and exits. There is silence, then TEDDY reaches under his bed and pulls out the braces. DUSTIN stops painting to watch him. TEDDY crosses to DUSTIN's bed and puts the braces back. TEDDY lies down on DUSTIN's bed. DUSTIN continues painting. TEDDY watches him intently.)

DUSTIN. What do you want?

TEDDY. Nothing. I was just watching you paint.

DUSTIN. Well, don't.

TEDDY (He rolls over onto his stomach.) Do you think you could teach me how to paint, Dustin?

DUSTIN. I told you it's too hard to teach. You would do better if you learned yourself.

TEDDY. But you could just teach me how to hold the brush, and then we could both paint.

DUSTIN. I've tried to teach you how to hold the brush. You won't listen to me.

TEDDY. I'll listen this time, I promise. Just put my hand on top of yours.

DUSTIN. No, Teddy. You're being stupid.

TEDDY. Please, Dustin. (TEDDY gets on his knees and walks over until he is standing next to DUSTIN.)

DUSTIN. Well, what would you want to paint?

TEDDY. Something clear.

DUSTIN. You can't paint something clear. Not unless you leave the canvas blank.

TEDDY. Blank canvas could be white.

DUSTIN. Who's the painter here anyway? Look, just go back to your side of the room and let me paint on my own.

TEDDY. Dustin—

DUSTIN. I'm not gonna let you if you're going to be stupid and paint something like rain.

TEDDY. Dustin, what's your problem?

DUSTIN. Just shut up!

TEDDY (He pauses thoughtfully in silence for a while.) Dustin, how come you hid your braces from Barbara?

DUSTIN. It doesn't matter.

TEDDY. Yes, it does.

DUSTIN. Because I didn't want to walk.

TEDDY. Why not?

DUSTIN. Could we just drop this?

TEDDY. No. I'm confused. Barbara said you wanted to walk.

DUSTIN. Well, I don't.

TEDDY. Why not? (DUSTIN *doesn't answer.*) You won't even try anymore.

DUSTIN. And you won't take off those damn glasses. We're even. What do you want to be blind for? Why the hell would you want to be blind?

TEDDY. If you tell me why you won't walk, I'll tell you why I wear these.

DUSTIN. I don't care why.

TEDDY. Well, I do.

DUSTIN. Teddy, there are more important things to me than walking, and . . .

TEDDY. And what?

DUSTIN. And that's all.

TEDDY. It's because you can't do it perfect, right? (DUSTIN *ignores him and returns to painting.*) How come you never tell Barbara anything? (DUSTIN *ignores him.*) I could tell her if you want.

DUSTIN. Look! I don't want you to do anything but let me finish this. Go someplace that's not in the way.

TEDDY (*Crosses over and lies down on the bed. Takes off his sunglasses, examines them for a while, then looks at* DUSTIN.) Dustin, you could wear these for a while if you let me paint with you.

DUSTIN. I don't want to wear your stupid dark glasses, Teddy. I'm busy. Just go away.

TEDDY. Okay. (TEDDY *goes to exit.*)

DUSTIN. Teddy?

TEDDY. What?

DUSTIN. Never mind.

TEDDY. Dustin, are you okay? (*Moves toward* DUSTIN *and puts his hand on* DUSTIN*'s shoulder.*)

DUSTIN. I'm fine. (TEDDY *turns to leave again and exits.*) Teddy—don't go.

(*Blackout.*)

Scene Three

The lights come up on TEDDY and BARBARA *sitting, eating cookies.* DUSTIN is *painting.*

TEDDY. Dustin says you can't paint things if they're clear.

BARBARA. No. I guess not. Dustin's the artist here.

TEDDY. But I've seen paintings of glass before, or a window.

BARBARA. Have you?

TEDDY. Yeah. When I was really little, my mom took me to this art place. I think there was a painting with glass in it.

BARBARA. Do you remember much of that place?

TEDDY. Only that Mom would hold me up so I could touch the paintings, even though she wasn't supposed to. (*Pause*) Barb, have you seen my mom?

BARBARA. No, sweetie.

TEDDY. I don't remember, but I bet she was pretty. Dustin, you should've met my mom. You would've liked her. She could even have helped you paint. Barbara, do you know where she is?

BARBARA. No, Ted. But you have some

people who want to be your mom and dad.

TEDDY. Do they want to be Dustin's too?

BARBARA. They only want one child, and they like you.

TEDDY. Is it because Dustin can't walk? *(DUSTIN turns to look at TEDDY.)*

BARBARA. No.

TEDDY. If Dustin could walk, would they take him too?

BARBARA. I don't think so, Ted.

TEDDY. I want to stay with Dustin. We do fine by ourselves, right, Dustin?

DUSTIN. I guess.

BARBARA. Have you done any walking lately?

TEDDY. Yeah, I've done a lot.

BARBARA *(laughs).* Not you. Dustin.

TEDDY. If you were trying to get me to walk instead of him, you wouldn't have to work anymore.

BARBARA. True, but we want Dustin to walk. It's a priority.

TEDDY. Whose priority?

DUSTIN. Teddy—

TEDDY. No. I want to know who wants him to walk.

BARBARA. Lots of people.

TEDDY. Does that mean Dustin too?

BARBARA. Well, Dustin agreed to it at the meeting in school. Right, Dustin?

DUSTIN. Yeah.

TEDDY. Then why isn't he walking?

DUSTIN. Teddy, cut it out.

TEDDY. I'm just trying to help. You said yourself . . .

DUSTIN. Teddy, shut up!

TEDDY. But you said . . .

DUSTIN. I can speak for myself.

TEDDY. Then why aren't you?

DUSTIN. If I wanted you to talk for me, I would have asked you. But I didn't ask. I don't need your help. Leave me alone and I'll do just fine.

BARBARA. Dustin— *(He wheels around to face her.)*

DUSTIN. And I don't need your help either. 'Cause you're not helping. You're always telling me I should walk. Why?

BARBARA. Because it's a sad thing to see a sixteen-year-old boy not be able to go outside and walk around because he won't try.

DUSTIN. It's sad for you, not me! Can't you see that?

BARBARA. But it's important for you to keep at it. You don't want to spend the rest of your life in a wheelchair, right?

DUSTIN. Maybe I do. How the hell would you know what I want? You never ask.

BARBARA. But it was your choice. You said . . .

DUSTIN. Yeah, of course I said I wanted to walk. They asked me when I was five. How was I supposed to know it meant wearing clumsy braces and dragging my feet along with my arms? Can't you see I don't want to do that?

BARBARA. Dustin, we had our first meeting, you said you'd start trying again. I'd hate to see you give all that up now.

DUSTIN. I haven't given anything up.

BARBARA. I know you feel awkward, but

that's just because you haven't practiced enough.

DUSTIN. Yeah. And if I keep practicing, I'll be running marathons, just like the people on TV.

BARBARA. I didn't say that, but at least you'd be able to get around.

DUSTIN. I get around fine!

BARBARA. I'm just trying to help you.

DUSTIN. Why? You don't care about me. I'm just another job for you. I'm just another file that sits on your desk.

BARBARA. That's not true. . . .

DUSTIN. Then maybe you do this to make yourself feel good. A fat lady can make a kid walk. Wow, what a miracle worker!

BARBARA. Wait a minute now, that's not fair.

DUSTIN. And what you're doing is?

BARBARA. I'm doing this for you. It hurts me to see you confined to a wheelchair when you don't have to be.

DUSTIN. That's all you can see, isn't it? My legs? Well, if you were more observant, you might see that I don't mind that much. And if you do, well then, that's your problem. Just keep it to yourself.

TEDDY. Dustin—

DUSTIN. Shut up, Teddy.

BARBARA. It's not just me. Your teachers want to help too.

DUSTIN. If they really did, then they would quit trying to make me do something I don't want to do. Just give me a box of paints and show me how to move my wheelchair around

better instead of trying to drag me out of it.

BARBARA. You can't just sit around and paint all the time.

DUSTIN. I want to paint. And if it will make you happy, I'll get onto the floor and do a few pushups every now and then.

BARBARA. Dustin—

DUSTIN. Barbara, just think of me instead of your job.

BARBARA. I am thinking about you. If you don't take the chance to walk now, I'm afraid you'll regret it later.

DUSTIN. And then I would blame you, and you would feel guilty, and you don't want that. See, you don't care about me, you care about yourself.

BARBARA. Dustin, maybe we could talk to your teachers about this.

DUSTIN. Maybe. But for right now I think I want to be alone.

BARBARA. All right. I think you should cool down. Come on, Teddy, let's go play.

TEDDY. In a minute. (BARBARA exits.) Dustin—

DUSTIN. Go play, Teddy.

TEDDY. Dustin, don't be mad at me.

DUSTIN. Just leave me alone. You're the one who got me into this mess in the first place.

TEDDY (frustrated, angry). You don't need to walk. You do it fine already.

DUSTIN. What?

TEDDY. It doesn't matter that you're in a wheelchair. You're always walking away. I can walk, but I'm still here.

DUSTIN. You're not talking about walking, you're talking about people turning away from each other. It's different, stupid.

TEDDY. You're the stupid one. All you care about is painting. I'm here, too, you know.

DUSTIN. Yeah, well, I want to be alone right now.

TEDDY *(suddenly).* Go away!

DUSTIN. What?

TEDDY. I hate you. That's all you ever tell me to do: "Go away, Teddy." "I don't want to play, Teddy." "I'm busy." Yeah, well, I don't care. I was just trying to be nice, that's all. But I don't care anymore. I wouldn't let you play if you wanted to.

(TEDDY *throws a beanbag at* DUSTIN. DUSTIN, *moving to avoid it, knocks his painting off the easel.)*

DUSTIN. What did you do? What the hell did you do?

TEDDY. It's your fault. You didn't catch it.

DUSTIN. I don't believe you. What are you trying to do?

TEDDY. Dustin, stop it. I didn't mean it.

DUSTIN. It was wet. You messed it up.

TEDDY. You can fix it, right?

DUSTIN. Maybe. Don't worry about it.

TEDDY. I thought you'd catch it. Honest I did.

DUSTIN. Never mind.

TEDDY. Dustin, I didn't mean it. Don't be mad.

DUSTIN. I'm not.

TEDDY. I'm sorry.

DUSTIN. Teddy—

TEDDY. Dustin, I love you.

DUSTIN. Aw, come on, Teddy.

TEDDY. You're my brother. I can love you if I want.

DUSTIN. Don't.

TEDDY. Why?

DUSTIN. Just don't. It makes things hard on both of us.

TEDDY. So what. You're my brother.

DUSTIN. I am not your brother.

TEDDY. I can love you anyway. (DUSTIN *looks at* TEDDY *for a minute in silence.)* Dustin? Why wouldn't you follow me out into the rain?

DUSTIN. It doesn't matter.

TEDDY. It does to me.

DUSTIN. I guess because people don't belong in rain. They just kind of stand out. It's like in painting. If you put a person, a real person, in a painting, they wouldn't seem to fit. They'd just look like they didn't belong in a perfect setting. You know what I mean?

TEDDY. No.

DUSTIN. Go play.

(Lights fade to black.)

Scene Four

T he stage is dimly lit. DUSTIN *is lying in bed sleeping, and* TEDDY *is packing a suitcase that is lying open on his bed. He is talking to no one in particular as he is packing. The sound of rain hitting against the windowpane is noticeable, but soft. It will grow more noticeable as the scene progresses.*

TEDDY. Ya know, sometimes I think it really wouldn't be so bad to be blind. You wouldn't have to worry about what everything looked like. You could make things look like you wanted them to. You could wear clothes that didn't match, and nobody would tell you you had no taste. They would think you dressed like that just 'cause you couldn't see. If we couldn't see, we'd start seeing the things inside people more.

(TEDDY *stops packing and wanders over to* DUSTIN's *easel. Picking up a paintbrush, he goes back to his bed, reaches under it, pulls out his bag of stuff, and adds the paintbrush to his collection.* TEDDY *picks up the suitcase and walks to the door. Putting the suitcase down, he turns to look at* DUSTIN.*)*

TEDDY. Dustin? *(Silence)* You awake, Dustin? *(Silence)* Dustin?

DUSTIN *(annoyed)*. What?

TEDDY. I want to talk to you.

DUSTIN. It's two o'clock in the morning. Go to sleep!

TEDDY. What's wrong?

DUSTIN. Just go to sleep.

TEDDY. Dustin? I'm leaving tomorrow. I want to talk to you.

DUSTIN. I'll talk to you in the morning. Now, go lie down.

TEDDY. Dustin—

DUSTIN. Teddy—leave me alone.

TEDDY. Dustin? *(When* DUSTIN *doesn't answer,* TEDDY *reaches up and gently puts his hand on* DUSTIN's *face.* DUSTIN *bolts to a sitting position.)*

DUSTIN. Quit it! You're not blind.

TEDDY. I'm cold. Just hold me a minute. *(The two boys look at each other for a minute, then* DUSTIN *turns over and lies down again with his back to*

TEDDY.*)* Dustin . . . this is the last time . . . this is the last time. . . . Can't you just . . . Forget it! This is the last time you'll see me. I'm the only thing you have, and I'm leaving.

DUSTIN. Good! Now, go to sleep.

*(*TEDDY *turns away and goes back to his bed. He curls up and softly begins crying.* DUSTIN *is silent for a while. He then pulls himself into his wheelchair, talking softly to* TEDDY.*)*

DUSTIN. I used to think that the morning light was yellow. That's the color streetlights are and the color the moon is and everything. Then one night I woke up and looked around. It was two o'clock, and it was blue. You know what I wanted to do, Teddy? I wanted to wake you up and show you that everything was blue, not yellow like I thought. But I didn't. It's different tonight. Everything should be blue in here, but it's not. Maybe I should paint the sky yellow, like you said, and red. Yeah, a red splash could mix in just fine. *(By this time the rain can be heard against the windowpane.* DUSTIN *has gotten into his wheelchair and now wheels over to* TEDDY's *bed.)* Teddy? *(Pause)* I need you. I'm scared.

TEDDY *(looks up and then goes to* DUSTIN *and sits in his lap)*. It's raining, Dustin. I can hear it.

DUSTIN. Yes, it's raining.

TEDDY. But you can't see it . . . no one can.

DUSTIN. It's too dark to see at night. You can hear it, and if you went outside, you could feel it.

TEDDY. I can feel it.

DUSTIN. Then let's paint it. *(TEDDY gets a canvas, palette, and brush and brings it to* DUSTIN. DUSTIN *puts* TEDDY*'s hand on his own, holding the brush. They begin making smooth strokes up and down, painting as they look out the window.)* When you paint rain, you have to move your hand gently. Yeah, like that. That's good.

TEDDY. As good as you?

DUSTIN. Better. You know how it feels, not just how it looks.

TEDDY. I'll show you how it feels.

DUSTIN. I was kidding when I said I wouldn't follow you out in the pouring rain. I would. We could go outside and play in the mud and climb trees. We could jump outside through the window too. It's only glass. You know how easy it is to break through glass.

Lights out

Responding to the Play
1. Why does Teddy pretend to be deaf and then blind?
2. Analyze Barbara's role in the boys' lives.
3. Would the play be as effective if the parts of Dustin and Teddy were played by girls? Support your answer.
4. If you were the set designer, what colors would you use to capture the play's mood? Why?
5. Name the props that you believe are essential to producing this play. Explain why.

More About Stage Crews
There are usually three different crews working on a stage production: the prop crew, the stage crew, and the scenery crew. The prop crew is responsible for all the props and any sets assigned to them. Prop crews are often very busy because they must find or build all the necessary props. The scenery crew often builds and paints the scenery, under the direction of a set designer. The set designer plans the scenery, and a technical director oversees its construction. Once prop and scenery crews have found or built the props and scenery, the stage crew takes over. They see to it that all the props and scenery are where they should be during the performance. The stage crew moves anything that has to be moved during the play and then readies them again for the next performance. In small theatres or schools, stage crews often work on prop and scenery crews also.

Creating and Performing
1. Draw a colored sketch of the set of *Painted Rain*. Include any scenery or props that you feel are important.
2. Find a scene that you feel captures the mood of the play. Rehearse it with a partner or partners. Be prepared to describe the mood of this scene.
3. Look at the stage directions for TEDDY on page 148. Choose the directions in either the first or second column, and act them out for the class.

Nothing But the Truth

The Play as Literature: Protagonist/Antagonist

In a work of literature, the character who moves the action forward is called the *protagonist*. Usually, the protagonist is the person with whom we identify most strongly. Any force that opposes the protagonist is called the *antagonist*. Most of the time the antagonist is another person, but sometimes the antagonist can be a situation or even the protagonist's own inner conflict.

As you read *Nothing But the Truth*, you will recognize the protagonist easily. Think carefully about who you would characterize as the antagonist in this drama.

The Play as Theatre: Creating a Character

Becoming someone else on stage is the ultimate goal (and the great challenge) of any actor. To play a character in a believable way, you must find a way to understand or identify with that character. Ask yourself the following questions about any character you wish to portray. Then act as you would act under similar circumstance.

- What is my character fighting for or against?
- What are my character's hopes, dreams, and goals?
- How does my character see himself or herself?
- How does my character see the characters around him or her?
- How does my character sound and move?
- How does my character change from the beginning to the end of the play?

Warm Up!

Imagine that you are to play the role of a young person who must choose between friendship and honesty. Your character has signed a school oath not to cheat, and to report anyone who does. Your character has just seen a good friend cheating on a test and is about to confront that friend. Think about how your character would feel, how he or she would approach the friend, and how the friend would respond. Then write a monologue that presents this confrontation.

Avi's

Nothing
But the Truth

Dramatized by Ronn Smith

Setting	Characters	Time
Almost any-where in the United States	**(IN ORDER OF APPEARANCE)**	The present

(IN ORDER OF APPEARANCE)

PHILIP MALLOY, student (14 years old)
MARGARET NARWIN, teacher (mid to late 50's)
BERNARD LUNSER, teacher
DR. GERTRUDE DOANE, principal
STUDENT #1
STUDENT #2
STUDENT #3
ALLISON DORESETT, student
COACH EARL JAMISON, teacher
BEN MALLOY, Philip's father
SUSAN MALLOY, Philip's mother
KEN BARCHET, student
LISA GIBBONS, student
JACOB BENISON, teacher
TODD BECKER, student
JANET BARSKY, student
DR. JOSEPH PALLENI, assistant principal
TED GRIFFEN, school board candidate
JENNIFER STEWART, reporter for the *Manchester Record*
DR. ALBERT SEYMOUR, school superintendent
JAKE BARLOW, talk radio host
MRS. GLORIA HARLAND, chairperson of school board
CALLER #1 (Steve)
CALLER #2 (Liz)
ROBERT DUVAL, reporter for the *St. Louis Post-Dispatch*
CALLER #3 (Roger)
CYNTHIA GAMBIA, student
JESSICA WITTINGTON
HANK MORGAN
CHARLES ELDERSON
CARLTON HAVEN
DAVID MAIK
LAURA JACOBS
ROLANDO MERCHAUD
MS. HARBOR
AMERICAN LEGIONNAIRE
GEORGE BROOKOVER, principal of Washington Academy
MISS ROONEY, teacher at Washington Academy

The following "memo" should be distributed to all audience members as they enter the theatre, or may be included as part of the program:

Memo

Harrison School District
Where Our Children Are Educated, Not Just Taught

Dr. Albert Seymour
Superintendent

Mrs. Gloria Harland
Chairman, School Board

STANDARD FORMAT FOR
MORNING ANNOUNCEMENTS ON
PUBLIC-ADDRESS SYSTEM

1. 8:05 A.M. The Principal, or in his stead, the Assistant Principal, or in his stead, a designated member of the faculty, will say, "Good morning to all students, faculty, and staff. Today is Monday (or whatever day), January (or whatever month) 3 (or whatever day). Today will be a Schedule A (or B) day" (depending on what schedule).

2. Say, "Today in history..." (Please consult *Book of Days* in Principal's office for appropriate references. Limit is three items.)

3. Say, "Please all rise and stand at respectful, silent attention for the playing of our national anthem."

4. Turn on tape of anthem.

5. After anthem is completed, say, "I have these announcements." All administration and faculty announcements shall be made at this point.

6. Say, "May I now introduce _____(name of student, grade) for today's sport and club news. Have a good day."

7. Student announcements.

8. All announcements should end by 8: 15 latest.

Dr. Joseph Palleni
Assistant Principal

Act One

Prologue

(Spot up on PHILIP MALLOY, *who is standing in the DC acting area)*

PHILIP MALLOY *(to the audience).* Two questions. Do you swear to tell the truth, the whole truth, and nothing but the truth? *(Pause)* Does anyone ever say no?

(Blackout)

Scene One

SLIDE: *"Tuesday, March 13. 10:35 P.M. From the Diary of Philip Malloy"*

(Lights up on PHILIP MALLOY, *standing in the DC acting area. He is holding his diary.)*

PHILIP MALLOY *(to the audience).* Coach Jamison stopped me in the hall today to say that I should try out for the track team! That with me on the Harrison High team we could be county champs. Fantastic! He wouldn't say that unless he meant it. Will have to ask the folks to help me get new shoes. But Dad was so excited I'm sure he'll help. *(He begins to leave, but then stops and turns back to the audience.)*

Oh, yeah. Sarah Gloss came over at lunch to say this girl, Allison Doresett, likes me. I wasn't sure who Allison was. Then I remembered. She's in my English class. Bet she heard about my running. Girls like guys who win. Ta-da! It's Malloy Magic time!

Talk about Malloy Magic. This time for—da-dum!—Miss Narwin. I mean, what can you do with an English teacher who's so uptight she must have been put together with superglue. She won't let people have their own minds about anything! And the stuff she makes us read! I can't believe how *boring* Jack London is! *The Call of the Wild.* Talk about dogs! Ma says *she* had to read it in school. There has to be better stuff to read. I thought high school was going to be different. *(Beat)* Have to figure out a way to run past Narwin.

SLIDE: *"10:45 P.M. From a Letter Written by Margaret Narwin to Her Sister, Anita Wigham"*

*(*PHILIP MALLOY *exits and* MARGARET NARWIN, *holding the letter, enters. She stops in the DC acting area.)*

MARGARET NARWIN *(to the audience).* Yes, a body gets a little tired after doing anything for twenty-one years. And I have been teaching at Harrison High for that long. But I still believe I was meant to bring fine literature to young minds. When the connection is made—and from time to time it is made—it's all worth it. The truth is, I like my work. *(Beat)*

But the other truth, Anita, is that students today are not what they used to be. There is no love of literature. They come to it reluctantly, fighting every inch of the way. I like them and their capacity for independence, but they seem to lack caring for anything other than themselves.

If they ask me once more "What's this have to do with us?" I think I'll scream.

For example, right now I'm teaching *The Call of the Wild*. This boy, Philip Malloy, raised his hand to say he didn't understand "who was calling who." Now if I were to laugh, he would have been insulted. And I would have lost him. You have to treat students with such care and fairness.

This Philip is only a middling student, which is a shame. He's a nice-looking boy. Intelligent. With real potential. Perhaps that's why he irritates me so, for he shows no desire to strive, to make sacrifices for the betterment of himself. Like so many students, he exhibits *no* desire to learn. But it's not even *that* that I mind so much. It's a certain something—a resistance—to the idea that literature is important. But it is. I know it is. If I could only convince students of this.

I can hear you saying, "Come down to Florida." Anita, I don't know if I am ready. Yes, I could take early retirement, but the truth is, I would be lost without my books, my teaching, my students.

Scene Two

 SLIDE: *"Thursday, March 15. 8:05 A.M. Bernard Lunser's Homeroom Class"*

(PHILIP MALLOY, STUDENT #1, STUDENT #2, STUDENT #3, *and* BERNARD LUNSER *in*

SL *acting area. General commotion.*)

> *SLIDE (on rear projection screen behind* SL *area): Classroom wall, maybe a blackboard or a row of windows.*

BERNARD LUNSER. Let's go! Let's go! Time to grab the moment!

INTERCOM (*voice of* DR. GERTRUDE DOANE) Good morning to all students, faculty, and staff. Today is Thursday, March fifteenth. Today will be a Schedule A day.

BERNARD LUNSER. Get that, bozos? *A* day!

INTERCOM. Today in history. On this day in forty-four B.C., Julius Caesar was assassinated.

BERNARD LUNSER. And right after that they all ate a Caesar salad.

INTERCOM. It was in eighteen-twenty that Maine was admitted to the United States.

BERNARD LUNSER. And by eighteen-twenty-one they wanted out.

INTERCOM. Please all rise and stand at respectful, silent attention for the playing of our national anthem.

(PHILIP MALLOY *and the other* STUDENTS *stand.* PHILIP MALLOY'*s attention is on the book lying open on his desk as the first verse of* The Star-Spangled Banner *is played over the intercom. [In following scenes, unless otherwise noted, fade out music soon after the dialogue has been concluded.])*

Oh, say, can you see by the dawn's early light,

What so proudly we hailed at the twilight's last gleaming? . . .

BERNARD LUNSER. Okay, Philip, is that your homework you're working on?

Whose broad stripes and bright stars, thro' the perilous fight . . .

PHILIP MALLOY. I'm trying to pass an exam.

BERNARD LUNSER. Ah, the famous wit and wisdom of Mr. Malloy. Put the book away.

O'er the ramparts we watched were so gallantly streaming? . . .

PHILIP MALLOY. Just one last paragraph?

BERNARD LUNSER. Away, Philip! Or I'll make you sing a solo!

And the rockets' red glare, the bombs bursting in air,

Gave proof thro' the night that our flag was still there.

Oh, say does that star-spangled banner yet wave

O'er the land of the free and the home of the brave?

 SLIDE: "11:05 P.M. From the Diary of Philip Malloy"

(PHILIP MALLOY *in the DC acting area. He is holding his diary.*)

PHILIP MALLOY *(to the audience).* Winter term exams next week. I hate them. Studying is so boring! Three exams scheduled in one day! The trick is getting past the teacher. It's like a race. You have to have a strategy, know when to take it easy, when to turn on the juice. Get teachers to think you're in control. Or when all else fails, make them laugh.

The exam I really want to study for is math. People think I'm weird, but I like math. I won't waste time on English. What can you say about a dog? Besides, it's just a matter of opinion! If only I could get Narwin to crack a smile. *(Beat)*

Been checking out Allison. She looked cool today. Dad says that girls really go for sports stars.

Sunny at first today. Then cloudy. Bit of rain. Then sunny again. Still, I got in a workout. Mostly wind sprints. Then twenty minutes on Dad's rowing machine. Track team practice starts next week. Can't wait. That's all Dad and I talk about.

Scene Three

 SLIDE: "Friday, March 16. Memo to Philip from Dr. Joseph Palleni, Assistant Principal"

(PHILIP MALLOY *in SL acting area. He is holding the memo.*)

SLIDE: School hallway.

PHILIP MALLOY *(reading).* "Dear Philip. As we head into Spring Term, the faculty committee has made some changes in homeroom assignments. This will facilitate the movements of students, as well as allow for a greater degree of freedom in the planning of Spring Term extracurricular schedules. Your new homeroom teacher is Miss Narwin, in room two-oh-six. Effective Wednesday, March twenty-eight. Thank you for your cooperation."

(PHILIP MALLOY *looks up at the audience, a look of horror on his face.*)

 SLIDE: *"8:20 P.M. Telephone Conversation between Philip and Allison Doresett"*

(PHILIP MALLOY *in the UC acting area.* ALLISON DORESETT *in DC acting area.*)

> SLIDE [*on rear projection screen behind UC area*]: *Kitchen wall in the Malloy household.*

PHILIP MALLOY. Can I speak to Allison, please?

ALLISON DORESETT. This is she.

PHILIP MALLOY. Oh, Allison. Hi, this is Phil Malloy.

ALLISON DORESETT. Oh, hi.

PHILIP MALLOY. Hey, I . . . I was wondering . . . the English exam. Did you read *The Call of the Wild* yet?

ALLISON DORESETT. I finished it last night. We're supposed to review it tomorrow for the exam.

PHILIP MALLOY. I lost my copy.

ALLISON DORESETT. You what?

PHILIP MALLOY. It wasn't my fault. See, I had this idea . . . I thought I'd read it to a dog.

ALLISON DORESETT. A dog!

PHILIP MALLOY. Well, it's about dogs, right? So I started to read it to him . . . this really mean dog . . . slobbering mouth, running eyes, the whole bit. Only, see he grabs it and starts to run away.

ALLISON DORESETT (*laughing*). This isn't true . . .

PHILIP MALLOY. No, listen! I'm serious! And I chased him into a yard and there he was . . .burying the book in the ground. I couldn't get it back. My point is, he hated it too!

ALLISON DORESETT. You're too much. I dare you to tell that to Narwin.

PHILIP MALLOY. You think I should?

ALLISON DORESETT. You always make remarks.

PHILIP MALLOY. Somebody's got to keep the class awake.

ALLISON DORESETT. I hate to tell you, Phil, but I liked the book.

PHILIP MALLOY. Whoops! Sorry, wrong number! Bye!

Scene Four

 SLIDE: *"Monday, March 19. Margaret Narwin's Winter Term Exam"*

(PHILIP MALLOY *and* MARGARET NARWIN *in the SL acting area, facing the audience. They are each holding a copy of the exam.*)

> SLIDE: *Classroom wall. [This image is not the same as the one used in Scene Two, but should be used for all subsequent scenes that take place in Margaret Narwin's classroom.]*

PHILIP MALLOY (*to the audience*). "Question four: What is the significance of Jack London's choice in making Buck, the dog in *The Call of the Wild*, the focus of the novel? Is the dog meant to be symbolic? Explain your answer. Can people learn from this portrayal of a dog? Expand on these ideas."

MARGARET NARWIN (*incredulous, reading*

PHILIP MALLOY's *answer*). "The significance of Buck in Jack London's *The Call of the Wild* is that Buck is symbolic of a cat. You might think that cats have nothing to do with the book, but that is the point. Dogs are willing to sit around and have writers write about them, which, in my personal opinion, makes them dumb. I think cats are smart. Cats don't like cold. A book that takes up so much time about a dog is pretty dumb. The book itself is a dog. That is what people learn from Jack London's *The Call of the Wild.*

PHILIP MALLOY (*reading* MARGARET NARWIN's *response*). "Philip, this is an unacceptable response. *The Call of the Wild* is an acknowledged masterpiece of American literature. You are not required to like it. You are, however, required to give it your respectful, thoughtful attention. When you get your Winter Term grade, consider it a warning. Exam grade: C minus."

(PHILIP MALLOY *looks up at the audience, surprised.*)

Scene Five

 SLIDE: *"Tuesday, March 20. Memo to Dr. Gertrude Doane, Principal, from Margaret Narwin"*

(DR. GERTRUDE DOANE *in SR acting area. She is reading the memo.*)

SLIDE *[on rear projection screen behind SR area]: Office wall.*

DR. GERTRUDE DOANE. "Attached please find my application for a summer grant-in-aid. I am applying to the State University for a summer program entitled, 'New Approaches to the Teaching of Literature for Today's Students.' It's an intensive two-week workshop in which university professors will present new ideas for the experienced high school English teacher. The application form requires both an approval and a recommendation from my head administrator, which is why I write you.

"I have been teaching for a long time. And I feel I am in need of new ideas, strategies, concepts to keep my teaching vital. The truth is—and I believe I can speak honestly to you about this—I feel that I am a little out of touch with the current crop of students. I want to find new works and new ways to reach them.

"In any case, you can easily see that the real beneficiaries of the program will be the students of Harrison High. I know how restricted district money is these days, but I have not asked for this kind of support before. The State University tuition, two thousand dollars, is quite beyond my personal budget. May I ask you to give this request your personal and immediate attention. Sincerely, Margaret Narwin."

Scene Six

 SLIDE: *"Friday, March 23. 10:30 P.M. From the Diary of Philip Malloy"*

(PHILIP MALLOY *in the DC acting area. He is holding his diary.*)

PHILIP MALLOY (*to the audience*). Got my term grades. Math, an A. Awesome wicked. B-minus in Biology. That's okay, too. And I got a C in History, which is cool. All of that stuff is dead anyway. A straight B in Health. But then I got a D in English! Narwin is so dumb she didn't get the joke. What she really wants is for us to write down the things she thinks. And now I'm going to get Narwin for a homeroom teacher, too. Not me.

Worked out with Mike at the track. Short sprints. Starts. Long runs. It calmed me down. Tryouts for the team are on Monday. Can't wait. I know I'll make it. Will have to ask the folks to spring for those new shoes. (*Beat*)

Sarah Gloss was reading this book, *The Outsiders.* She said it was the best book she'd ever read. Said she'd loan it to me when she was done.

Saw Allison today. Did this thing. (PHILIP MALLOY *sweeps off his imaginary hat and makes a big, theatrical bow.*) She cracked up. I'm getting to her.

Went out to this restaurant tonight called Treasure Island. Seafood place. Dad said I could have anything on the menu except lobster. I ordered a hamburger and fries. Dad was pretty sore. I wish people would say what they mean.

Scene Seven

 SLIDE: *"Monday, March 26. Memo to Margaret Narwin from Dr. Doane"*

(MARGARET NARWIN *in SL acting area. She is reading the memo.*)

SLIDE: *Classroom wall*

MARGARET NARWIN. "As much as I would like to be supportive of your desire to take the 'New Approaches to the Teaching of Literature' workshop, I am afraid I cannot give it formal approval. The problem is severely limited district money. Such funds as are available for this kind of support have already been allocated.[1] In fact, the last of them just went to Kimberly Howard, the music teacher, who will be taking a summer course in marching band techniques . . . something that will give pleasure to so many people, and, it is hoped, encourage greater attendance at athletic events. (*Beat*)

I do want to say, on a personal level, how much I admire your willingness to expand your intellectual and teaching horizons. You have always been one of our best teachers, and I know you will continue to be so. Sincerely, Dr. Gertrude Doane."

 SLIDE: *"11:20 A.M. Coach Earl Jamison's Office"*

(COACH EARL JAMISON *and* PHILIP MALLOY *in SR acting area.* COACH EARL JAMISON *is holding a copy of* PHILIP MALLOY'S *grades.*) SLIDE: *Coach's office, maybe with trophies.*

---

1. allocate (al′ə kāt) to set apart money for a special purpose

COACH JAMISON. Look, Phil, I've got a copy of your winter term grades here. You know, there's a school rule—a district rule—that you can't be on a team unless you've got a passing grade in every subject.

PHILIP MALLOY. A passing grade?

COACH JAMISON. Yeah. In high school, a passing grade.

PHILIP MALLOY. I didn't know.

COACH JAMISON. Well . . . the point is, Phil, it looks like you don't have high grades. There's a D here. I guess we have a problem.

PHILIP MALLOY. We do?

COACH JAMISON. A D isn't—by the rules—

PHILIP MALLOY. It's Miss Narwin. I keep trying to get her to like me, but she won't.

COACH JAMISON. Is there any point in your talking with her?

PHILIP MALLOY. What do you mean?

COACH JAMISON. The rule . . . as it stands now, you're not even allowed to try out.

PHILIP MALLOY. I didn't know about that rule.

COACH JAMISON. The rule has been around for a long time. You need passing grades.

PHILIP MALLOY. I mean, you can't kid around with her or anything.

COACH JAMISON. Phil, sometimes you have to go along to get along. That's the whole thing about sports. You have to go with the flow.

PHILIP MALLOY. I think it's a personal

thing with her. She has it in for me. I shouldn't be in her class. Could you get me switched?

COACH JAMISON. Maybe if you just talk with her. Do some catch-up work. How about it?

PHILIP MALLOY. I mean, if I knew it was a rule—

COACH JAMISON. Yeah, well, a rule is a rule. It isn't always easy.

PHILIP MALLOY. I didn't know.

Scene Eight

 SLIDE: "Tuesday, March 27. 6:23 P.M. The Malloy Kitchen"

(BEN *and* SUSAN MALLOY *in UC acting area.*)

SLIDE: Kitchen wall.

SUSAN MALLOY. Honey, did you have a chance to look at Phil's grades?

BEN MALLOY. Uh, sort of. Where is he?

SUSAN MALLOY. In the basement. On your rowing machine. Did you?

BEN MALLOY. I'm looking at them now. Not too bad. Except for English. What's the problem?

SUSAN MALLOY. He says it's the teacher.

BEN MALLOY. I've seen him read.

SUSAN MALLOY. He's reading some paperback. *Insiders. Outsiders.* I don't know. That doesn't seem to be the problem.

BEN MALLOY. I never was one for reading much.

SUSAN MALLOY. Ben, he could flunk that course.

BEN MALLOY. Won't be the end of the

world. What would he have to do, go to summer school?

SUSAN MALLOY. The last couple of days he's been very moody.

BEN MALLOY. Come on, he's fourteen.

SUSAN MALLOY. He doesn't want to talk to me. Maybe you should spend more time with him.

BEN MALLOY. I know. But at work I'm all tied up in this—

SUSAN MALLOY. But work's better, isn't it?

BEN MALLOY. Some. *(Beat)* Did Phil make the track team?

SUSAN MALLOY. I forgot to ask him. Maybe that's the problem.

BEN MALLOY. I'll talk to him.

 SLIDE: "8:05 P.M. The Malloy Basement"

(PHILIP MALLOY is in the DC acting area, doing sit-ups. BEN MALLOY enters.)

BEN MALLOY. Can I talk to you?

PHILIP MALLOY. Sure.

BEN MALLOY. Uh, Phil . . . school stuff. Straight up. What's the story with English?

PHILIP MALLOY. What do you mean?

BEN MALLOY. I saw your grades. What's with English?

PHILIP MALLOY. You want the truth?

BEN MALLOY. Well?

PHILIP MALLOY. It's the teacher. Narwin. She has it in for me.

BEN MALLOY. How come?

PHILIP MALLOY. I don't know. Nobody likes her.

BEN MALLOY. Want me or your mother to talk to her?

PHILIP MALLOY. No, I can handle it.

BEN MALLOY. What are you reading in school?

PHILIP MALLOY. *Julius Caesar.* Shakespeare.

BEN MALLOY. Uh-oh.

PHILIP MALLOY. So bad. No one understands it. Narwin says it's English, but it must have been English before the English got there.

BEN MALLOY. Well, reading is important. *(Beat)* How are you getting on with the track team? Phil?

PHILIP MALLOY. I, ah . . . was thinking I wouldn't try out.

BEN MALLOY. But high school track is. . . . Why?

PHILIP MALLOY. Lots of reasons.

BEN MALLOY. Like what? I want to know.

PHILIP MALLOY. Just because you did it doesn't mean I have to.

BEN MALLOY. Now wait a minute. We just got you new shoes. And you're good. Better than I ever was. I love watching you run. And here you are working out. I don't get it. What's going on?

PHILIP MALLOY. Nothing.

BEN MALLOY. Didn't you tell me the coach asked you to be on the team?

PHILIP MALLOY. Doesn't mean. . . . It's my choice.

BEN MALLOY. Phil, let me tell you something. If God gives you a ticket, you better use it.

PHILIP MALLOY. Ticket to what?

BEN MALLOY. Running.

PHILIP MALLOY. I'll think about it.

SLIDE: *"9:24 P.M. From a Letter Written by Margaret Narwin to Her Sister"*

(MARGARET NARWIN *in SL acting area. She is holding the letter.*)

MARGARET NARWIN *(to the audience).* The truth is I'm hurt. Never in all the years I've been at Harrison High have I asked for anything in the way of extra funds. If it were a case of no money available for anyone, I could accept that. But a certain Kimberly Howard, who has been here for only two years, and who has a husband who works for some large corporation, she receives money! And for some idiotic course in marching band music!

I think there's a question of fairness here. Call it pride, call it vanity, but I would like some respect for all I have done here. From the community. From the administration. *(Beat)*

The truth is it's our superintendent's doing. He sent out a memo to everybody warning that the budget vote might fail again. He is a *very* political person. But then, all he wants is to keep his job. I am so angry. . . .

SLIDE: *"10:40 P.M. From the Diary of Philip Malloy"*

(PHILIP MALLOY *in the UC acting area. He is holding his diary.*)

PHILIP MALLOY *(to the audience).* Dad talked to me about the grades. I told him the truth. He seemed to understand. But then he asked me about

my being on the track team. I didn't know what to say.

I just realized two things that make me want to puke. Track practice starts tomorrow and I'm *not* on the team. Also, I start homeroom with *Narwin!* I have to find a way to get transferred out.

Scene Nine

SLIDE: *"Wednesday, March 28. 7:30 A.M. Philip and Ken Barchet on the Way to the School Bus"*

(PHILIP MALLOY *and* KEN BARCHET *in DC acting area*)

PHILIP MALLOY. What's happening, man?

KEN BARCHET. Nothing. Got room changes. Who'd you get?

PHILIP MALLOY. Narwin.

KEN BARCHET. So do I. She's okay.

PHILIP MALLOY. Can't stand her.

KEN BARCHET. Doesn't matter. It's just homeroom.

PHILIP MALLOY. No way. I've got her for English, too. I'm going to get transferred out of both.

KEN BARCHET. Why?

PHILIP MALLOY. Told you. I can't stand her.

KEN BARCHET. How you going to do that?

PHILIP MALLOY. I'm working on it.

KEN BARCHET. Sure . . . Malloy Magic, right?

PHILIP MALLOY. You'll see.

SLIDE: *"8:03 A.M. Margaret Narwin's Homeroom Class"*

(MARGARET NARWIN, PHILIP MALLOY, KEN BARCHET, ALLISON DORESETT, *and* LISA GIBBONS *in SL acting area.*)

SLIDE: *Classroom wall.*

MARGARET NARWIN. Ladies and gentlemen, please settle down. For the moment just take any seat you wish. We'll work out problems later. Yes?

LISA GIBBONS. Am I supposed to be in this room?

MARGARET NARWIN. What's your name?

LISA GIBBONS. Lisa Gibbons.

MARGARET NARWIN (*checking her list*). Lisa? Yes, you're on my list. Just take any seat. Yes, Allison, you are here.

INTERCOM (*voice of* DR. GERTRUDE DOANE). Good morning to all students, faculty, and staff.

MARGARET NARWIN. Please, let's get done with the morning business.

INTERCOM. Today is Wednesday, March twenty-eight. Today will be a Schedule B day. Today in history: In the year A.D. one-ninety-three the Roman Emperor Pertinax was assassinated. On this day in eighteen-sixty-two the Civil War battle in Glorieta, New Mexico, was fought. Please all rise and stand at respectful, silent attention for the playing of our national anthem.

Oh, say, can you see by the dawn's early light . . .

(PHILIP MALLOY *starts humming.*)

MARGARET NARWIN. Is that someone humming?

What so proudly we hailed at the twilight's last gleaming? Whose broad stripes and bright stars . . .

MARGARET NARWIN. Who is that?

. . . thro' the perilous fight, O'er the ramparts we watched were so gallantly streaming? . . .

MARGARET NARWIN. Is that you, Philip?

PHILIP MALLOY. Just humming.

MARGARET NARWIN. Please stop it.

Gave proof thro' the night that our flag was still there. . . .

PHILIP MALLOY. Mr. Lunser doesn't mind. I just—

MARGARET NARWIN. Stop it now.

PHILIP MALLOY. But—

Oh, say does that star-spangled banner yet wave . . .

MARGARET NARWIN. Now! Thank you.

O'er the land of the free and the home of the brave?

 SLIDE: *"10:30 A.M. Margaret Narwin and Jacob Benison, Science Teacher, in the Faculty Room"*

(MARGARET NARWIN *and* JACOB BENISON *in DC acting area*)

JACOB BENISON. Morning, Peg. How's it going?

MARGARET NARWIN. I'll get through it.

JACOB BENISON. Sometimes I think it's not worth the trouble. I'll be glad to get out of it. Forty-four more days!

MARGARET NARWIN. I sometimes think I should join you.

JACOB BENISON. Can't wait. Get you some coffee? Kim brought in muffins.

MARGARET NARWIN. Kim?

JACOB BENISON. Kimberly Howard. Music.

MARGARET NARWIN. Oh.

JACOB BENISON. Something the matter, Peg?

MARGARET NARWIN. Oh, stupid business. I suppose it's this changing of homeroom classes. The announcements and so on. And when the national anthem comes on, the students are supposed to stand in silence.

JACOB BENISON. Right. I think the rule reads, "Respect, silence, and attention."

MARGARET NARWIN. Exactly. I had a student who started to hum. Very loudly.

JACOB BENISON. Uh-oh. Who was that?

MARGARET NARWIN. Philip Malloy.

JACOB BENISON. Oh, sure. Phil. Nice kid. Bright . . . when he gets around to doing some work. He's got being fast on the brain. Humming? What was he doing that for?

MARGARET NARWIN. I don't know. I had to ask him to stop.

JACOB BENISON. Did he?

MARGARET NARWIN. Not at first. He claimed he always did it in Bernie Lunser's class.

JACOB BENISON. Well, the term won't last forever.

MARGARET NARWIN. Sometimes I wonder.

 SLIDE: "12:15 P.M. Philip and Todd Becker in Front of Philip's Locker"

(PHILIP MALLOY *and* TODD BECKER *in SL acting area.*)

SLIDE: School hallway.

TODD BECKER. Hey, how come you aren't going out for track?

PHILIP MALLOY. Too much to do.

TODD BECKER We could use you. Need some power.

PHILIP MALLOY. I'll think about it. Just don't bug me.

TODD BECKER Just asking. Who's your new homeroom teacher?

PHILIP MALLOY. Narwin.

TODD BECKER I like her.

PHILIP MALLOY. I hate her.

TODD BECKER Yeah? How come?

PHILIP MALLOY. You know how they play *The Star-Spangled Banner* in the morning . . .?

TODD BECKER Yeah. . . .

PHILIP MALLOY. Well, I started to sing it. . . .

TODD BECKER Why?

PHILIP MALLOY. Felt like it. She told me to stop.

TODD BECKER Stop what?

PHILIP MALLOY. Humming.

TODD BECKER I thought you said singing.

PHILIP MALLOY. Whatever.

TODD BECKER How come she made you stop?

PHILIP MALLOY. I don't know. She really has it in for me. I mean, she's always on me about something.

TODD BECKER What did you do?

PHILIP MALLOY. I told you. Nothing.

TODD BECKER I mean when she told you to stop humming.

PHILIP MALLOY. I stopped. *(Beat)* Humming, would you believe it? No way I'm staying in her classes.

 SLIDE: "1:40 P.M. Margaret Narwin's English Class"

(MARGARET NARWIN, PHILIP MALLOY, *and the three* STUDENTS *in SL acting area.)*

SLIDE: Classroom wall.

MARGARET NARWIN. Now, scene two, line fifty-two. Brutus says, "No, Cassius; for the eye sees not itself / But by reflection, by some other things." What does he mean by that? Anyone? Yes?

STUDENT #1. That he can't see himself.

MARGARET NARWIN. Close. Yes, Philip?

PHILIP MALLOY. But what if he's cross-eyed? He'd see himself then, wouldn't he?

MARGARET NARWIN. I'm not even going to respond to that!

 SLIDE: "3:15 P.M. Philip and Allison on the School Bus"

(PHILIP MALLOY *and* ALLISON DORESETT *in DC acting area)*

ALLISON DORESETT. Can I sit next to you?

PHILIP MALLOY. Oh, sure.

ALLISON DORESETT. What's the matter? You look like death warmed over.

PHILIP MALLOY. I'm okay.

ALLISON DORESETT. You got Miss Narwin mad today with that joke.

PHILIP MALLOY. She's always mad at me.

ALLISON DORESETT. Is something the matter?

PHILIP MALLOY. Nothing.

ALLISON DORESETT. How come you didn't go to track tryouts?

PHILIP MALLOY *(shrugs).* Had to do something.

ALLISON DORESETT. Todd said you were really great.

PHILIP MALLOY. Yeah.

ALLISON DORESETT. Boy, you're in a mood!

PHILIP MALLOY. Just don't feel like talking.

ALLISON DORESETT. Well, excuse me!

(ALLISON DORESETT *exits.)*

PHILIP MALLOY. Hey, Allison, wait. . . . Damn!

 SLIDE: "3:20 P.M. Margaret Narwin and Bernard Lunser Outside the School's Main Office"

(MARGARET NARWIN *and* BERNARD LUNSER *in SR acting area.)*

SLIDE: School hallway

MARGARET NARWIN. Bernie! I need to ask you something.

BERNARD LUNSER. What's that?

MARGARET NARWIN. Do you allow your students to sing the national anthem in your morning homeroom?

BERNARD LUNSER. Sing? I thought the kids are supposed to be quiet.

MARGARET NARWIN. One of my new homeroom students informed me that you always allow singing. Do you?

BERNARD LUNSER. The rule says keep quiet. . . .

MARGARET NARWIN. But do you allow singing?

BERNARD LUNSER. Hey, Peg, do I look like a guy who goes around breaking important rules?

MARGARET NARWIN. Thanks.

 SLIDE: "7:15 P.M. Discussion between Philip and His Parents During Dinner"

(PHILIP MALLOY *plus* BEN *and* SUSAN MALLOY *at the dinner table in the UC acting area. They are eating dinner, which can be mimed.*)

SLIDE: Kitchen wall.

BEN MALLOY. What did you decide to do about the track team? *(Pause)*

SUSAN MALLOY. Philip, your father asked you something.

PHILIP MALLOY. I'm not on the team.

BEN MALLOY. I know that. But I'd like to know why.

PHILIP MALLOY. What would you say if a teacher said I wasn't allowed to sing *The Star-Spangled Banner?*

BEN MALLOY. Anywhere?

PHILIP MALLOY. In class.

SUSAN MALLOY. What's this have to do with your running?

PHILIP MALLOY. I'm trying to tell you. You know, when school starts, homeroom, when they play the song over the speaker system. It's a tape.

BEN MALLOY. Come again?

PHILIP MALLOY. I'm trying to explain!

BEN MALLOY. No need to raise your voice!

SUSAN MALLOY. The both of you. . . .

BEN MALLOY. Philip, just tell us what. . . . Obviously something has happened. Why are you upset?

PHILIP MALLOY. Everybody got new homeroom teachers in school today. Anyway, I got this Miss Narwin. She's a real witch.

BEN MALLOY. Phil!

PHILIP MALLOY. Do you want to know what happened or not?

SUSAN MALLOY. Honey, let the boy tell it his way.

PHILIP MALLOY. So they always start off playing *The Star-Spangled Banner.* Okay. It's stupid, but, sometimes I sort of sing along. . . . Or I hum. No big deal. But this teacher got real mad and yelled at me.

BEN MALLOY. She yelled at you because you were—?

PHILIP MALLOY. Right. Humming. That's all I was doing.

BEN MALLOY. And she yelled at you?

SUSAN MALLOY. That's not what I'd call fair.

PHILIP MALLOY. Yeah.

 SLIDE: "8:32 P.M. From a Letter Written by Margaret Narwin to Her Sister"

(MARGARET NARWIN *in DC acting area. She is holding the letter.*)

MARGARET NARWIN *(to the audience).* I do think it's the best thing Barbara Pym ever wrote. It was so soothing to come home to that quiet, thoughtful, civilized British world. *(Beat)* The truth is, I needed something soothing. Today was "Spring Changeover Day," when our students, after six months of struggling to learn exactly where to go, are tossed pell-mell here, there, anywhere. Of course, bedlam is always the result. But one has to be vigilant[2] and firm. As well as consistent and fair. That's the key with students these days. Sometimes I haven't the stamina for it. Ah, well. . . .

 SLIDE: "9:05 P.M. From the Diary of Philip Malloy"

(PHILIP MALLOY *in UC acting area. He is holding his diary.*)

PHILIP MALLOY (*to the audience*). Today was rotten. Nothing was right. I felt like punching Narwin in the face. It all just stinks.

 SLIDE: "10:45 P.M. Philip and His Father in His Bedroom"

(PHILIP MALLOY *and* BEN MALLOY *in UC acting area.*)

SLIDE: *Philip Malloy's bedroom.*

BEN MALLOY: Now, look, about this business about not being allowed to sing the national anthem—

PHILIP MALLOY. I was humming.

BEN MALLOY. Whatever. Now, your mother and I want you to understand that whatever it is, we're on your side.

PHILIP MALLOY. I didn't think you were interested.

BEN MALLOY. Of course I'm interested.

PHILIP MALLOY. It's just that the teacher—

BEN MALLOY. No, wait. Straight up, I think she's wrong. You're right to be bugged. Now, your mother and I are no great—well—big patriots. But that doesn't mean we don't love our country. We just don't make a big thing about it. But not

being allowed to sing *The Star-Spangled Banner* . . . well, that's sort of like not being allowed to pray. A personal thing. The point is, in America, it doesn't seem right. And we just want you to know we're with you.

PHILIP MALLOY. Thanks. (*Beat*) You're not mad?

BEN MALLOY. Of course not. I have half a mind to talk to Ted Griffen. He's running for school board. That can mean something.

PHILIP MALLOY. He's always chasing me off his lawn.

BEN MALLOY. Yeah. But you were a kid then. Phil, let me tell you something. You really have to stick up for your rights. Your mother and I will stand with you. Don't worry.

PHILIP MALLOY. Right.

Scene Ten

 SLIDE: "Thursday, March 29. 8:02 A.M. Margaret Narwin's Homeroom Class"

(MARGARET NARWIN, PHILIP MALLOY, STUDENT #1, *and* STUDENT #3 *in SL acting area.*)

SLIDE: *Classroom wall.*

MARGARET NARWIN. Ladies and gentlemen, please take your assigned seats. I need to take attendance.

STUDENT #3. Miss Narwin.

MARGARET NARWIN. Yes?

STUDENT #3. Peggy Lord is sick.

————————
2. vigilant (vij′ə lənt), alertly watchful

MARGARET NARWIN. Thank you.

INTERCOM (*voice of* DR. GERTRUDE DOANE). Good morning to all students, faculty, and staff. Today is Thursday, March twenty-nine. Today will be a Schedule A day. Today in history: In the year seventeen-ninety our tenth president, John Tyler, was born. In nineteen-eighteen singer Pearl Bailey was born. Please rise and stand at respectful, silent attention for the playing of our national anthem.

Oh, say, can you see by the dawn's early light . . .

(PHILIP MALLOY *starts humming.*)

MARGARET NARWIN. Philip, is that you again?

What so proudly we hailed at the twilight's last gleaming?
Whose broad stripes and bright stars . . .

MARGARET NARWIN. I spoke with you yesterday about this.

. . . thro' the perilous fight,
O'er the ramparts we watched were so gallantly streaming?

MARGARET NARWIN. Now, please, stop it.

And the rockets' red glare, the bombs bursting in air . . .
Gave proof thro' the night that our flag was still there . . .

MARGARET NARWIN. Philip, leave this room instantly. Report to Dr. Palleni's office. Now!

 SLIDE: "8:35 A.M. Dr. Joseph Palleni's Office"

(PHILIP MALLOY *and* DR. JOSEPH PALLENI *in SR acting area.*)

SLIDE: Office wall.

DR. PALLENI. You must have some idea about what seems to be the problem. Miss Narwin asked you to leave the class. What happened?

PHILIP MALLOY. She wouldn't let me sing *The Star-Spangled Banner.*

DR. PALLENI. What?

PHILIP MALLOY. It's just a thing I like to do. Sing along.

DR. PALLENI. You mean, when the morning tape plays? . . .

PHILIP MALLOY. Yeah.

DR. PALLENI. There's a rule about being quiet at that time.

PHILIP MALLOY. Yeah, well, it's sort of a . . . patriotic thing with me. But the whole thing is, she always has it in for me.

DR. PALLENI. Did Miss Narwin ask you to stop?

PHILIP MALLOY. I wasn't being loud or anything like that.

DR. PALLENI. But when Miss Narwin asked you, did you stop?

PHILIP MALLOY. It was just to myself.

DR. PALLENI (*looking through a desk drawer*). Where is that thing? Here it is. This is a memo from Dr. Doane. Go on, read it. What does it say? "Silent." Right? But you were singing. Miss Narwin asked you to stop singing. You didn't. You were disobedient. So she asked you to leave.

PHILIP MALLOY. How can you ask someone not to sing *The Star-Spangled Banner?*

DR. PALLENI. It's the rule.

PHILIP MALLOY. Is a memo a rule?

DR. PALLENI. Philip, look, I've got more important things to do with my time than argue with you about following simple, basic rules.

PHILIP MALLOY. Put me in another homeroom. And another English class.

DR. PALLENI. What's English have to do with this? *(Pause)* Philip, I asked you something.

PHILIP MALLOY. She and I don't get along.

DR. PALLENI. Look, Philip, you are here to get an education. You've given me your side of the story. I'll check with Miss Narwin, but it seems pretty clear to me . . . . Here's a note that says I spoke to you. Scoot.

PHILIP MALLOY. But—

DR. PALLENI. Hey, Phil, be cool. I heard you're a runner. It's a great day for running. Go join the track team. They could use you. Have a nice day.

 SLIDE: *"6:10 P.M. The Malloy Kitchen"*

(BEN *and* SUSAN MALLOY *in UC acting area.*)

SLIDE: *Kitchen wall.*

SUSAN MALLOY. What's wrong?

BEN MALLOY. I got chewed out by Dexter.

SUSAN MALLOY. What for?

BEN MALLOY. Some job estimate that went wrong. Wasn't even anything I did.

SUSAN MALLOY. I hope you stood up for yourself.

BEN MALLOY. And get myself in his bad books?

SUSAN MALLOY. You wouldn't get yourself—

BEN MALLOY. You don't understand. I'm sorry I mentioned it. Look, I'm just not in a position of power there. Okay? Just forget it.

SUSAN MALLOY. Sorry I asked.

 SLIDE: *"7:10 P.M. The Malloy Kitchen"*

(PHILIP MALLOY *plus* BEN *and* SUSAN MALLOY.)

SLIDE: *Kitchen wall.*

PHILIP MALLOY. It happened again.

SUSAN MALLOY. What happened?

PHILIP MALLOY. In school. This morning I was singing *The Star-Spangled Banner.* The teacher kicked me out. She sent me to the assistant principal's office.

BEN MALLOY. I hope you stood up for yourself.

SUSAN MALLOY. What did he say?

PHILIP MALLOY. He sided with Narwin.

BEN MALLOY. Listen to me. Don't give in to that crap. There must be some mistake.

PHILIP MALLOY. That's the way she is.

BEN MALLOY. You have to stick up for yourself, Phil. We'll stand behind you.

 SLIDE: *"9:45 P.M. From a Letter Written by Margaret Narwin to Her Sister"*

(MARGARET NARWIN *in DC acting area. She is holding the letter.*)

MARGARET NARWIN (*to the audience*). So you see, Anita, it was gratifying to hear Gertrude talk this way . . . exactly the kind of support teachers need. Certainly it's what I needed. Many teachers have almost nothing good to say about their administrators, complaining that they fail to support them. Or that they show only slight concern about their problems. My principal is different. I'm lucky. . . .

SLIDE: "11:05 P.M. *From the Diary of Philip Malloy*"

(PHILIP MALLOY *in UC acting area. He is holding his diary.*)

PHILIP MALLOY (*to the audience*). Lots of kids bad-mouth their parents, say they never stick up for them or understand them or pay any attention to them. Stuff like that. My parents are different. I'm lucky.

Scene Eleven

SLIDE: "Friday, March 30. 8:05 A.M. *Margaret Narwin's Homeroom Class*"

(MARGARET NARWIN, PHILIP MALLOY, STUDENT #1, *and* STUDENT #2 *in SL acting area.*)

SLIDE [which remains on through the end of the scene]: Classroom wall.

(PHILIP MALLOY *is singing along with the tape, which is being broadcast over the intercom system.*)

What so proudly we hailed at the twilight's last gleaming?
Whose broad stripes and bright stars, thro' the perilous fight . . .

MARGARET NARWIN. Philip, is that you singing again?

PHILIP MALLOY. I have the right to do it.

O'er the ramparts we watched were so gallantly streaming?
And the rockets' red glare, the bombs bursting in air . . .

MARGARET NARWIN. The what?

PHILIP MALLOY. The right.

Gave proof thro' the night that our flag was still there. . . .

MARGARET NARWIN. I want you to stop it immediately. Your actions are thoroughly disrespectful.

PHILIP MALLOY. It's you who's being disrespectful.

Oh, say does that star-spangled banner yet wave . . .

MARGARET NARWIN. Philip!

PHILIP MALLOY. I'm being patriotic. It's a free country. You have no right to stop me.

MARGARET NARWIN. Philip Malloy, you will leave this room immediately! Report to the principal's office.

PHILIP MALLOY. You can't keep me from being patriotic.

MARGARET NARWIN. Leave!

(PHILIP MALLOY *crosses to SR acting area, which has now become* DR. PALLENI'*s office.* DR. JOSEPH PALLENI *enters and sits behind the desk. SLIDE [which remains on through the end of the scene]: Office wall.)*

DR. PALLENI. Something happened. What's going on?

PHILIP MALLOY. Miss Narwin, she won't let me sing *The Star-Spangled Banner.*

DR. PALLENI. Isn't this what we were talking about the last time?

PHILIP MALLOY. She's against me being patriotic.

DR. PALLENI. I thought we agreed that when we have rules in schools, we stick with them.

PHILIP MALLOY. Get me out of her classes.

DR. PALLENI. Look, Philip, what do you want me to do? Change the rules just for you?

PHILIP MALLOY. No, but . . . she's wrong. I was just singing. That's all.

DR. PALLENI. That's all you have to say?

PHILIP MALLOY. It's a free country.

DR. PALLENI. Nothing is free.

PHILIP MALLOY. Get me out of her classes.

DR. PALLENI. Phil, sit out in the hall for a while. Cool off. Otherwise, I call your folks, they come get you—boom!—two-day suspension. Automatic.

PHILIP MALLOY. But she's wrong.

DR. PALLENI. I'll level with you, Philip. You're the one who is wrong. You're here to get an education. Rules are rules. Now clear out.

(DR. JOSEPH PALLENI crosses to SL acting area.)

DR. PALLENI. Excuse me, Miss Narwin, may I have a word with you?

MARGARET NARWIN. Class, continue on with that scene. I'll be right back.

DR. PALLENI. Sorry to bother you, Peg, but it's about Phil Malloy.

MARGARET NARWIN. Something is certainly bothering that boy.

DR. PALLENI. Any idea what it's about?

MARGARET NARWIN. No.

DR. PALLENI. I offered to get him out of this business by giving him the chance to come back and apologize, but he won't.

MARGARET NARWIN. Maybe it would be better to switch him into another homeroom.

DR. PALLENI. That's what he suggested. And out of your English class, too.

MARGARET NARWIN. He's doing poorly there.

DR. PALLENI. Let's start with a homeroom change. The parents might want to talk with you.

MARGARET NARWIN. I understand. I wish I could reach him.

DR. PALLENI. Yeah, a good kid. Maybe something going on at home. Or hormones. Does he have a girlfriend?

MARGARET NARWIN. Joe, I wouldn't know.

(MARGARET NARWIN returns to her class.)

(DR. JOSEPH PALLENI crosses back to SR acting area.)

DR. PALLENI. Now, Philip, Miss Narwin is in agreement with you. You did break the rules. She also said that she is prepared to let bygones be bygones if you apologize and promise not to do it again.

PHILIP MALLOY. No.

DR. PALLENI. It would be a shame to put something down on your record. But I'm prepared to call one of your parents to come get you. You'll be out for the rest of the day and. . . . How about Monday? Give you a long weekend to think it over.

PHILIP MALLOY. I'm not going to change my mind.

DR. PALLENI. Okay, who do you want me to call?

PHILIP MALLOY. My father doesn't like to be called at work.

DR. PALLENI. Too bad. Is your mother reachable? *(Pause)* Phil?

PHILIP MALLOY. She works too.

DR. PALLENI. Where?

PHILIP MALLOY. At the telephone company.

DR. PALLENI. I'll call her. *(Beat)* Last chance, Phil.

PHILIP MALLOY. Can't you just—

DR. PALLENI. An apology.

PHILIP MALLOY. Call her.

(DR. JOSEPH PALLENI *picks up the phone.*)

(SUSAN MALLOY *in DC acting area*)

DR. PALLENI. Hello? Is this Mrs. Malloy, Phil's mother?

SUSAN MALLOY. Yes, it is.

DR. PALLENI. This is Dr. Palleni, assistant principal at Harrison High. I'm afraid we've had a little incident here . . . rule-breaking.

SUSAN MALLOY. What happened?

DR. PALLENI. And breaking the rule twice in one week after he'd been warned.

SUSAN MALLOY. What rule?

DR. PALLENI. Philip was offered a chance to apologize to the teacher, but he won't. So, I'm afraid—and let me stress that this is Phil's decision, not mine—what we have here is a two-day suspension. I'm afraid you'll have to come and take him home.

SUSAN MALLOY. Now?

DR. PALLENI. Yes.

SUSAN MALLOY. What rule did he break?

DR. PALLENI. We—you, me, and Philip—can talk about it when you get here.

SUSAN MALLOY. I'll get permission and then come right over.

DR. PALLENI. Thank you.

 SLIDE: *"10:05* A.M. *Phone Conversation between Philip Malloy's Parents"*

(SUSAN MALLOY *in DC acting area.* BEN MALLOY *in UC acting area.*)

BEN MALLOY. What's up?

SUSAN MALLOY. I have to go and get Phil at the school. They're going to suspend him.

BEN MALLOY. Why?

SUSAN MALLOY. Some rule. I'm really upset.

BEN MALLOY. I'm going to give them a piece of my mind.

SUSAN MALLOY. Don't you think we should—

BEN MALLOY. Susan, the kid has done nothing!

SUSAN MALLOY. We can speak—

BEN MALLOY. Honey, I have to go. Something just came up.

SLIDE: "10:42 A.M. Dr. Palleni's Office"

(DR. JOSEPH PALLENI, PHILIP MALLOY, *and* SUSAN MALLOY *in SR acting area.*)

SLIDE: Office wall.

DR. PALLENI. Philip broke a rule. Twice. He and I talked it over earlier this week and I made it clear what would happen. If a student creates a disturbance in a classroom, that's breaking the rule. An important rule. Now, we offered Philip an opportunity to apologize. I'll offer it again. Philip?

PHILIP MALLOY. She really dislikes me.

DR. PALLENI. Who is that?

PHILIP MALLOY. Narwin.

SUSAN MALLOY. Philip has been saying that—

DR. PALLENI. Look , Mrs. Malloy, Philip admits that he broke a rule.

SUSAN MALLOY. What rule?

DR. PALLENI. Disturbing a class.

PHILIP MALLOY. Singing the national anthem.

SUSAN MALLOY. Is that the rule?

DR. PALLENI. Yes, disturbing the class.

SUSAN MALLOY. I just can't believe that—

DR. PALLENI. Excuse me. Philip, did you break the rule?

PHILIP MALLOY. It's a dumb rule.

DR. PALLENI. See? Mrs. Malloy, it is my job to make sure the school works together in harmony—the kids, the staff, and the teachers. We can't have the students deciding which rules to follow and which rules not to follow.

I'll have to suspend Philip for the rest of today. And Monday. Be back on Tuesday.

SUSAN MALLOY. I just want to say that I don't think this is right.

DR. PALLENI. Excuse me. Are you saying that kids should only follow the rules they want to?

SUSAN MALLOY. No, but—

DR. PALLENI. Then we're in agreement. Thank you for coming in.

 SLIDE: "11:02 A.M. Conversation between Philip and His Mother on Their Way Home"

(PHILIP MALLOY *and* SUSAN MALLOY *in the DC acting area*)

SUSAN MALLOY. Phil, what is this all about?

PHILIP MALLOY. I told you, Narwin . . .

SUSAN MALLOY. You've never been suspended.

PHILIP MALLOY. It's her.

SUSAN MALLOY. But why?

PHILIP MALLOY. I don't know.

SUSAN MALLOY. They said you could apologize.

PHILIP MALLOY. There's nothing to apologize for.

SUSAN MALLOY. We'll talk it out with your father when he gets home tonight.

PHILIP MALLOY. Yeah, well, he told me I should stick up for myself. That she was wrong and I was right.

SUSAN MALLOY. Sometimes I think we should have sent you to Washington Academy.

PHILIP MALLOY. Geeky private school? No way.

SLIDE: "12:46 P.M. Conversation between Margaret Narwin and Dr. Palleni"

(MARGARET NARWIN *and* DR. JOSEPH PALLENI *in DC acting area*)

DR. PALLENI. Oh, Peg! I know you're rushing off. Look, I just want you to know I took care of the Malloy boy. Talked to his mother. She understands. Couple of days' suspension. No big deal.

MARGARET NARWIN. Did you have to suspend him?

DR. PALLENI. Two infractions in one week. I put a memo in your box. Also, switched him back to Bernie Lunser for homeroom. What about his English class?

MARGARET NARWIN. I don't want to give up on him yet.

DR. PALLENI. Whatever you say.

MARGARET NARWIN. He's really a nice boy. Thanks for taking care of it.

DR. PALLENI. No problem.

 SLIDE: "3:45 P.M. Phone Conversation between Ken and Allison"

(KEN BARCHET *and* ALLISON DORESETT *at opposite sides of SL acting area*)

ALLISON DORESETT. Is this Ken?

KEN BARCHET. Yeah.

ALLISON DORESETT. This is Allison Doresett.

KEN BARCHET. Oh, hi.

ALLISON DORESETT. Is it true that Phil got suspended?

KEN BARCHET. Yeah.

ALLISON DORESETT. Why?

KEN BARCHET. You were there.

ALLISON DORESETT. The singing?

KEN BARCHET. Yeah. Narwin got him kicked out.

ALLISON DORESETT. You're kidding. She wouldn't do that.

KEN BARCHET. She did. You saw it.

ALLISON DORESETT. For how long?

KEN BARCHET. Two days.

ALLISON DORESETT. Wow. He must have really gotten on her nerves. Well, I just wanted to know. People are talking.

KEN BARCHET. What are they saying?

ALLISON DORESETT. You know. Weird.

 SLIDE: "6:45 P.M. Discussion between Philip Malloy's Parents"

(BEN *and* SUSAN MALLOY *in UC acting area.*)

SLIDE: Kitchen wall.

BEN MALLOY. Where's Philip?

SUSAN MALLOY. Up in the shower. He just got back from running.

BEN MALLOY. You talk with him about what happened?

SUSAN MALLOY. When I drove him home. But I had to get right back to work. It's just what I told you. How was your day?

BEN MALLOY. Rotten. Dexter is still sore at me.

 SLIDE: "7:00 P.M. From a Letter Written by Margaret Narwin to Her Sister"

(MARGARET NARWIN *in DC acting area. She is holding the letter.*)

MARGARET NARWIN (*to the audience*). Do

you remember my writing to you about Philip Malloy? I'm convinced there is something going on in this boy's private life that is deeply troubling him. Twice this week I had to send him out for being disruptive. Our society is always asking schools to do what is not done at home. Then Joe Palleni, the assistant principal, felt compelled to suspend him for a bit—something I *never* believe is productive. Philip is a nice boy, so I do feel badly about the whole thing. Next week, when he comes back, I intend to sit down with him and have a heart-to-heart talk.

 SLIDE: "7:12 P.M. The Malloy Kitchen"

(PHILIP MALLOY *plus* BEN *and* SUSAN MALLOY *in UC acting area.*)

SLIDE: Kitchen wall.

BEN MALLOY. We're on your side. But I have to know what happened.

PHILIP MALLOY. See, they play *The Star-Spangled Banner* at the beginning of school. . . . A tape.

BEN MALLOY. Okay.

PHILIP MALLOY. When I was in Mr. Lunser's class, he was like, almost asking me to sing out loud. But this teacher—

BEN MALLOY. Mrs. Narwin.

PHILIP MALLOY. It's Miss.

BEN MALLOY. Figures.

SUSAN MALLOY. That has nothing to do with it, Ben!

BEN MALLOY. Go on.

PHILIP MALLOY. She won't let me. She

threw me out of class.

SUSAN MALLOY. The principal said it was the rule.

PHILIP MALLOY. The assistant principal.

BEN MALLOY. But why does that mean suspension?

PHILIP MALLOY. She threw me out twice this week.

BEN MALLOY. It seems arbitrary.[3]

SUSAN MALLOY. Stupid rules.

BEN MALLOY. Right. How can you have a rule against singing *The Star-Spangled Banner?*

PHILIP MALLOY. Ask Narwin.

BEN MALLOY. You know who I bet would be interested in this?

PHILIP MALLOY. Who?

BEN MALLOY. Ted Griffen.

SUSAN MALLOY. Why?

BEN MALLOY. He's a neighbor. A friend. And he's running for school board. He should be interested. That's what the board does. Keeps the schools in line.

PHILIP MALLOY. He won't be able to do anything. If I could just get out of her classes . . .

BEN MALLOY. Maybe. Maybe not. But Phil, we intend to support you on this.

 SLIDE: "8:40 P.M. Conversation between Philip Malloy, Ben Malloy, and Ted Griffen"

(PHILIP MALLOY, BEN MALLOY, *and* TED GRIFFEN *in DC acting area.* TED GRIFFEN *holding a telephone.*)

---

3. arbitrary (ärʹbə trer/ē), depending on individual preference, convenience, or random chance

BEN MALLOY. Got a minute, Ted? This a bad time?

TED GRIFFEN. Well, I am in the middle of a talk with . . . why, what's up?

BEN MALLOY. Something about school. And Phil here . . .

TED GRIFFEN. I'm not on the school board yet, Ben. Trying, but not yet.

BEN MALLOY. That's the point. Phil was suspended for singing *The Star-Spangled Banner.*

TED GRIFFEN. What?

BEN MALLOY. He was kicked out of school for singing the national anthem.

TED GRIFFEN. Are you serious?

BEN MALLOY. I know. It's crazy.

TED GRIFFEN *(to* PHILIP MALLOY*).* That true?

PHILIP MALLOY. Yes, sir.

BEN MALLOY. We couldn't believe it at first either. But they called Susan at work to bring him home. Two-day suspension. For *singing.*

TED GRIFFEN. Who did it?

BEN MALLOY. The principal.

PHILIP MALLOY. Assistant principal.

TED GRIFFEN. Were you singing?

BEN MALLOY. Tell him.

PHILIP MALLOY. They play the national anthem in the morning. And I . . . I was singing it. Mostly to myself. Then, I have this teacher . . . and she threw me out of the class and—

TED GRIFFEN. Wait a minute. I want to get this straight. Look, I have a reporter I'm talking to, Jennifer Stewart, from the *Manchester Record.*

School beat. How about talking to me with her there?

BEN MALLOY *(to* PHILIP MALLOY*).* What do you say?

PHILIP MALLOY. A reporter?

TED GRIFFEN. She's covering the school board elections around the state. A good person.

PHILIP MALLOY. I don't know. . . .

TED GRIFFEN. Very straightforward. I'd like her to hear about this. Just tell her the truth. You don't mind, do you, Ben?

BEN MALLOY. No.

TED GRIFFEN. Phil?

PHILIP MALLOY. Well . . .

TED GRIFFEN. Sure. Just tell her the truth. Nothing but the truth. Come on.

 SLIDE: *"11:34 P.M. From the Diary of Philip Malloy"*

*(*PHILIP MALLOY *in UC acting area. He is holding his diary.)*

PHILIP MALLOY *(to the audience).* It really hit the fan today. So much happened I have a headache. It's going to take a while to think out. Actually, I don't feel so great. In a way, the whole thing is stupid. But everybody says I was right. *(Beat)* And I was.

Scene Twelve

 SLIDE: *"Saturday, March 31. 10:00 A.M. Phone Conversation between Jennifer Stewart of the* Manchester Record *and Dr. Albert Seymour, Superintendent of Schools"*

(JENNIFER STEWART *and* DR. ALBERT SEYMOUR *on opposite sides of the DC acting area.*)

JENNIFER STEWART. May I speak to Dr. Albert Seymour, please.

DR. SEYMOUR. Speaking

JENNIFER STEWART. Dr. Seymour, this is Jennifer Stewart of the *Manchester Record.* I'm the education reporter. I hope you don't mind a call at home.

DR. SEYMOUR. Oh, no.

JENNIFER STEWART. I wanted to check some facts with you.

DR. SEYMOUR. Certainly.

JENNIFER STEWART. Sir, does the Harrison School District have a rule that forbids students from singing *The Star-Spangled Banner?*

DR. SEYMOUR. Of course not. Whatever gave you that idea?

JENNIFER STEWART. There's been a claim.

DR. SEYMOUR. Hogwash. You should check your sources.

JENNIFER STEWART. I'm checking them right now.

DR. SEYMOUR. The answer is no. We do not have such a rule. Absolutely.

JENNIFER STEWART. May I quote you?

DR. SEYMOUR. Of course.

JENNIFER STEWART. Thank you.

 SLIDE: "10:15 A.M. Phone Conversation between Jennifer Stewart and Dr. Gertrude Doane, Principal, Harrison High"

(JENNIFER STEWART *and* DR. GERTRUDE DOANE *in DC acting area, except* JENNIFER STEWART *is on the opposite side of the area from where she was in the previous scene.*)

JENNIFER STEWART. May I speak to Dr. Doane, please.

DR. DOANE. This is she.

JENNIFER STEWART. Dr. Doane, this is Jennifer Stewart, of the *Manchester Record.* I do the school stories. Sorry to bother you on a Saturday.

DR. DOANE. Yes?

JENNIFER STEWART. I'm checking out an item that's come to our attention. It would appear that one of your students, Philip Malloy—

DR. DOANE. Ninth grade.

JENNIFER STEWART. You know him?

DR. DOANE. Oh, yes. Nice boy. Know him well. Has something happened to him?

JENNIFER STEWART. This is in reference to his suspension from school.

DR. DOANE. Suspension?

JENNIFER STEWART. Isn't that something that as principal you would know about?

DR. DOANE. Oh, yes. . . .

JENNIFER STEWART. Philip Malloy claims, as his parents claim, that he was suspended yesterday for two days.

DR. DOANE. Discipline problems are usually in the hands of my assistant principal, Dr. Palleni.

JENNIFER STEWART. Wouldn't Dr. Palleni discuss such a suspension with you first?

DR. DOANE. That would depend on . . . Ms. . . .

JENNIFER STEWART. Stewart.

DR. DOANE. Ms. Stewart, I'm not sure I should be discussing this matter with you. Records regarding our children are of a confidential nature.

JENNIFER STEWART. It's already a matter of public record. The boy and his father made a public statement. They claim he was suspended.

DR. DOANE. That's what you say. You call me up and inform me about something of which I have had no prior information.

JENNIFER STEWART. Then you didn't know about this? Ms. Doane—

DR. DOANE. Dr. Doane.

JENNIFER STEWART. Excuse me, Dr. Doane, Philip Malloy, who is a student at your school, and who you claim to know well, has made a statement to the effect that he was suspended for singing *The Star-Spangled Banner.*

DR. DOANE. Oh, really!

JENNIFER STEWART. His father claims this is true. I just spoke to your superintendent . . .

DR. DOANE. Dr. Seymour?

JENNIFER STEWART. That's right. And he says that Harrison School District has no such rule. I'm just trying . . .

DR. DOANE. I see no reason to be talking to a reporter about a student's problem. In any case, it doesn't seem to have happened. The superintendent told you we have no such rule.

JENNIFER STEWART. Would a student in your school run into difficulty by singing the national anthem?

DR. DOANE. Of course not. But I repeat: Discipline problems of a minor nature are handled by my assistant principal.

JENNIFER STEWART. Palleni?

DR. DOANE. That's right. Dr. Joseph Palleni.

JENNIFER STEWART. Thank you.

 SLIDE: "10:30 A.M. Discussion between Philip and His Mother"

(PHILIP MALLOY *and* SUSAN MALLOY *in UC acting area.* PHILIP MALLOY *has a letter in his hand.*)

SLIDE: Kitchen wall.

PHILIP MALLOY. Hey, Ma, look at this letter! It just came in the mail. They shifted me out of Narwin's homeroom class. Back to Mr. Lunser.

SUSAN MALLOY. Well, that's something. They must have seen that something was wrong. Maybe you can go back to school Monday.

PHILIP MALLOY. Says it won't happen till Tuesday. When I go back.

SUSAN MALLOY. May be just as well. I don't want you to have to deal with that woman again.

PHILIP MALLOY. But I still have her for English.

SUSAN MALLOY. Didn't they change that?

PHILIP MALLOY. No.

SUSAN MALLOY. But if they admit they're wrong about the one thing . . .

PHILIP MALLOY. Bet they forgot to say that. Where's Dad?

SUSAN MALLOY. He went to the store. Feel better?

PHILIP MALLOY. Yeah. But the English . . .

SUSAN MALLOY. You just said they forgot.

PHILIP MALLOY. I guess.

SLIDE: "10:40 A.M. *Conversation between Jennifer Stewart and Dr. Joseph Palleni, Assistant Principal, Harrison High*"

(JENNIFER STEWART *and* DR. JOSEPH PALLENI *in DC acting area, except* JENNIFER STEWART *is on the opposite side of the area from where she was in the previous scene.*)

DR. PALLENI. Hello. This is Dr. Palleni.

JENNIFER STEWART. Dr. Palleni, this is Jennifer Stewart. I'm a reporter for the *Manchester Record.* I've already spoken with your—

DR. PALLENI. What is this about?

JENNIFER STEWART. Dr. Palleni, according to Dr. Seymour, the Harrison School District has no rule that would keep a student from singing *The Star-Spangled Banner.*

DR. PALLENI. Did you say *singing?*

JENNIFER STEWART. Yes. Is that your understanding?

DR. PALLENI. Well . . .

JENNIFER STEWART. Now Dr. Doane, your principal, says that you are in charge of discipline in the school.

DR. PALLENI. With her. I always keep her informed.

JENNIFER STEWART. Did you inform her that on Friday you suspended a student, Philip Malloy, for singing *The Star-Spangled Banner?*

DR. PALLENI. I did no such thing!

JENNIFER STEWART. You didn't inform her or you didn't suspend the boy? Which? *(Pause)* Dr. Palleni? Are you still there?

DR. PALLENI. I don't wish to talk to you.

JENNIFER STEWART. No comment?

DR. PALLENI. No comment. But you've got your facts all wrong.

JENNIFER STEWART. Is that your comment?

DR. PALLENI. No comment.

JENNIFER STEWART. I'm sorry. Should I call you back?

DR. PALLENI. Not to talk about this.

JENNIFER STEWART. May I quote you?

SLIDE: "11:00 A.M. *Phone Conversation between Jennifer Stewart and Margaret Narwin*"

(JENNIFER STEWART *and* MARGARET NARWIN *in DC acting area, except* JENNIFER STEWART *is on the opposite side of the area from where she was in the previous scene*)

JENNIFER STEWART. Margaret Narwin, please.

MARGARET NARWIN. Speaking.

JENNIFER STEWART. Miss Narwin, my name is Jennifer Stewart, of the *Manchester Record.* The education reporter. I'm trying to write a story regarding an incident . . . something that appears to have happened in one of your classes. I understand you are a teacher.

MARGARET NARWIN. An English teacher. Yes.

JENNIFER STEWART. Have you taught there long?

JENNIFER STEWART. For twenty-one years. What incident are you referring to? I'm not aware . . .

JENNIFER STEWART. I'm simply trying to get the facts correct. I'm sure you can appreciate that.

MARGARET NARWIN. Are you sure this has something to do with me?

JENNIFER STEWART. That appears to be the case. I spoke to your superintendent, your principal, and your assistant principal, as well as Philip Malloy and his father.

MARGARET NARWIN. Who?

JENNIFER STEWART. Philip Malloy. I believe he is one of your students.

MARGARET NARWIN. Well . . .

JENNIFER STEWART. Now, as I understand it, the boy was suspended from school because he sang *The Star-Spangled Banner* in your class. He says it's a question of patriotism with him. *(Pause)* Miss Narwin? Are you there?

MARGARET NARWIN. Yes. . . .

JENNIFER STEWART. Could you give me your side of the story?

MARGARET NARWIN. The boy was creating a disturbance.

JENNIFER STEWART. By singing the national anthem?

MARGARET NARWIN. We have a rule . . .

JENNIFER STEWART. Your superintendent, Dr. Seymour, says there is no rule.

MARGARET NARWIN. I don't think I should be talking about this.

JENNIFER STEWART. But you do acknowledge that you sent him from your room?

MARGARET NARWIN. I think you need to speak to our principal.

JENNIFER STEWART. I did speak with her.

MARGARET NARWIN. Then I have nothing more to say.

JENNIFER STEWART. Are you sure?

MARGARET NARWIN. Quite sure.

JENNIFER STEWART. Thank you, Miss . . . or is it *Mrs.* Narwin?

MARGARET NARWIN. Miss.

JENNIFER STEWART. Thank you.

 SLIDE: "11:45 P.M. From the Diary of Philip Malloy"

(PHILIP MALLOY *in a spotlight in UC acting area. He is holding his diary.*)

PHILIP MALLOY *(to the audience).* Aside from getting out of Narwin's homeroom, not much of anything today. Boring! Newspapers to deliver. Collection day. Can't understand how people who want the paper think they can get away with not paying for it. And it comes out of my pocket. Then folks made me do yard work. Clean up room. Ken came over. Been trying to figure a way to get on the school track team. Maybe—like the coach said—I should ask Narwin for extra work. Be worth it. I hate working out without a team. . . .

(Blackout)

End of Act One

The following "article" should be distributed during the intermission.

Suspended for Patriotism
by J. Stewart, *Education Reporter*

Harrison. While it may appear to be an April Fools' Day joke, tenth-grader Philip Malloy of Harrison High School was suspended for singing, *The Star-Spangled Banner.*

His parents, Susan and Benjamin Malloy of Harrison Township, do not consider themselves superpatriotic, but they did raise their son to have pride in our country. It was only natural then for Philip to sing along when the national anthem was played on tape during the morning exercises. According to Harrison School superintendent, Dr. A. Seymour, there is no rule against singing the anthem. Indeed, in every other class Philip did just that. His new homeroom teacher, Ms. Margaret Narwin, however, changed the rules. Every time Philip lifted his voice to sing she threw him out of the class, insisting a disturbance was being created.

School principal Dr. Gertrude Doane, who admits that the student has no previous bad marks on his record, saw the issue only as one of discipline, and referred all questions regarding school policy to Dr. Joseph Palleni, assistant principal. Dr. Palleni, however, refused to be interviewed regarding the incident.

Act Two

Scene One

 SLIDE: "Sunday, April 1. 8:30 A.M. Phone Conversation between Dr. Seymour and Dr. Doane"

(DR. ALBERT SEYMOUR *and* DR. GERTRUDE DOANE *on opposite sides of the DC acting area. She is holding several sections of the newspaper.*)

DR. SEYMOUR: Gertrude, Al Seymour here. Did you see this morning's paper?

DR. DOANE. I was just reading it.

DR. SEYMOUR. Well, look at section D, page two. School News.

(DR. GERTRUDE DOANE *looks through the newspaper.*)

DR. DOANE. Oh, my!

DR. SEYMOUR. Is any of this true?

DR. DOANE. Al, the boy was not suspended because of singing the national anthem. He was suspended because he was creating a disturbance. That's according to Joe.

DR. SEYMOUR. Joe?

DR. DOANE. Joe Palleni.

DR. SEYMOUR. Who is this Narwin woman?

DR. DOANE. An English teacher. A good teacher. She's been on the staff for years.

DR. SEYMOUR. Oh, yes. I think I know her. And that's all there is to it?

DR. DOANE. As far as I know. Al, no one could take this seriously.

DR. SEYMOUR. I hope not. With the budget vote soon . . . and the school board—

DR. DOANE. Do you want me to call the newspaper?

DR. SEYMOUR. Ah . . . no. But if you get any calls, refer them to me.

DR. DOANE. I will.

DR. SEYMOUR. This is not going to do us any good.

DR. DOANE. No one reads about schools.

DR. SEYMOUR. Let's hope so.

 SLIDE: "9:20 A.M. Phone Conversation between Philip and Ken"

(PHILIP MALLOY *in UC acting area.* KEN BARCHET *in DC acting area.*)

PHILIP MALLOY. What's happening?

KEN BARCHET. Did you see today's paper?

PHILIP MALLOY. I deliver it. I don't read it.

KEN BARCHET. There's an article in it about you.

PHILIP MALLOY. Sure. April fool.

KEN BARCHET. No, really. Look at section D, page two.

PHILIP MALLOY. Right.

KEN BARCHET. It ain't true, but it's funny.

 SLIDE: "9:50 A.M. Conversation between Philip Malloy's Parents"

(SUSAN *and* BEN MALLOY *in UC acting area.* SUSAN MALLOY *is looking through the newspaper.*)

SLIDE: Kitchen wall.

SUSAN MALLOY. Look here, Ben. Here's the story about Philip.

BEN MALLOY. You're kidding! Let me see.

SUSAN MALLOY. Here.

(BEN MALLOY *takes the newspaper from* SUSAN MALLOY.)

BEN MALLOY. I'll be. . . . See, the superintendent says there's no rule. It was just the teacher.

SUSAN MALLOY. It doesn't seem right.

BEN MALLOY. She should be fired. Is Philip around?

SUSAN MALLOY. I think so.

BEN MALLOY. Philip! Come in here and look at this.

(PHILIP MALLOY *enters UC acting area.* SUSAN MALLOY *points out the article to* PHILIP MALLOY.)

BEN MALLOY. See? If you stick up for yourself, you get action. How's that make you feel? *(Beat)* Philip?

SUSAN MALLOY. What's the matter?

PHILIP MALLOY. I don't know. Weird.

SUSAN MALLOY. It was the teacher. Just as you said.

BEN MALLOY. Just shows you—

SUSAN MALLOY. Where are you going?

PHILIP MALLOY. Upstairs.

(PHILIP MALLOY *exits*)

SUSAN MALLOY. That Ted Griffen knows how to get things done.

BEN MALLOY. He gets my vote.

 SLIDE: "2:30 P.M. Phone Conversation between Margaret Narwin and Her Sister"

(MARGARET NARWIN *in DC acting area*)

MARGARET NARWIN. I just don't understand why they would ever print such a thing. *(Pause)* But it's so slanted. And full of errors. *(Pause)* Yes, I suppose you're right, people won't pay

much attention to it. It's just. . . .

 SLIDE: "7:30 P.M. Ted Griffen Delivers a Speech to a Meeting of the Harrison Sunday Fellowship"

(TED GRIFFEN *in SR acting area..*)

SLIDE: Church assembly room

TED GRIFFEN *(to the audience).* And if I am elected to the Harrison School Board, I will, one, keep the cost of education down to a reasonable level—which is to say that I will keep our taxes down—and two, I will work with the rest of the board to support basic American values. For I—and I can only speak for myself—I am shocked that a student should be suspended from one of our schools because he desires to sing the national anthem. Yes, my friends, it is true. This sad story is in today's *Record.* And, I say, what is the point of installing computers, which my generation never seemed to need, if our young people are not allowed to practice the elemental values of American patriotism?

 SLIDE: "11:20 P.M. From the Diary of Philip Malloy"

(PHILIP MALLOY *in DC acting area. He is holding his diary.*)

PHILIP MALLOY *(to the audience).* Folks excited by the newspaper story. Dad keeps telling me how great I am. I wonder what will happen now. Maybe they'll kick Miss Narwin out. Wonder if she saw the article. It's her fault. Not mine. *(Beat)* No one called. I guess I don't go to school tomorrow. *(Beat)* Finished *The Outsiders.* Not bad. Wonder what it would be like to live without parents. You could do what you'd like.

Scene Two

 SLIDE: "Monday, April 2. 8:05 A.M. The Jake Barlow Talk Show"
(JAKE BARLOW *in SR acting area.*)

SLIDE: Radio station studio.

JAKE BARLOW. Okay. Okay. Here we go! All sorts of things we can talk about. Wanting—and waiting—to hear from you on WLRB, your talk radio with your loudmouthed host Jake Barlow. Ready. Willing. And able! All kinds of things going on. We can talk about that demonstration in Washington. I don't know about that. Or that point-shaving scandal over at the university? Come on, guys, is that an education or what?

Now here's a bit of a story that just came in over the wires. Let me read it to you. Now, listen up! This is America. I mean it! WLRB asking you—Jake Barlow asking you—what you think of *this*.

"Kicked out of school for patriotism."

Right, you heard me correct. I'm not making this up. None of it. I'm *reading it!*

"Harrison." Where in the *world* is Harrison? In the United States? In America? All their auto plates read "Live free or die." Well, something died, because this is going on there right now! Here it is. Right in the morning news.

"A tenth-grader was suspended from his local school because he sang *The Star-Spangled Banner* during the school's morning exercises. The boy, Philip Malloy, who wished to sing in the spirit of patriotism, was then forced to remain at home alone, since both his parents work. English teacher Margaret Narwin, who brought about the suspension, maintains the boy was making a nuisance of himself."

Would you believe it? Okay, this is WLRB, all-talk radio. Take a short break, then come right back to talk about whatever you want. Man, but I'm telling you. What's happening to this country!

Now this. . . .

 SLIDE: "8:07 A.M. Phone Conversation between Mrs. Gloria Harland, Chairperson, Harrison School Board, and Dr. Seymour"
(MRS. GLORIA HARLAND *and* DR. ALBERT SEYMOUR *on opposite sides of the DC acting area.*)

MRS. HARLAND. Albert, this is Gloria Harland. Good morning.

DR. SEYMOUR. Gloria! Good morning.

MRS. HARLAND. Al, last night I attended a meeting of the Harrison Sunday Fellowship—

DR. SEYMOUR. Oh, yes. Couldn't make it.

MRS. HARLAND. Well, Ted Griffen made a speech. He's running for the school board.

DR. SEYMOUR. Yes, right.

MRS. HARLAND. Albert, part of Ted's speech was an attack on the present board in regard to what he claims is the suspension of a student for singing the national anthem in one of the schools. One of the high schools, I think.

DR. SEYMOUR. Oh, Lord, is he going to make a thing about this?

MRS. HARLAND. What happened? It's not true, is it?

DR. SEYMOUR. I can assure you nothing of the kind occurred. Nothing. But let me make some further inquiries and then get back to you.

MRS. HARLAND. This is *not* what we need. Not with the budget vote so—

DR. SEYMOUR. Exactly, I understand.

 SLIDE: "8:10 A.M. The Jake Barlow Talk Show"

(JAKE BARLOW *in SR acting area.*)

SLIDE: Radio station studio.

JAKE BARLOW. Okay. Back again. And ready to take you on. We've got the scandal at the university. The demonstration in Washington, D.C. The kid kicked out of school for being an American patriot. Anything you want. Here we go. First call. Hello?

CALLER #1 *(voice only).* Is this Jake?

JAKE BARLOW. Jake Cruising-for-a-Bruising Barlow. Who's this?

CALLER #1. This is Steve.

JAKE BARLOW. Steve! How you doing, big guy?

CALLER #1: Great. Look, about that kid.

JAKE BARLOW. The one kicked out of school?

CALLER #1: Yeah. That gripes me. Really does.

JAKE BARLOW. Right! What are schools for, anyway?

CALLER #1: People might call me a . . . a . . .

JAKE BARLOW. Jerk?

CALLER #1: Yeah, maybe. But like they used to say: America, love it or leave it. And that school—

JAKE BARLOW. It was a teacher.

CALLER #1: Yeah, teacher. She shouldn't be allowed to teach. That's my opinion.

JAKE BARLOW. Right. I'm with you there, Steve. I mean, there are the three R's—reading, 'riting, and 'rithmetic—and the three P's—prayer, patriotism, and parents. At least, that's my notion of schooling.

CALLER #1: Right. I'm right with you.

JAKE BARLOW. Okay, Steve. Like what you said. Let's see if we got any ultra-liberals out there who'll call in and try to defend this—I was about to say woman—person. Steve! Thanks for calling.

CALLER #1. Yeah.

JAKE BARLOW. Who's next?

 SLIDE: "8:30 A.M. Conversation between Dr. Seymour and Dr. Doane"

(DR. ALBERT SEYMOUR *and* DR. GERTRUDE DOANE *on opposite sides of the DC acting area*)

DR. SEYMOUR. Gert, Al here. Look, I just got a call from Gloria Harland about this boy who was suspended for singing.

DR. DOANE. Al, I told you, that's not why he was suspended.

DR. SEYMOUR. Maybe yes. Maybe no. But Gloria was at a meeting last night at which Ted Griffen claimed it's school policy to keep kids from singing—

DR. DOANE. That's absolutely untrue.

DR. SEYMOUR. It doesn't matter if it's true or not, Gert. What's important is what people are saying. Will be saying. I want a report on my desk. Make it short and to the point. Soon as you can.

DR. DOANE. Al—

DR. SEYMOUR. Gert, believe me. I'm sensitive to this sort of thing. Just do as I've requested.

 SLIDE: "8:35 A.M. The Jake Barlow Talk Show"

(JAKE BARLOW *in SR acting area.*)

SLIDE: Radio station studio.

JAKE BARLOW. Okay. Who's this?

CALLER #2 (*voice only*). My name is Liz.

JAKE BARLOW. Liz baby! How you doing?

CALLER #2: Just fine.

JAKE BARLOW. Liz, what's on your pretty mind this morning?

CALLER #2. Jake, I'm a mother. I have three kids. All school-age. But if I had a teacher like that—

JAKE BARLOW. Whoa! Back off. Like who?

CALLER #2: The one who forbade that child to show his patriotism. . . .

JAKE BARLOW. Right.

CALLER #2. I'd take my kids out of school.

JAKE BARLOW. You would? What about the teacher?

CALLER #2: Wouldn't let my kids go back

unless she was removed.

JAKE BARLOW. The teacher doesn't have rights?

CALLER #2: It's a free country. But she has no right to do what she did. My husband was in the military. She's taking away rights.

JAKE BARLOW. Then you know.

CALLER #2: Yes, I do.

 SLIDE: "9:17 A.M. Conversation between Robert Duval, Reporter for the St. Louis Post-Dispatch, *and Dr. Doane"*

(ROBERT DUVAL *and* DR. GERTRUDE DOANE *on opposite sides of the DC acting area*)

ROBERT DUVAL. Is this Miss Doane, principal of Harrison High School?

DR. DOANE. Dr. Doane. Yes.

ROBERT DUVAL. Thank you. Of course. Dr. Doane, my name is Robert Duval. I'm a reporter with the *St. Louis Post-Dispatch.* I'm attempting to follow up on an AAP release that indicates your school suspended a student because he sang *The Star-Spangled Banner.*

DR. DOANE. Did you say St. Louis?

ROBERT DUVAL. Yes, ma'am. Missouri. Took the story off the wire service. And we ran it. Now you see, we have our state American Legion convention going on here. Someone noticed the item and called to see if we had any more information.

DR. DOANE. Are you serious?

ROBERT DUVAL. Certainly am.

DR. DOANE. Is it being sent out over the whole country?

ROBERT DUVAL. Well, actually, it has been sent out. Would you like to comment, ma'am?

DR. DOANE. There has been some mistake, and . . . None of this is true.

ROBERT DUVAL. None of it? The boy was not suspended, then?

DR. DOANE. Yes, suspended, but not for those reasons. Look, Mr. Duval, I have to sort this out.

ROBERT DUVAL. When can I call back?

DR. DOANE. Give me a few hours.

ROBERT DUVAL. Yes, ma'am.

 SLIDE: "9:32 A.M. The Jake Barlow Talk Show"

(JAKE BARLOW *in the SR acting area.*)

SLIDE: Radio station studio.

JAKE BARLOW. Back again. Who's on?

CALLER #3 (*voice only*). This is Roger.

JAKE BARLOW. Roger Rabbit?

CALLER #3. Not quite.

JAKE BARLOW. How many kids do you have?

CALLER #3. Ah . . . two.

JAKE BARLOW. Get hopping, Roger, get hopping. Ha! Okay, Roger, what's on your mind?

CALLER #3: About all these calls about the boy who was kicked out.

JAKE BARLOW. Makes me sick. Sick!

CALLER #3: Well, you've read the story a few times, so I think I understand it. And it seems to me that couldn't be the whole story.

JAKE BARLOW. What do you mean?

CALLER #3: Well, the story is slanted from the point of view of the boy. It doesn't really indicate what the teacher's position is.

JAKE BARLOW. Roger—let me get this right—you are defending this so-called teacher?

CALLER #3: No, I don't say that. But the story you read is the boy's, not the teacher's. Why should we assume that the teacher is wrong?

JAKE BARLOW. Come on. Give us a break. The kid was suspended, right?

CALLER #3: So it would appear.

JAKE BARLOW. Suspended for singing the national anthem, right?

CALLER #3: That's the story you read.

JAKE BARLOW. Now, how could singing the national anthem ever . . . ever be making a nuisance?

CALLER #3: Well . . .

JAKE BARLOW. Roger, what's your point? Let me guess. You're a teacher!

CALLER #3: Actually, I'm a salesman.

JAKE BARLOW. What do you sell?

CALLER #3: That doesn't make—

JAKE BARLOW. Come on! Out with it!

CALLER #3: Well, books, but—

JAKE BARLOW. Yeah, see? Exactly. And here you are defending this creep of a teacher. What does the kid know other than his own, natural-born patriotism? And then this teacher comes along and squelches it. And this country has all these problems with morality, drugs, pornography. No way, José.

CALLER #3: But—

JAKE BARLOW. Good-bye! Always one rotten apple. Hey, out there. Do you agree with this guy? Tell you what! Why don't we start a crusade. I want you all to write to the teacher. Hey, free country! Do you agree with what she did? Okay, tell her. If you disagree, tell her that. Let's see, here's her name. Margaret Narwin. N—a—r—w—i—n. Just write her. Postcard. Brick. Hey, just kidding. Okay! Now this . . .

 SLIDE: *"10:00 A.M. Conversation between Dr. Doane, Margaret Narwin, and Dr. Palleni"*

(DR. GERTRUDE DOANE, MARGARET NARWIN, *and* DR. JOSEPH PALLENI *are in the SL acting area.*)

SLIDE: *Classroom wall.*

DR. DOANE. I know you're upset, but I have to get it down clearly. Peg, just tell me what happened. We all need to tell the same story.

DR. PALLENI. Amen. Gert's trying to be helpful, Peg.

MARGARET NARWIN. It's terribly unsettling.

DR. DOANE. Well, yes . . . to all of us. Now, once more. Please.

MARGARET NARWIN. Very well. Philip Malloy, from the first day he entered my homeroom last week . . . during the time the students are asked to stand in silence—

DR. PALLENI. The rule is "respectful silence." It's in your memo about opening exercises. Isn't in the student handbook. But I think it should be.

DR. DOANE. Good point.

MARGARET NARWIN. During the playing of the national anthem, he sang. Loudly. To make a commotion.

Obviously. The first time he did it, I asked him to stop, and he did. After a bit. The second two times, he didn't. He refused. That's when I sent him to Joe.

DR. PALLENI. The boy admitted it, Gert.

MARGARET NARWIN. Deliberately provocative.

DR. DOANE. Do we know why, Peg?

MARGARET NARWIN. I haven't the slightest idea.

DR. DOANE. Joe?

DR. PALLENI. Nope. No problems before. Ever.

DR. DOANE. Maybe I should talk to some students.

MARGARET NARWIN. He's always been restless in English class. Sort of a wise guy. I don't know why. In his last exam he wrote a very foolish answer. Mocking me.

DR. DOANE. You?

MARGARET NARWIN. Oh, yes. Absolutely. Mocking.

DR. DOANE. Do you still have it?

MARGARET NARWIN. I always return exams to students.

DR. DOANE. Too bad. But there must be some reason. . . .

MARGARET NARWIN. I agree.

DR. PALLENI. Home, Gert. Ninety-nine point nine times out of a hundred, you get a thing like this, a kid acting out, believe me, it's home.

DR. DOANE. But we don't know that.

DR. PALLENI. Hey, what's the difference? The parents always blame the school.

DR. DOANE. As far as I'm concerned, this is strictly a discipline problem.

That's what I intend to tell people. Do you agree?

DR. PALLENI. Well, the thing is, it's the truth.

MARGARET NARWIN. I don't think it was wise to suspend him.

DR. PALLENI. Two infractions in one week, Peg. That's the rule. If we start breaking the rules each time—

DR. DOANE. Joe, draft something—keep it strictly to the facts—to give to Seymour. Do it immediately. I want to speak to some students.

 SLIDE: "11:00 A.M. From the Drafted Memo Written by Dr. Palleni"

(DR. JOSEPH PALLENI *in DC acting area*)

DR. PALLENI Three. On March twenty-eighth, twenty-ninth, and thirtieth, Philip Malloy caused a disturbance in his homeroom class (Margaret Narwin, teacher) by singing the national anthem in a loud, raucous,[4] *disrespectful* manner.

Four. When asked by Miss Narwin on the first occasion to cease, Philip Malloy reluctantly did so. But on the second and third occasions, he refused and was sent to Assistant Principal Joe Palleni for discipline.

Five. Philip Malloy does not dispute the above facts.

Six. On the third occurrence, Philip Malloy was asked to promise not to show such a disrespectful attitude, and to apologize to the teacher and his fellow classmates. *He refused.*

 SLIDE: "11:15 A.M. Conversation between Dr. Doane and Ken Barchet"

(DR. GERTRUDE DOANE *and* KEN BARCHET *in SR acting area.*)

SLIDE: Office wall.

DR. DOANE. Ken, I'm just trying to understand what happened there. Is this clear?

KEN BARCHET. Yes.

DR. DOANE. I hope you can speak freely. In your view—what occurred?

KEN BARCHET. Well, you know, the music went on—

DR. DOANE. Which day was this?

KEN BARCHET. Wednesday.

DR. DOANE. Okay.

KEN BARCHET. Right. The music went on. And we were just standing there. And the next thing, Miss Narwin was telling Philip to stop.

DR. DOANE. Stop what?

KEN BARCHET. I'm not sure. The news-paper said singing.

DR. DOANE. What about the other days?

KEN BARCHET. You know, he was, again . . . sort of, I guess . . . singing.

DR. DOANE. In what way?

KEN BARCHET. Just singing.

DR. DOANE. Loudly?

KEN BARCHET. Not really.

DR. DOANE. But you heard him?

KEN BARCHET. I guess.

---

4. raucous (rô′kəs), disorderly; disruptive

DR. DOANE. How close to Philip do you sit?

KEN BARCHET. Across the room.

DR. DOANE. So, loudly enough for you to hear?

KEN BARCHET. Well . . .

DR. DOANE. Then what happened?

KEN BARCHET. Miss Narwin got mad.

DR. DOANE. Why?

KEN BARCHET. Well, you know . . . like you said . . . Philip was singing. And I guess we're not supposed to.

DR. DOANE. Did Philip stop?

KEN BARCHET. Yeah. When she told him to get out.

DOANE. Not before?

DR. KEN BARCHET. No.

DR. DOANE. What did the class do?

KEN BARCHET. I wasn't paying attention.

 SLIDE: "11:45 A.M. *Phone Conversation between Ken and Philip"*

(KEN BARCHET *in SL acting area.* PHILIP MALLOY *in UC acting area.*)

SLIDE: School hallway.

KEN BARCHET. Hey, man, what's happening?

PHILIP MALLOY. Nothing. What's happening there?

KEN BARCHET. Just spoke to Doane.

PHILIP MALLOY. How come?

KEN BARCHET. She called me in to find out what happened.

PHILIP MALLOY. What did you tell her?

KEN BARCHET. What happened. The whole thing. Lot of people talking about it.

PHILIP MALLOY. Yeah, but what did you tell her?

KEN BARCHET. I thought I should tell her how funny it was.

PHILIP MALLOY. Come on! What?

KEN BARCHET. Nothing. I mean, it wasn't anything. I don't know why they're making a fuss about it.

PHILIP MALLOY. I still have English with Narwin, but they switched me back to Lunser's homeroom.

KEN BARCHET. He's okay. Tells good jokes. Someone told me he has a collection of joke books. That's where he gets all those one-liners. *(Beat)* We going to work out this afternoon?

PHILIP MALLOY. Yeah.

KEN BARCHET. Catch you later.

 SLIDE: "11:50 A.M. *Conversation between Dr. Doane and Cynthia Gambia, Student"*

(DR. GERTRUDE DOANE *and* CYNTHIA GAMBIA *in SR acting area*).

SLIDE: Office wall.

DR. DOANE. Cynthia, I'm trying to find out what happened in Miss Narwin's homeroom class. With Philip Malloy.

CYNTHIA GAMBIA. Yes, I understand. I wasn't paying much attention.

DR. DOANE. That's all right. Just tell me what happened as you saw it.

CYNTHIA GAMBIA. Well, during *The Star-Spangled Banner,* when the tape went on, Philip started to hum.

DR. DOANE. *Hum?*

CYNTHIA GAMBIA. I think so.

DR. DOANE. Not sing?

CYNTHIA GAMBIA. It could have been. I

wasn't paying attention. Not at first.

DR. DOANE. And then?

CYNTHIA GAMBIA. Miss Narwin asked him to leave.

DR. DOANE. Which days were these?

CYNTHIA GAMBIA. All three.

DR. DOANE. Was Philip causing a disturbance?

CYNTHIA GAMBIA. Well, I heard him. I mean, it wasn't loud or anything. Not like the paper said. But he wouldn't stop. And she did ask him. I guess that was the disturbance.

DR. DOANE. So he wasn't loud.

CYNTHIA GAMBIA. Maybe the last time.

DR. DOANE. What day was that?

CYNTHIA GAMBIA. Ah . . . I'm not sure. Wednesday? Thursday?

DR. DOANE. What did the other students do?

CYNTHIA GAMBIA. Nothing.

DR. DOANE. Do you have any idea why Philip did this?

CYNTHIA GAMBIA. No.

DR. DOANE. Do you want to add anything?

CYNTHIA GAMBIA. No. I guess not. I mean, he was being sort of rude.

DR. DOANE. Philip?

CYNTHIA GAMBIA. Miss Narwin did ask him to stop. You're supposed to be quiet. Everybody says that's the rule. He certainly wasn't. She's a fair teacher. All the kids say so.

 SLIDE: "12:30 P.M. Ted Griffen Delivers a Speech to the Harrison Rotary Club"

(TED GRIFFEN *in DC acting area*)

TED GRIFFEN (*to the audience*). And, if elected, I will work with the rest of the board to support basic American values. I am shocked that a Harrison student should be expelled from one of our schools simply because he desires to sing the national anthem. What is the point of installing computers if our young people are not allowed to practice the elemental values of American patriotism? Is that the way we budget our education dollars?

 SLIDE: "12:50 P.M. Conversation between Dr. Doane and Allison Doresett"

(DR. GERTRUDE DOANE *and* ALLISON DORESETT *in SR acting area.*)

SLIDE: Office wall.

DR. DOANE. Now, as I understand it, you are in Miss Narwin's homeroom class. So you were there all three times?

ALLISON DORESETT. Uh-huh.

DR. DOANE. Tell me what you saw.

ALLISON DORESETT. Well, Philip, he doesn't like Miss Narwin.

DR. DOANE. Do you know why?

ALLISON DORESETT. It's what people are saying. In English class he just sits there, like he's bored and can't stand anything she says. It's just the way he looks. But then he suddenly makes some remark, a joke or something. Something funny.

DR. DOANE. Do you think this has anything to do with what happened?

ALLISON DORESETT. Well, it was so obvious he was trying to get at her.

DR. DOANE. What do you mean?

ALLISON DORESETT. Get her mad.

DR. DOANE. Because he doesn't like her?

ALLISON DORESETT. I think he was doing it to get Miss Narwin in trouble.

DR. DOANE. I wish you'd tell me more.

ALLISON DORESETT. Well, he's been angry a lot lately. I go home on the same bus with him. The other day I—you know—tried to sit next to him. On the bus. He wouldn't talk to me.

DR. DOANE. Do you know why?

ALLISON DORESETT. That's the way he is.

DR. DOANE. Allison, I appreciate your help.

ALLISON DORESETT. Can I say something?

DR. DOANE. Of course.

ALLISON DORESETT. I like Miss Narwin.

DR. DOANE. I'm glad. Your telling the truth can only help her.

 SLIDE: "1:30 P.M. Memo to Dr. Seymour as Rewritten by Dr. Doane"

(DR. GERTRUDE DOANE in SR acting area.)

SLIDE: Office wall.

DR. DOANE. Three. On March twenty-eighth, twenty-ninth, and thirtieth Philip Malloy deliberately caused a disturbance in his homeroom class (Margaret Narwin, teacher) by singing the national anthem in a loud, raucous, *disrespectful* fashion, thereby drawing attention to himself.

Four. When requested by Miss Narwin on the first occasion to cease, Philip Malloy did so, albeit reluctantly. On the second and third occasions, he repeated his disrespectful behavior, and when he refused to stop, he was sent—standard procedure—to Assistant Principal Dr. Joseph Palleni for discipline.

Five. Philip Malloy did not dispute the above facts.

Six. A random selection of students who were in the classroom at the time confirms these events. Indeed, there is evidence that Philip Malloy's acts were indicative of some personal animosity he feels toward the homeroom teacher, Miss Narwin. His rudeness was also on display in the English classes he had with her. His grade there indicates inferior work.

Seven. On the third occurrence, Philip Malloy was asked to: one) promise not to show such a disrespectful attitude toward our national anthem and, two) apologize to his teacher and his classmates for his behavior. He refused, choosing the option afforded him of suspension.

 SLIDE: "2:22 P.M. Telegrams"

(JESSICA WITTINGTON, HANK MORGAN, and CHARLES ELDERSON in DC acting area)

JESSICA WITTINGTON *(to the audience).* Telegram to Margaret Narwin, Harrison High School. From Young Americans for America. "On behalf of our membership we strongly condemn your suppression of patriotism in the American school system. Sincerely, Jessica Wittington, Executive Secretary, Tampa, Florida."

HANK MORGAN *(to the audience).* Telegram

to Philip Malloy. From the Society for the Preservation of Free Speech. "We applaud your defense of the freedom of speech in a public arena. One is never too young to fight for our constitutional rights, which are under constant assault from right-wing forces. Stand firm. Stand tall. Please call us for active support. Hank Morgan, Chicago, Illinois."

CHARLES ELDERSON *(to the audience).* Telegram to Principal, Harrison High. "People like Margaret Narwin should be kicked out of teaching. Charles Elderson, Woodbank, North Carolina."

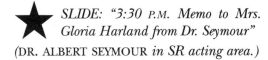 *SLIDE: "3:30 P.M. Memo to Mrs. Gloria Harland from Dr. Seymour"*
(DR. ALBERT SEYMOUR *in SR acting area.)*

SLIDE: Office wall.

DR. SEYMOUR. Three. On March twenty-eighth, twenty-ninth, and thirtieth, Philip Malloy deliberately caused a disturbance in his homeroom class (Margaret Narwin, a teacher of twenty years' standing) by singing the national anthem in a loud, raucous, *disrespectful* fashion, thereby drawing attention to himself and away from the words. There are strong indications that he was acting out some personal animosity[5] toward the teacher in question for reasons unknown. His school performance has been inferior. (It has been suggested that there may be problems in the home area. Please note, however, that the law *requires* schools to keep such personal information confidential.)

Four. When requested by his teacher, Miss Narwin, on the first occasion to maintain a dignified response to the national anthem, Philip Malloy did so, though reluctantly. On the second and third occasions, he repeated his disrespectful acts, and when he refused to stop, he was—as a matter of course—sent to Assistant Principal Dr. Joseph Palleni for discipline.

Five. Philip Malloy, when given the opportunity, did *not* dispute the above facts.

Six. Students who were in the classroom at the time of the incidents confirm these events.

Seven. On the third occurrence, Philip Malloy was requested to: one) promise that he would show an attitude of respect toward our national anthem, and two) apologize to his teacher and his classmates for his rude behavior. He refused, choosing the option of suspension *himself.*

 SLIDE: "6:20 P.M. Conversation between Philip Malloy's Parents"
(SUSAN *and* BEN MALLOY *in UC acting area.)*

SLIDE: Kitchen wall.

BEN MALLOY. Hi! Where's Philip?

SUSAN MALLOY. He just got in. Washing up.

BEN MALLOY. People were talking about him today. Amazing how many folks saw that thing in the paper.

SUSAN MALLOY. At my place, too.

BEN MALLOY. Makes you feel good.

SUSAN MALLOY. We should celebrate.

---

5. animosity (an ə măs′ə tē), ill will or resentment causing hostility

(PHILIP MALLOY enters.)

BEN MALLOY. Well, how do you feel?

PHILIP MALLOY. Okay.

SUSAN MALLOY. You should be pleased with yourself.

BEN MALLOY. What do you think of all the telegrams?

PHILIP MALLOY. I don't know. Who are those people? I never heard of them before.

BEN MALLOY. They've heard of you. You're famous. Just shows you. One person, standing up for what he believes in, makes a difference.

SUSAN MALLOY. I'm just so glad it's worked out all right. Aren't you?

PHILIP MALLOY. I suppose.

BEN MALLOY. What's the problem now?

PHILIP MALLOY. It'll be weird going back. What kids will say.

BEN MALLOY. They'll be on your side. Just make sure you sing in the morning. People will look to that.

PHILIP MALLOY. I'll be in Mr. Lunser's class.

BEN MALLOY. You said he likes kids singing.

PHILIP MALLOY. Sort of.

BEN MALLOY. I think you should go over and speak to Ted Griffen, too.

PHILIP MALLOY. Why?

BEN MALLOY. Someone at work heard him at some speech he gave—the school board thing—he mentioned this whole business. . . .

PHILIP MALLOY. He did?

SUSAN MALLOY. And he brought in that reporter.

BEN MALLOY. Come on, Philip, people are really on your side!

PHILIP MALLOY. I guess.

 SLIDE: "7:30 P.M. Ted Griffen Delivers a Speech to a Meeting of the Harrison Chamber of Commerce"

(TED GRIFFEN in SR acting area)

> *SLIDE: Meeting room.*

TED GRIFFEN *(to the audience).* I am a great believer in basic American values. But what I say is—most emphatically—what is the point of installing computers if our young people are not allowed to practice the elemental values of American patriotism? And to think—because this story has been picked up by the national press—how shocking it is that this is the way our town of Harrison should come to be known. It should not be condoned.[6]

 SLIDE: "8:10 P.M. Phone Conversation between Margaret Narwin and Dr. Gertrude Doane"

(MARGARET NARWIN and DR. GERTRUDE DOANE on opposite sides of DC acting area)

DR. DOANE. Yes, Peg, hello. How are you?

MARGARET NARWIN. Gert, I . . .

DR. DOANE. Peg, are you all right?

MARGARET NARWIN. Gert, I just got a call from my sister in Florida . . . about a newspaper story—

DR. DOANE. I know, Peg. I've already heard about it. I just didn't see any point in upsetting you any more.

---

6. condoned (kən dōn′), pardoned, overlooked, or treated as not important

MARGARET NARWIN. But why?

DR. DOANE. I already received a call from some midwestern reporter. There have been telegrams—

MARGARET NARWIN. Telegrams?

DR. DOANE. At school. I told the office to hold them. Peg, it's gotten out of hand.

MARGARET NARWIN. I want to see them. What do the telegrams say?

DR. DOANE. Well, they believe what the story says and—

MARGARET NARWIN. Were they addressed to me?

DR. DOANE. Well, to me, and yes, some to you, but—

MARGARET NARWIN. I want to see them.

DR. DOANE. Peg, I assure you, I have complete confidence in you.

MARGARET NARWIN. It's so monstrous, so . . .

DR. DOANE. Peg, we're just going to have to weather it and . . . maybe you'll want to take the day off tomorrow.

MARGARET NARWIN. No, I can't give in to this—

DR. DOANE. Peg, believe me. It will calm down.

 SLIDE: "10:33 P.M. From the Diary of Philip Malloy"

(PHILIP MALLOY *in UC acting area. He is holding his diary.*)

PHILIP MALLOY (*to the audience*). Weird day not doing much. Got these telegrams from people I never heard of before, talking about something I didn't get. Folks all high. Be glad to be back in school. I hate sitting around. Glad to be in Lunser's homeroom class again. Get things back to normal. Guess I'll still be in Narwin's English. Better speak to her and see if I can do some extra work. So I can get on the track team. Wonder what she'll say? (*Beat*) Did some extra time on Dad's rowing machine. (*Beat*) I'm a little nervous.

Scene Three

 SLIDE: "Tuesday, April 3. Letters sent to Margaret Narwin"

(CARLTON HAVEN, DAVID MAIK, *and* LAURA JACOBS *in DC acting area*)

CARLTON HAVEN (*to the audience*). "Dear Margaret Narwin. As a teacher in the Dayton, Ohio school system for ten years, I am dismayed and horrified that in this day and age a colleague of mine should suspend a student from school for singing the national anthem. We suffer enough from unfair criticism. The profession does not need people like you who make it so hard for the rest of us. Carlton Haven."

DAVID MAIK (*to the audience*). "Margaret Narwin. I'm a veteran who fought for this country and gave his blood and I really hate people like you. David Maik, Eugene, Oregon."

LAURA JACOBS (*to the audience*). "Margaret Narwin. It seems to me that people like you, who don't believe in patriotism, cause the problems. Surely you have something better to do with your classroom authority than attacking kids who express their love of our country. Or maybe you should find a better profession for your lack of ability. Laura Jacobs, San Diego, California."

 SLIDE: "7:15 A.M. Conversation between Dr. Seymour and Dr. Doane in the Superintendent's Office"

(DR. ALBERT SEYMOUR *and* DR. GERTRUDE DOANE *in SR acting area. They are each holding a number of telegrams.*)

DR. DOANE. How many are there?

DR. SEYMOUR. *Telegrams?* Ten. Fifteen. Every one of them demanding we fire this Narwin woman.

DR. DOANE. Not this one.

DR. SEYMOUR. Well, the overwhelming majority. And I had twelve calls at my home last night.

DR. DOANE. From whom?

DR. SEYMOUR. People in town. People who vote. They're outraged.

DR. DOANE. And they believe that story. . . .

DR. SEYMOUR. I'm beginning to believe it. . . .

DR. DOANE. Al!

DR. SEYMOUR. What do you expect me to do?

DR. DOANE. I expect you to support Peg Narwin.

DR. SEYMOUR. A TV network wants to interview people.

DR. DOANE. You're not going to let them. . . .

DR. SEYMOUR. No. No. But the board wants me to issue a statement. Gert, I have an appointment with this Ted Griffen at nine-fifteen.

DR. DOANE. Griffen is running for board . . . .

DR. SEYMOUR. Exactly. He's already made speeches about this business. Look, Gert, I'm sorry, but between you and me—quote me and I'll deny it—I don't care about the board. I can handle them. But the budget . . . if we lose again . . .

DR. DOANE. I know.

DR. SEYMOUR. People scream if kids are not educated. Then they scream if you ask them for the money to do it.

DR. DOANE. Yes, I know.

DR. SEYMOUR. I want to see the file on Narwin.

DR. DOANE. Why?

DR. SEYMOUR. I have to decide what to do.

DR. DOANE. Before your meeting with this Griffen?

DR. SEYMOUR. Exactly.

 SLIDE: "7:30 A.M. Conversation between Philip and His Parents During Breakfast"

(PHILIP MALLOY *plus* SUSAN *and* BEN MALLOY *in UC acting area.*)

SLIDE: Kitchen wall.

BEN MALLOY. You don't have to be nervous about anything. You were right. The fact that they moved you out of that woman's class proves you were right.

PHILIP MALLOY. Just homeroom. I still have English with her.

SUSAN MALLOY. I'm sure she won't give you any more trouble.

PHILIP MALLOY. It's just the other kids . . .

BEN MALLOY. You said they hated her, too.

PHILIP MALLOY. Yeah . . . .

SUSAN MALLOY. Do you want me to drive you?

PHILIP MALLOY. I'm meeting Ken.

SUSAN MALLOY. You'll be fine.

BEN MALLOY. As I've told you, half your runs are won at the start. Leap out of the blocks. Show them what you can do.

PHILIP MALLOY. Easy for you—

SUSAN MALLOY. Phil, you better go if you don't want to miss your bus.

 SLIDE: "7:40 A.M. Conversation between Philip and Ken on the Way to the School Bus"

(PHILIP MALLOY *and* KEN BARCHET *in DC acting area*)

PHILIP MALLOY. What's happening?

KEN BARCHET. Nothing. What's with you?

PHILIP MALLOY. Not much. We going to run this afternoon?

KEN BARCHET. Can't. Got track team right after school. Coach told us it's going to be at least three hours. You really should have tried out, man. You know that Polanski kid?

PHILIP MALLOY. Brian?

KEN BARCHET. Right. Coach has him down for the four hundred.

PHILIP MALLOY. Can't do anything.

KEN BARCHET. Best we got. *(Beat)* You mad at the coach or something?

PHILIP MALLOY. No. Why?

KEN BARCHET. You should change your mind about being on the team.

PHILIP MALLOY. Yeah, I might. *(Beat)* Want to know why I didn't go out? Narwin.

KEN BARCHET. What did she have to do with it?

PHILIP MALLOY. She almost flunked me in English. That meant I wasn't allowed to try out.

KEN BARCHET. That's why you're mad at her?

PHILIP MALLOY. But I'm going to ask her if I can do extra work. For credit.

KEN BARCHET. Think she'll give it to you?

PHILIP MALLOY. I don't know. I'll ask.

KEN BARCHET. Be great if you could get on the team.

PHILIP MALLOY. That's what I've been thinking.

 SLIDE: "7:45 A.M. Conversation between Margaret Narwin and Dr. Doane"

(MARGARET NARWIN *and* DR. GERTRUDE DOANE *in SR acting area. A mail bag full of letters sits beside the desk.*)

SLIDE: Office wall.

MARGARET NARWIN. I don't believe it!

DR. DOANE. It is incredible.

MARGARET NARWIN. How many telegrams are there?

DR. DOANE. Here? Almost two hundred. *(Beat)* The superintendent's office put out a statement explaining the true situation.

MARGARET NARWIN. What did he say? May I see it?

DR. DOANE. Of course. Here.

(DR. GERTRUDE DOANE *hands* MARGARET

NARWIN *the statement, which she reads.)*

DR. DOANE. What's the matter?

MARGARET NARWIN. This doesn't support me. I pleaded with Joe not to suspend him.

DR. DOANE. Peg, it does.

MARGARET NARWIN. Where?

DR. DOANE. Peg, understand that. . . . I need to tell you I said no to some TV people.

MARGARET NARWIN. No. Absolutely not.

DR. DOANE. *Exactly.* They can't come in without permission. Peg, do you want to take the day off?

MARGARET NARWIN. No. They'll come to my home. *(Beat)* Gert, I don't understand. I have been teaching—

DR. DOANE. People believe what they read.

MARGARET NARWIN *(looking at her watch).* I have my class . . . .

DR. DOANE. Peg, I've moved Philip from your English class. He's with Mr. Keegan.

MARGARET NARWIN *(surprised).* Gert, people will misconstrue.

DR. DOANE. We are trying to be even-handed . . . .

MARGARET NARWIN. He's a student. I'm a teacher. Hands are not meant to be even.

DR. DOANE. That's my decision.

 SLIDE: "7:55 A.M. Conversation between Philip and Allison"

(PHILIP MALLOY *and* ALLISON DORESETT *in DC acting area)*

ALLISON DORESETT. Philip!

PHILIP MALLOY. Oh, hi.

ALLISON DORESETT. I just want you to know that I think what you did was really mean.

PHILIP MALLOY. What?

ALLISON DORESETT. Narwin is one of the best teachers. All the kids say so. It's really embarrassing.

PHILIP MALLOY. What are you talking about?

ALLISON DORESETT. You were just doing that to annoy her.

PHILIP MALLOY. Who?

ALLISON DORESETT. Miss Narwin. Everybody knows it. She's so fair.

(ALLISON DORESETT *exits.)*

PHILIP MALLOY. That's not true.

 SLIDE: "8:03 A.M. Discussion in Bernard Lunser's Homeroom Class"

(BERNARD LUNSER, PHILIP MALLOY, STUDENT #1, *and* STUDENT #2 *in SL acting area.)*

SLIDE [the one used at the beginning of Scene Two]: Classroom wall.

BERNARD LUNSER. Let's go! Let's go! Seats. My God, it's Philip Malloy, Harrison High's own Uncle Sam. Take any empty seat, Philip. I'll set it later.

INTERCOM *(voice of* DR. GERTRUDE DOANE*).* Good morning to all students, faculty, and staff. Today is Tuesday, April third. Today will be a Schedule B day.

BERNARD LUNSER. That's B for bozos, boys and girls. B!

INTERCOM. Today in history. On this day, in the year thirteen-sixty-six, King Henry the Fourth of England was born.

BERNARD LUNSER. Not to be confused with a fifth of scotch.

INTERCOM. In nineteen-sixty-one, actor Eddie Murphy was born.

BERNARD LUNSER. My only competition.

INTERCOM. Please all rise and stand at respectful, silent attention for the playing of our national anthem.

BERNARD LUNSER. Philip!

PHILIP MALLOY. What?

BERNARD LUNSER. You want to sing?

STUDENTS. Yeah, sing!

BERNARD LUNSER. Keep your lip buttoned, Brian! Philip?

PHILIP MALLOY. No. . . .

BERNARD LUNSER. Okay. Just making sure your rights are protected.

Oh, say can you see by the dawn's early light,
What so proudly we hailed at the twilight's last gleaming?

BERNARD LUNSER. You sure, Philip?

PHILIP MALLOY. Yeah. . . .

Whose broad stripes and bright stars, thro' the perilous fight,
O'er the ramparts we watched were so gallantly streaming? . . .

 SLIDE: "Letters sent to Philip Malloy"

(ROLANDO MERCHAUD, MS. HARBOR, *and* AMERICAN LEGIONNAIRE *in DC acting area*)

ROLANDO MERCHAUD (*to the audience*). "Dear Philip. We support your defense of America. Keep on singing. We all join in. Rolando Merchaud, Red Oak, Iowa."

MS. HARBOR (*to the audience*). "Dear Philip. We, Ms. Harbor's fourth grade class at the Robert Fulton School, like to sing *The Star-Spangled Banner*, too. You can come to our school. Ms. Harbor's fourth grade class, Robert Fulton School, Brooklyn, New York."

AMERICAN LEGIONNAIRE (*to the audience*). "To Philip Malloy. American Legion Post number sixteen of Newport, Rhode Island, salutes you for your defense of American values. Fight the good fight. Thumbs-up!"

 SLIDE: "8:16 A.M. Conversations between Philip and Students in the Hallway on the Way to First Class"

(PHILIP MALLOY, TODD BECKER, STUDENT #2, *and* STUDENT #3 *in SL acting area.*)

SLIDE: School hallway.

TODD BECKER. Hey, Philip, what's happening?

PHILIP MALLOY. Nothing.

TODD BECKER. You going to have a press conference?

PHILIP MALLOY. Get off!

STUDENT #2: Look out! Here comes Uncle Sam! That's what Mr. Lunser called him.

STUDENT #3: What's it like to be famous, newspapers and all?

PHILIP MALLOY. Come on. I have to get to class.

TODD BECKER. Oh, let the big man go.

STUDENT #3: Hey, Philip? How come you went after Narwin? I heard it was because you were failing English! That true?

PHILIP MALLOY. I have a class!

(PHILIP MALLOY *exits.*)

STUDENT #2: Let Uncle Sam go.

 SLIDE: "9:20 A.M. Conversation between Dr. Seymour and Ted Griffen"

(DR. ALBERT SEYMOUR *and* TED GRIFFEN *in SR acting area.*)

SLIDE: Office wall.

DR. SEYMOUR. Mr. Griffen. Nice to meet you. Come right in.

TED GRIFFEN. Thank you.

DR. SEYMOUR. Get you some coffee?

TED GRIFFEN. No, thanks.

DR. SEYMOUR. Look, Mr. Griffen—

TED GRIFFEN. Call me Ted.

DR. SEYMOUR. Fine. Ted. I'm Al. I've heard you speak a couple of times . . . was very interested in what you had to say. . . . I thought it would be a good idea, generally, to meet you. Sort of talk things over.

TED GRIFFEN. I appreciate that, Al.

DR. SEYMOUR. Now, what we've got here . . . well, the media . . . they never pay attention to us unless something bad—

TED GRIFFEN. Right. I never trust anything that's in print.

DR. SEYMOUR. Exactly. But we've got these elections coming up . . . budget.

TED GRIFFEN. And the board.

DR. SEYMOUR. Exactly. I'm prepared to work with anyone who's on the board. . . . But the budget thing—

TED GRIFFEN. Have to keep costs down.

DR. SEYMOUR. Absolutely. But, Ted, I'll be frank with you. All this publicity—

negative publicity—won't do us any good.

TED GRIFFEN. I understand.

DR. SEYMOUR. That first budget was tight. And this second budget . . . to the bone. Get any closer and we're scooping marrow. Now, I understand no one wants to pay a cent more. But without that budget, education is in big trouble here in Harrison.

TED GRIFFEN. People want to hold the line on taxes.

DR. SEYMOUR. I sympathize. I pay taxes, too. But there's been a real misunderstanding regarding this national anthem thing. Let me share some facts with you. We have no rule against singing the national anthem. Never have had. Never will.

TED GRIFFEN. But the boy was suspended.

DR. SEYMOUR. Just getting to that. What I suspect here . . . we've got a personal problem.

TED GRIFFEN. With the boy? He seems—

DR. SEYMOUR. Now, Ted, I'm speaking in confidence.

TED GRIFFEN. Sure.

DR. SEYMOUR. Then we understand. It's not the boy. It's the teacher.

TED GRIFFEN. Well, I thought . . . what kind of a problem?

DR. SEYMOUR. Let me quote from a letter she wrote just a few weeks ago to her principal. I can't give you a copy, you understand, but I can read part of it to you . . . so you can understand what I'm up against.

TED GRIFFEN. Sure.

DR. SEYMOUR. She says here, and I'm quoting her, "The truth is . . . I feel that sometimes I am a little out of touch with contemporary teaching, and, just as important, the students who come before me." In other words, she's been around since history began.

TED GRIFFEN. Oh, boy. You've got a problem there.

DR. SEYMOUR. Exactly. The question is, what are you and I going to do about it?

 SLIDE: *"1:30 P.M. Conversation between Philip and Margaret Narwin"*

(PHILIP MALLOY *and* MARGARET NARWIN *in SL acting area.*)

SLIDE: *Classroom wall.*

PHILIP MALLOY. Miss Narwin?

MARGARET NARWIN. Philip? What are you doing here? What do you want?

PHILIP MALLOY. My class.

MARGARET NARWIN. You're . . . you're not in this section anymore. You were switched.

PHILIP MALLOY. I was?

MARGARET NARWIN. You're in Mr. Keegan's class.

PHILIP MALLOY. But . . .

MARGARET NARWIN. What?

PHILIP MALLOY. To get my grade up . . . I was going to ask for extra work. . . .

MARGARET NARWIN. Philip, you are no longer in my class.

PHILIP MALLOY. So I could get on the track team and . . .

MARGARET NARWIN. You are not in my class.

PHILIP MALLOY. But what about the grade?

MARGARET NARWIN. Please leave the room.

PHILIP MALLOY. But—

MARGARET NARWIN. Go!

PHILIP MALLOY. I'm leaving.

MARGARET NARWIN. Speak to Dr. Doane.

 SLIDE: *"2:50 P.M. Conversation between Philip and Coach Earl Jamison"*

(PHILIP MALLOY *and* COACH JAMISON *in SL acting area*)

PHILIP MALLOY. Can I talk to you a minute?

COACH JAMISON. Yeah. Sure.

PHILIP MALLOY. Remember, you said I should ask Miss Narwin for some extra work. . . .

COACH JAMISON. Sure.

PHILIP MALLOY. So I could get my grade up, get on the team.

COACH JAMISON. Okay.

PHILIP MALLOY. She won't let me.

COACH JAMISON. She won't let you what?

PHILIP MALLOY. Do more work.

COACH JAMISON. Well, Phil, you did one hell of a number on her. . . .

PHILIP MALLOY. I mean, I'm not even in her class anymore. She must have kicked me out. If I could stay in her class I—

COACH JAMISON. Philip, you want my advice? I'm always telling you guys— it's what sports is all about. A rule is a rule—to get along you have to play along. Know what I'm saying?

PHILIP MALLOY. What about my running with the team?

COACH JAMISON. Look, Philip, you did a number on Miss Narwin. She's a good person. You have to be a team player. So you can't just come around now and start asking for things. It just doesn't work that way.

 SLIDE: "3:30 P.M. Conversation between Margaret Narwin and Dr. Doane"

(MARGARET NARWIN *and* DR. GERTRUDE DOANE *in SR acting area.*)

SLIDE: Office wall.

DR. DOANE. Would you like a cup of coffee?

MARGARET NARWIN. My nerves are too tight as it is.

DR. DOANE. It's astonishing. . . . I had another call from a TV reporter—

MARGARET NARWIN. You wanted to see me.

DR. DOANE. Just that some good has come out of all this. . . .

MARGARET NARWIN. That would be nice. What is it?

DR. DOANE. It concerns your application for funds for that summer refresher course, English teaching. I talked to Al Seymour and—

MARGARET NARWIN. Don't mention him to me. His statement—

DR. DOANE. But he managed to find some money, and you can take it. . . .

MARGARET NARWIN. Well, I'm very grateful.

DR. DOANE. There is only one thing. . . . Peg, he wants you to take the rest of the term off.

MARGARET NARWIN. What?

DR. DOANE. The rest of the term.

MARGARET NARWIN. But—

DR. DOANE. Take the time off, full pay, of course, and then, take that course. You'll come back fall term . . . and, well, things will be fine. It's very kind of Al.

MARGARET NARWIN. In other words, he wants me to leave.

DR. DOANE. No. No. You misunderstand. It would be an administrative leave. With pay. You'll lose no time on your pension. You could be with your sister. . . .

MARGARET NARWIN. No.

DR. DOANE. Peg, you have to see it from his, our side. . . .

MARGARET NARWIN. Aren't we on the same side?

DR. DOANE. That's not the point.

MARGARET NARWIN. What is the point?

DR. DOANE. Peg, Al is deeply worried about out budget.

 SLIDE: "6:30 P.M. Conversation between Philip Malloy's Parents"

(SUSAN *and* BEN MALLOY *in UC acting area.*)

SLIDE: Kitchen wall.

SUSAN MALLOY. He's very upset.

BEN MALLOY. About the telegrams?

SUSAN MALLOY. Something at school.

BEN MALLOY. The teacher again?

SUSAN MALLOY. He wouldn't say. He wouldn't talk about it.

BEN MALLOY. Strange.

SUSAN MALLOY. I almost thought he was going to start crying. Maybe you should talk to him.

BEN MALLOY. Sure.

SUSAN MALLOY. Dinner will be ready in twenty minutes. *(Beat)* Hon, my sister called.

BEN MALLOY. From Conover?

SUSAN MALLOY. She said Philip could go to school in their district.

BEN MALLOY. That's absurd!

SUSAN MALLOY. Maybe it isn't. Maybe this is too much.

BEN MALLOY. Susan . . .

SUSAN MALLOY. Just a thought.

 SLIDE: "8:50 P.M. From the Diary of Philip Malloy"

(PHILIP MALLOY in DC acting area. He is holding his diary.)

PHILIP MALLOY *(to the audience).* Things stink. And it's all so unfair. Nobody takes my side. They all think Narwin's great. Nobody pays any attention to what she did to me. Coach Jamison won't let me on the team. I hate that school.

Scene Four

 SLIDE: "Wednesday, April 4. 7:20 A.M. Phone Conversation between Margaret Narwin and Dr. Doane"

(MARGARET NARWIN and DR. GERTRUDE DOANE on opposite sides of the DC acting area)

DR. DOANE. Yes, Peg.

MARGARET NARWIN. I won't be coming in today.

DR. DOANE. Oh.

MARGARET NARWIN. I'm too exhausted.

DR. DOANE. I think that's wise.

MARGARET NARWIN. I need some time to think.

DR. DOANE. You do that. No problem here. We'll get a substitute.

 SLIDE: "7:30 A.M. Conversation between Philip and His Parents at Breakfast"

(PHILIP MALLOY plus SUSAN and BEN MALLOY in UC acting area.)

SLIDE: Kitchen wall.

PHILIP MALLOY. No way I'm going to school today.

BEN MALLOY. Why?

PHILIP MALLOY. I just won't.

SUSAN MALLOY. Philip, you must tell us. Has that teacher done something else?

PHILIP MALLOY. I'm not in her class anymore.

BEN MALLOY. But . . . look at the telegrams. Everybody says you did the right thing.

PHILIP MALLOY. I'm not going.

BEN MALLOY. Philip, you must go.

PHILIP MALLOY. I'd rather go to another school. You said there was a private school.

SUSAN MALLOY. But—

BEN MALLOY. Oh, sure! Go to a private school! The only money we've got is the money we set aside for your college.

PHILIP MALLOY. I could go to Aunt Becky's. We could move.

BEN MALLOY. That's ridiculous. Look, it's clear *something* has happened. If we don't know, how can we help you?

PHILIP MALLOY. The kids hate me!

BEN MALLOY. Why?

PHILIP MALLOY. I'm not going.

BEN MALLOY. Philip, you will go!

 SLIDE: "7:40 A.M. Conversation between Philip and Ken on the Way to the School Bus"

(PHILIP MALLOY and KEN BARCHET in DC acting area)

PHILIP MALLOY. What's happening?

KEN BARCHET. Nothing. What's with you? I thought maybe you weren't going to school.

PHILIP MALLOY. My folks . . .

KEN BARCHET. Did you hear what Allison and Todd were planning to do?

PHILIP MALLOY. No, what?

KEN BARCHET. They want to get a petition going to get you to say you were wrong.

PHILIP MALLOY. No way.

KEN BARCHET. And you know who gave them the idea?

PHILIP MALLOY. No.

KEN BARCHET. Coach Jamison. That's what Brian told me. I want to start another petition to get Narwin to apologize. Or we could get you to sing together. Be boss.

PHILIP MALLOY. Would you stop bugging me!

KEN BARCHET. Hey, man, can't you take a joke?

PHILIP MALLOY. Forget it.

(PHILIP MALLOY exits.)

KEN BARCHET. Hey! Come on, Phil. Where you going? I was just kidding!

 SLIDE: "8:55 A.M. Phone Conversation between Philip and His Mother"

(PHILIP MALLOY in UC acting area. SUSAN MALLOY in SR acting area.)

PHILIP MALLOY. Just wanted you to know I'm home.

SUSAN MALLOY. Home? Why?

PHILIP MALLOY. I told you. I'm not going to school. Not that school.

SUSAN MALLOY. Well . . . stay home today. That's okay. We'll talk it out when I get home.

PHILIP MALLOY. Just don't tell Dad, will you?

SUSAN MALLOY. Okay.

 SLIDE: "8:30 P.M. Ted Griffen Delivers a Speech to a Meeting of the Harrison Downtown Association"

(TED GRIFFEN in DC acting area)

TED GRIFFEN *(to the audience).* That I can be a forceful, productive member of the board is clear. It was I who made public this sad story regarding the boy who was removed from class because he wanted to express his patriotism.

I was able to meet with the superintendent and discuss in a calm, rational fashion what might be done. When it became clear that the problem was not with school policy itself, but the misguided judgment of a particular teacher—a teacher out of touch with Harrison values—a solution was worked out that is equitable to all. And preserves the good name of our community. The boy is back in class, where he belongs and wants to be. The teacher in question will get a needed refresher course in our values and return to her duties next year, better able to teach.

Our community will support just these kinds of productive compromises. And therefore I urge all of you, on April fifth, to support the school budget proposal set before the voters. It is a thoughtful budget, fiscally prudent, and I, for one, support it.

 SLIDE: "10:55 P.M. Conversation between Philip Malloy's Parents"

(SUSAN *and* BEN MALLOY *in UC acting area*).

SLIDE: Kitchen wall.

SUSAN MALLOY. Ben, he refuses to go back!

BEN MALLOY. I've never heard of anything so crazy. He won! But he acts as if he lost.

SUSAN MALLOY. He says he'll just wait till we're out of the house and then come home.

BEN MALLOY. Of all . . .

SUSAN MALLOY. He has to go to some school.

BEN MALLOY. Right.

SUSAN MALLOY. I'm going to call Washington Academy.

BEN MALLOY. That's his college money!

SUSAN MALLOY. Should I call my sister?

Scene Five

 SLIDE: "Friday, April 6. Report from the Manchester Record *on School Elections"*

(JENNIFER STEWART *in DC acting area*)

JENNIFER STEWART *(to the audience).* Harrison School Elections. Final results, vote for school budget: six hundred forty-five in favor and seventeen hundred eighty-four against. Budget defeated. The following were elected to the Harrison School Board for three-year terms: Susan Eagleton, Ted Griffen, Gloria Harland, Ernest Johnson, and Crawford Wright. Percentage of eligible voters casting ballots: twenty-two percent.

Scene Six

 SLIDE: "Monday, April 9. 8:25 A.M. Conversation between Philip and George Brookover, Principal of Washington Academy"

(PHILIP MALLOY *and* GEORGE BROOKOVER *in SR acting area.*)

SLIDE: Office wall.

GEORGE BROOKOVER. Philip, I just want to tell you that we're very pleased to have you at Washington Academy. We do know a good bit about you. You're famous.

PHILIP MALLOY. Yes, sir.

GEORGE BROOKOVER. We like what we hear. Anyway, we're all pretty much a family at Washington. I'm sure you'll make new friends.

PHILIP MALLOY. Yes, sir.

GEORGE BROOKOVER. You'll be in Miss Rooney's class. You'll find her a good teacher. I'm sure you'll do just fine. Have you any interest in sports?

PHILIP MALLOY. Track.

GEORGE BROOKOVER. Well, we don't have a track team here at Washington. There's never been enough interest. But now that you're here, maybe there can be. Your dad says you're a crackerjack runner. We do have soccer. You could do a lot of running there. Think that might interest you?

PHILIP MALLOY. I don't know.

GEORGE BROOKOVER. Okay. Let me take you on down to class now. Should be just getting under way.

 SLIDE: "8:30 A.M. Miss Rooney's Homeroom Class, Washington Academy"

(MISS ROONEY *and* PHILIP MALLOY *in DC acting area.* MISS ROONEY *has her arm around* PHILIP MALLOY's *shoulder, as if she is introducing him to the class.*)

MISS ROONEY *(to the audience).* Class, this is Philip Malloy, who has just joined our school. Philip, you can sit right over there. But we were about to begin our day. In fact, we usually begin by singing the national anthem. Maybe you would like to lead us in that? *(Beat)* Philip? Philip, what's the matter?

(*The* Star-Spangled Banner *begins to play.*)

(PHILIP MALLOY *petrified, just stands there.* PHILIP MALLOY *then begins to cry.*)

PHILIP MALLOY *(finally).* I don't know the words.

(The Star-Spangled Banner *gets louder as . . .*

Slides of the American flag on all three rear projection screens fade up.

PHILIP MALLOY *continues crying as . . .*

The national anthem and slides fade out very, very slowly until . . .

Blackout)

End of Play

Nothing But the Truth

Responding to the Play

1. Analyze Philip's attitudes from the beginning to the end of the play. Do you think he matures? Why or why not?
2. How does Philip, as the protagonist, move the action forward?
3. Who is the antagonist of this play? Explain your answer.
4. The author has created characters who honestly seem to believe they are telling "nothing but the truth." Who comes closest?
5. Look back at the suggestions for creating a character on page 164. Jot down how you would apply them to Margaret Narwin, Dr. Palleni, or Jennifer Stewart. Share your notes with the class.

About Acting Styles

Actors today generally use one of two main approaches to developing a character: the *presentational* or the *representational* style. Presentational actors work "from the inside out." That is, they develop feelings, motivations, and thoughts for their characters. Then they let those determine the character's behavior. Representational actors work "from the outside in." They work out the physical habits and characteristics of the character, hoping that those details will provide clues to the character's inner life. Presentational acting is especially popular with "method actors," in both dramatic and comic roles. Improvisers tend to favor representational acting, which offers immediate tools for quick takes and short skits.

Creating and Performing

1. What do you think Ms. Narwin does after Wednesday, April 4? Write a brief letter from Ms. Narwin to her sister telling of her plans.
2. Actors often have to develop a character in a way that fits the director's concept. Trade notes regarding Philip with another classmate. Then perform a monologue or scene in which you play the character as your classmate sees him.
3. Look back at your notes on creating a character for question 5 above. With a partner, perform a scene between two of the characters.

Avi's *Nothing But the Truth* dramatized by Ronn Smith   **221**

Before Reading

This Is a Test

The Play as Literature: Style

An author's *style,* the way he or she writes about a subject, puts a personal stamp on each of the author's works. Style includes the way the author writes dialogue, how the characters are made to interact, and the situations in which the author puts the characters. Authors strive to write in a style that best conveys the subject's theme.

In *This Is a Test*, Stephen Gregg's style effectively conveys the anxiety and self-consciousness of a high-school student. In Gregg's hands, the simple act of taking a test becomes the character's waking nightmare. Gregg's play may be offbeat and unusual, but it hits a common nerve. This is a test we've all taken.

The Play as Theatre: Pacing and Timing

An actor has many things to think about when playing a part on stage: "What's my next line?" "What's my motivation?" "Where do I move?" Just as important, however, are questions of pacing and timing.

The *pacing* of a dramatic work involves how quickly or slowly the acts and scenes move along. *Timing* involves when and at what rate an actor says his or her lines. Actors must be careful not to rush scenes while also not letting them drag. They must be aware that waiting a beat before responding can give a line extra emphasis, and that jumping in and clipping off another actor's line can add drama.

This Is a Test requires quick timing and smooth pacing. As you read, try to imagine how you would pace your dialogue if you were Alan.

WARM UP!

The actions of the chorus in this play are based on a theatre game called "This Is A." To play, choose small, one-syllable objects you can hold in your hand, such as a key. The entire class forms a circle. One person is the "starter" of the game. The starter initiates the dialogue (see left) and offers an object to the person on the right. The person on the right takes the object on his/her last line of dialogue. Then he or she initiates the same dialogue with the next person. The starter repeats the activity with a second object, then a third, and a fourth. Each person receives and then gives an object.

222 *This Is a Test* by Stephen Gregg

This is a pen.

A pen.

pen.

A what?

Oh, a pen

This is a

A what??

A shoe.

shoe.

This Is a Test

by Stephen Gregg

pe.

This is a key

key.

This is a

Oh, a

key.

A what?

pen.

A pen.

pen.

Oh, a pen

This is a book.

Setting	Characters	Time
A classroom	ALAN LOIS MOTHER TEACHER EVAN CHRIS PAT THE CHORUS OTHER STUDENTS THE VOICE	The 1980's

There *is a high-pitched whine of the type that comes on the television during the emergency broadcast system tests.*

VOICE. This is a test. For the next sixty minutes, this classroom will conduct a test of your emergency information retrieval system. This is only a test.

Lights come up on five desks and, behind them, a large blackboard. Two of the desks are occupied by LOIS *and* ALAN. LOIS *is neatly groomed.* ALAN *is a mess. His shirt is buttoned incorrectly, his socks do not match, and his hair sticks out at odd angles. His expression is both dazed and frantic.*

ALAN. I shouldn't have done this.

LOIS. It's going to be worth it.

ALAN. This was not a good idea.

LOIS. You know the stuff, right?

ALAN. I don't feel good.

LOIS. You're going to get an A and you're going to thank me.

ALAN. No. I should have slept.

LOIS. I told you, a little sleep is worse than no sleep.

ALAN. For you maybe. You do this all the time. I'm not used to this. I shouldn't have done it. I should have taken my phone off the hook.

LOIS. You did the right thing.

ALAN. It didn't work! I don't know anything.

LOIS. Yes, you do.

ALAN. I don't. *(He reaches under his desk, gets his books, and frantically thumbs through them.)* I have to study some more.

LOIS. Relax!

ALAN *(stopping at a random place and seeing the word "Saladin").* "Saladin. A Moslem sultan of Egypt in the twelfth century. *(He pauses.)* His name means 'keeper of the faith.' *(He pauses.)* He grew up in Lower Mesopotamia."

LOIS *(reaching over and shutting* ALAN*'s book).* Stop it. It's too late to study now. You either know it or you don't. The best thing you can do now is just relax.

ALAN. I can't! I don't know anything! Nothing stuck with me. You know what I learned last night? I learned that the Battle of Hastings was in ten-sixty-six and I learned that Thomas Edison's middle name was Alva. That's it. That's all I know. If we're asked when the Battle of Hastings was, I can say, "The Battle of Hastings was in ten-sixty-six." If he asks, "What was Thomas Edison's middle name?" I can say, "Alva." Other than that, I'm completely sunk.

LOIS. No, you're not.

ALAN. Evan wouldn't have done this.

LOIS. What does Evan have to do with this?

ALAN. He has the best grades in the class and he didn't stay up all last night.

LOIS. Who cares?

ALAN. He's going to get a better grade than I am and he didn't have you calling him every half hour to say, "Are you still awake?" *(He snarls.)* Yes, Lois, I am still awake. I am still awake, Lois. I am still awake!

LOIS. Calm down!

ALAN *(after a pause, much calmer).* I'm sorry. *(He pauses.)* It's all that caffeine. It makes me nervous.

LOIS. I know.

ALAN. I lose my concentration.

LOIS. Me too.

ALAN. I lose my concentration.

LOIS. Don't worry.

ALAN. I have to study some more. *(He goes for his books. LOIS stops him.)*

LOIS. No! Trust me. Just close your eyes . . . *(ALAN closes his eyes. After a pause.)* . . . and relax. Think about something else.

(THE CHORUS, ONE, TWO, and THREE, walks onstage.)

LOIS. Are you thinking about something else?

ONE *(after a pause, holding a pen).* This is a pen.

ALAN. Yes.

TWO *(after a pause of about two beats).* A what?

ONE *(after the same length pause).* A pen.

TWO *(after a pause of about two beats).* A what?

ONE *(after the same length pause).* A pen.

TWO *(after a shorter pause, taking the pen from ONE).* Oh, a pen. *(TWO turns and addresses THREE.)* This is a pen.

THREE. A what?

TWO. A pen.

THREE. A what?

TWO. A pen.

THREE. Oh, a pen.

ONE *(to TWO, holding a shoe).* This is a shoe. *(ONE and TWO go through the same dialogue: "A what?" "A shoe." "A what?" "A shoe." "Oh, a shoe." When TWO takes the shoe, he or she immediately turns to THREE and says, "This is a shoe." Simultaneously, ONE—holding a spoon—says, "This is a spoon" to TWO. THREE responds, "A what?" to TWO at the same time that TWO turns and responds, "A what?" to ONE. ONE and TWO, who turns back to THREE, say, "A spoon" and "A shoe." TWO and THREE respond, "Oh, a spoon" and "Oh, a* shoe" *and take the respective objects.* TWO *immediately says,* "This is a spoon" *to* THREE *while* ONE *says,* "This is a match" *to* TWO *and the process repeats with* ONE *presenting objects,* THREE *receiving them, and* TWO *both presenting to* THREE *and receiving from* ONE. *After the match, they pass these objects through the chain: a coin, a cup, a watch, a key, a shirt, a sock, a glass, a book, a bell, the time, a test. Soon after* THE CHORUS *begins to go through this routine,* ALAN *opens his eyes, squints, and shakes his head from side to side. When* ONE *says,* "This is a shirt," LOIS *notices* ALAN *shaking his head back and forth and the following dialogue—all the way down to* ALAN's *line,* "Fine!" *over- laps* THE CHORUS.)

LOIS. What's the matter?

ALAN. It's that drama exercise we did yesterday.

LOIS. What about it?

(With no interruption in the dialogue, PAT *and* CHRIS, *both students, enter and sit in the empty chairs. They notice* ALAN *contort- ing[1] his face and banging his head.)*

ALAN. That's what I'm thinking about.

LOIS. So?

ALAN. It's stuck.

LOIS. What do you mean "it's stuck"?

ALAN. It's stuck in my head.

LOIS. Think about something else.

ALAN. I can't! *(A loud bell rings, signaling the beginning of class.)*

(The TEACHER *enters, carrying tests.)*

TEACHER. Good morning. *(The* STU- DENTS *acknowledge him. He watches* ALAN *for a moment.)* I hope we're all

rested and ready to go. I know I am. There are a couple of things I'd like for you to keep in mind while you take this test. First, you really shouldn't think of this as a test. It is a test, of course, but it's also quite a bit more. *(He has been watching* ALAN *who has been shaking back and forth and hitting the side of his head.)* Alan, are you all right?

ALAN *(a little wildly).* Fine! *(THE CHORUS stops, even if it isn't finished with the list of objects.)*

TEACHER. Good. As I was saying, keep in mind that this isn't only a test. This is your mid-term. How you do today, this morning, will determine to a large extent how you do for the rest of this course. And, of course, how you do in this class has a large impact on your overall grade point which is a major factor in determin- ing what, if any, colleges you might be accepted into. It might help if you didn't think of this as a test so much as you think of it as your future. Your future in . . . *(He looks at his watch.)* fifty-eight minutes. Any last minute questions? *(CHRIS raises a hand.)* Chris?

CHRIS. Uh, what was Thomas Edison's middle name?

TEACHER. Alva. But don't worry. That's not on the test. Anything else? *(A pause)* All right then. Let's get going. *(He hands out the tests, face down.)* Think carefully about each question and be sure not to leave anything blank. Most of the questions come

---

1. contort (kən tôrt′), twist or bend out of shape

right off the review sheets, so if you studied them you'll be fine.

ALAN *(panicked).* Review sheets?

TEACHER. Yes. These. *(He holds up a stack of at least ten sheets of paper, stapled together.)* I handed them out last week. Didn't you get them?

ALAN. No.

TEACHER. Well, I don't know how that could have happened. Were you here last Monday?

ALAN. Of course.

TEACHER. I don't understand. Everyone who *did* get the review sheets, raise your hands. *(The other students raise their hands. The* TEACHER *stares at* ALAN *and shakes his head.)* That's a shame. They might have helped you. *(Pause)* But do your best, Alan. I'm sure you'll do fine. Is everyone ready? You have . . . *(He checks his watch.)* fifty-seven minutes to take this test. Begin. *(The students look at their papers.* PAT *immediately begins to write. A clock starts to tick loudly. It ticks through the entire play.* ALAN *reads his test.)*

VOICE. Section One. Multiple choice. Question One. In what year was the Battle of Hastings? *(Pause)* A: ten-sixty-two.

ALAN. No.

VOICE. B: ten-sixty-three.

ALAN. Nope.

VOICE. C: ten-sixty-four.

ALAN. No.

VOICE. D: ten-sixty-five.

ALAN. No.

VOICE. E: ten-sixty-seven.

ALAN. What? What happened to ten-sixty-six?

PAT *(raising a hand).* May I have another bluebook,[2] please?

TEACHER. Of course. *(He gives a bluebook to* PAT.*)*

ALAN *(frantically).* What happened to ten-sixty-six? *(*CHRIS *raises a hand.)*

TEACHER. Chris?

CHRIS. How much time to do we have left?

TEACHER. Fifty-six minutes.

ALAN. Where is ten-sixty-six?

TEACHER. Something the matter, Alan?

ALAN. No. It's just . . . *(He stares at* THE TEACHER *for a moment.)* I can't answer the first question.

TEACHER. Well, that shouldn't be a problem. It's not worth too much, is it? *(*ALAN *looks at the test.)*

VOICE. Five points.

ALAN. No.

TEACHER. Then just go on to something you do know.

ALAN. But that was all I knew!

TEACHER. Really? Did you study?

ALAN. Yes, I did. I studied all night.

TEACHER. Did you study efficiently?

ALAN. Well . . . yes, I did. I even made a list of all the things I needed to study. *(He stares straight ahead, daydreaming.* PAT *taps a pencil four times to the beat of "This is a test." Pause.* CHRIS *taps "A what?" Pause.* PAT *taps "A test." Pause.* CHRIS *taps "Oh, a test," then:)*

---

2. bluebook (blü′bůk), a small booklet with lined paper and a blue cover, used for taking exams in college and some high schools

ONE. This is a desk. *(And so on while* ALAN *says:)*

ALAN. This desk is a mess. I can't work in a mess like this. I'll just clean everything up and then I'll be able to work.

ONE. This is a phone. *(And so on while* ALAN, *miming the phone, says:)*

ALAN. Oh, hi, Lois. Of course I'm still awake. No, I haven't quite started yet. I had to clean my room.

ONE. This is a book. *(And so on while* ALAN *picks up a book and pretends to read.)*

ALAN. *Flowers of Northern Michigan.* Wow, this is really interesting. I'll get to work in just a minute.

ONE. This is a phone. *(And so on while* ALAN, *miming the phone, says:)*

ALAN. Hi, Lois. No, I haven't done . . . a whole lot.

ONE. This is a Mork.

TWO and THREE *(sincerely puzzled).* A what?

ONE. A Mork.

ALAN *(staring at an imaginary television).* And Mindy! My favorite show.

TWO and THREE. A what?

ALAN. What's it doing on at two in the morning?

ONE. A Mork.

ALAN. I'll just watch it for a quick study break.

TWO and THREE *(sarcastically).* Oh, a Mork.

ONE. This is a phone. *(And so on while* ALAN, *miming the phone, says:)*

ALAN. Hi, Lois. 'Course I'm still awake. How's my studying going?

ONE. This is a lie.

ALAN. Great.

TWO and THREE. A what?

ALAN. It's going just great.

ONE. A lie.

TWO and THREE. A what?

ALAN. Study, study, study.

ONE. A lie.

ALAN. I'll see you in a few hours.

TWO and THREE. Oh, a lie.

ALAN. It's five in the morning.

ONE. This is the pits. *(And so on while* ALAN *stares blankly.)*

TEACHER *(after "oh, the pits," putting a hand on* ALAN's *shoulder and shaking him gently).* Alan? *(Pause)* Alan. *(*ALAN *looks up.)* This is a test.

ONE, TWO and THREE *(softly).* A what?

TEACHER. You seem to be daydreaming. Don't you think you should be writing something?

ALAN. Yes, of course. That first question threw me a bit is all. *(He smiles weakly.)*

TEACHER. Glad to hear it.

ALAN *(to himself).* Now concentrate. *(*CHRIS *raises a hand.)*

TEACHER. Chris? *(*ALAN *looks a bit annoyed.)*

CHRIS. How much time do we have left?

TEACHER. Fifty-three minutes.

ALAN *(to himself).* Concentrate. And remember, it could be worse. Sometimes caffeine doesn't just confuse me. Sometimes it actually makes me . . . paranoid.

(As ALAN *tries to concentrate,* PAT *slowly leans over and looks at* LOIS's *test.* LOIS *seems to be aware of this, but doesn't stop it.*

ALAN *glances over to see* PAT *doing this and* PAT *immediately stops.* ALAN *looks horrified, but continues to try to concentrate. As he works,* CHRIS *slowly takes off his/her watch and begins to read something off the back of it. Again,* ALAN *catches him/her in the act and* CHRIS *quickly puts the watch back on. One by one, each of the* STUDENTS, *except* ALAN, *develops a mannerism which is probably, though not initially certainly, a signal to at least one of the others.* LOIS *might, for example, begin to thumb her nose. After noticing this,* PAT *might develop a significant sounding cough.* CHRIS *might tap a pencil on the desk in ways that seem less and less random. And so on.*

In addition to developing an idiosyncrasy,[3] each STUDENT *should occasionally notice what another* STUDENT *is doing and subtly acknowledge it or write down some information—all except* ALAN *who is becoming more and more agitated by what's going on around him. He looks at the other* STUDENTS *and then up at the* TEACHER *who always seems to be looking in the wrong place—glancing over someone's shoulder, perhaps, or just not paying attention. Finally, when he's certain that he's caught one of his classmates signaling to another,* ALAN *raises his hand to attract the* TEACHER*'s attention.)*

TEACHER *(pleasantly).* Alan?

ALAN. I was just curious about something . . . that I forgot to ask. *(He hesitates.)*

TEACHER. Yes?

ALAN. Is this test going to be graded on a curve?

TEACHER *(cheerfully, matter-of-factly).* Yes, of course. The better everyone else does, the worse you'll do.

ALAN. Thank you. *(The* TEACHER *nods and then turns away. As* ALAN *starts to work,* PAT *takes out semaphore flags[4] and begins to calmly, with almost mechanical movements, send signals to the other* STUDENTS. ALAN *notices and watches, horrified, as the other* STUDENTS *watch and take down answers. The* TEACHER *doesn't notice. After this has gone on for a while,* CHRIS *pulls out a flashlight from his vest, points it at the other students, and begins to click it on and off, sending Morse code messages which everyone but* ALAN *dutifully copies down. Finally,* LOIS *removes a large sign from underneath her desk or, better yet, she removes the entire top of the desk, on the bottom of which is a sign that says, "The answer to six is 'The Gaza Strip.'"* LOIS *waves the sign once to everyone. all, except* ALAN, *see it and copy it down.* ALAN *has seen what's happened and is horrified but he doesn't notice until it's too late to get the answer. He is panicked.)* It's what? The answer to number six is what?

TEACHER *(suspiciously).* Question, Alan?

ALAN. No!

TEACHER. There's nothing you want to ask me or . . . *(With much meaning)* anyone else?

ALAN. No.

TEACHER. I'm sure I don't have to remind anyone here that we're all on our honor. *(Pause)* Not that it makes any sense to cheat anyway because when you think about it, when you

---

3. idiosyncrasy (id′ē ə sing′krə sē), a strange or unusual way of behaving
4. semaphore flags (sem′ə fôr′), flags used for sending signals. Each position of the flags has its own meaning

really think about it, who is it that you're really hurting when you cheat?

CHRIS *(raising a hand, with much sincerity)*. You're really only hurting yourself, sir.

TEACHER. That's right, Chris. You're really only hurting yourself. I'm glad you feel that way. *(He turns his back on* CHRIS.*)* All right, let's get back to work. *(*CHRIS *holds up a sign that says, "Hurt me" to* PAT. PAT *holds up a sign that says "2D is False." * CHRIS *holds up a sign that says "Hurt me more." * PAT *holds up a sign that says "7 is Truman." * ALAN *has been staring back and forth in open-mouthed astonishment. Suddenly, the* TEACHER *spins around.* CHRIS *and* PAT *both still have their signs up.)*

TEACHER. Well! I see we can't all keep our eyes on our own papers, can we . . . Mr. Lefenfeld?

ALAN. What?

TEACHER. Eyes on your own paper, Alan. I don't want to have to speak to you again.

ALAN. No, sir. *(To himself)* Don't pay any attention to them. Concentrate. Concentrate and ignore them. Go on to the next section.

VOICE. Section Two. True or false.

ALAN *(to himself)*. Yes, much better. This is more my speed.

VOICE. Number One. Explain the nature of the universe.

ALAN. What? Wait a minute. That's not true or false. *(He frantically looks around, then looks down at his paper and mouths the words as the* VOICE *says:)*

VOICE. Explain the nature of the universe.

ALAN *(having no idea what to do)*. I . . . I don't know. *(Pause)* Next question.

VOICE. Athens.

ALAN. What?

VOICE. Athens.

ALAN. Athens? *(Pause)* Athens. *(Pause)* False. Athens is false.

VOICE. Renaissance.

ALAN *(after a pause)*. True.

VOICE. Geometry.

ALAN. True.

VOICE. Thomas Edison.

ALAN. False.

VOICE. One hundred and twelve.

ALAN *(growing more and more frenzied)*. True.

VOICE. Athletic ability.

ALAN. False.

VOICE. Biceps.

ALAN. False.

VOICE. Facial hair.

ALAN. False!

VOICE. Social life.

ALAN. False! *(Pause. Calmer, but panting a bit.)* This isn't so hard. *(Pause)* Wait a minute! I have a social life. I've had dates. *(Pause)* I've had a date. *(Pause)*

ONE. This is a date *(and so on)*. This is a girl *(and so on)*. *(The girl may be represented by a Barbie doll, a mannequin, or a real girl.)* This is a zit *(and so on, while* ALAN, *grabbing a spot on his face, says:)*

ALAN. Why? Why always before a date?

ONE. This is a dance *(and so on, while* ALAN *says:)*

ALAN. I hate dancing. I'm a terrible dancer.

ONE. This is a hand *(and so on, while* ALAN *says:)*

ALAN *(pretending to hold a hand).* Does her hand always sweat this much?

ONE. This is a kiss *(and so on, while* ALAN *says:)*

ALAN. Stop it. This is so embarrassing.

ONE. This is a kiss *(and so on, while* ALAN *says:)*

ALAN. Still. Still the same kiss?

ONE. This is a kiss *(and so on. The* TEACHER *and the other* STUDENTS *notice that* ALAN *is talking to himself.)*

ALAN. Still going? Listen, I think I'm in a little over my head here.

ONE. This is a breast *(and so on, while* ALAN *says:)*

ALAN. Put that away! I don't know what to do with it!

ONE. This is a faint *(and so on, while* ALAN *says:)*

ALAN *(defensively).* I did *not* faint. I just passed out momentarily!

ONE. This is his heart *(and so on. The response here is "His what?" one holds, then slowly rips in half a large paper valentine heart, while* ALAN *says:)*

ALAN *(desperately, almost angrily).* Go ahead. Break my heart! It's only flesh!

TEACHER. Alan?

ALAN *(a little wildly).* What?

TEACHER. Are you all right?

ALAN. I'm fine! *(To himself.)* Now concentrate. Think hard. (CHRIS *raises a hand.)*

TEACHER. Chris.

CHRIS. How much time do we have left?

ALAN *(to* CHRIS, *yelling).* Would you stop that! Why don't you get a watch? Some of us are trying to concentrate here and it's almost impossible with you asking the time every five minutes!

TEACHER. Alan, what is the matter with you?

ALAN *(suddenly meek).* I'm sorry. That's not really like me, is it?

TEACHER. Not at all.

ALAN *(addressing everyone).* I'm really sorry. I don't know what came over me. I'm calm now. *(To* CHRIS) What was it you wanted to know?

CHRIS. How much time do we have left?

TEACHER. Nine minutes.

ALAN. What? What happened to the last forty-five minutes?

TEACHER. They passed.

ALAN. Already?

TEACHER. Yes.

ALAN. Are you sure?

TEACHER. Lois, how much time do we have left?

LOIS *(looking at her watch).* Eight minutes.

TEACHER. Is everyone almost finished? *(all but* ALAN *ad lib "just about," etc.)* How much more do you have to do, Alan?

ALAN *(flipping through at least six pages that he hasn't gotten to, lying).* A little bit.

(EVAN walks in with a football sticking out of his backpack.)

TEACHER. Hello, Evan.

EVAN. Hi, Teach. Sorry I'm late. I was at practice.

TEACHER. No problem. *(He hands a test to* EVAN.*)* Here's the test. I'll tell you what. You don't really have time to take it. Why don't you just look it over and see how you would have done.

EVAN *(looking at the test, nodding his head occasionally).* Mmm-hmm. Yeah. Yup. *(Pause)* I think I know all but the second to the last one.

TEACHER. Which one? Oh, that's a hard one. Here, let me show you. *(He takes* EVAN*'s paper and begins to write on it.* ALAN *looks on, disgusted.)*

EVAN. Uh-huh. Yeah. Okay. That's pretty much what I would have put.

TEACHER. Is it?

EVAN. Yup.

TEACHER *(skeptically).* Is it really?

EVAN. Uh-huh.

TEACHER *(convinced).* All right, then. Nicely done. *(He writes on* EVAN*'s test with red ink.)* One hundred percent. Congratulations. See you in class tomorrow. *(EVAN starts to leave.)*

ALAN. Wait a minute!

TEACHER. Alan?

ALAN. That's not fair!

TEACHER. I beg your pardon?

ALAN. He didn't answer the questions.

TEACHER. But he knew the answers.

ALAN. That's what he told you!

TEACHER. Alan, are you doubting the word of one of your classmates?

ALAN. Well . . . no.

TEACHER. Evan always gets hundreds. You know that.

ALAN. I know, but . . .

TEACHER. Besides . . . it really doesn't matter what Evan gets on his tests anymore.

ALAN. Why not?

TEACHER. Because he was recently admitted to the college of his choice.

ALAN *(to* EVAN*).* You were?

EVAN. Yeah. Early decision.

ALAN. To where?

TEACHER. Majestica University. I believe that's the school you were going to apply to, wasn't it, Alan?

ALAN. What? How? How could they let him in already?

TEACHER. Alan, do I detect within you the . . . green and withering voice of envy?

ALAN. No. Well, yes, of course. *(To* EVAN*)* I mean, I'm happy for you, but . . . It just seems so early.

TEACHER. I don't want to hear a word about it. Evan has worked hard and this is his reward.

ALAN. But it's only October.

TEACHER. Not another word.

ALAN *(despondently[5]).* But we're only sophomores.

TEACHER. I don't want to hear it. Back to work.

ALAN *(to himself).* He's only a sophomore and he's already into Majestica. I'll never get in there. I'm not a good student. *(Pause)* Or a good athlete. And I'm funny looking.

ONE. This is his face *(and so on, while* THREE *draws the outline of a face on the*

---

5. despondently (di spän′dənt lē), in an unhappy, hopeless manner

chalkboard. The responses in this section are "His what?").

ONE. This is his nose *(and so on, while* THREE *draws an exaggeration of* ALAN*'s nose).*

ONE. These are his ears *(and so on, while* THREE *draws an enormous set of ears).*

ONE. This is his mouth *(and so on, while* THREE *draws a mouth, perhaps with large buck teeth).*

ONE. This is his hair *(and so on, while* THREE *draws wild hair).*

ONE. This is his skin *(and so on, while* TWO *and* THREE *draw spots all over the face and one labels the picture "Alan").*

TEACHER *(overlapping "This is his skin").* And remember, how you do today can affect your whole future.

ALAN. My future?

ONE. This is your life *(and so on, holding and then passing a sign that says "dull" in large block letters, while* ALAN *says:)*

ALAN *(despondently).* My future.

ONE. This is your job *(and so on, passing a sign that says "duller").*

ONE. This is your town *(and so on, passing a sign that says "dullsville").*

ONE. This is your wife *(and so on, passing a sign that says "dullard").*

PAT. May I have two more bluebooks, please?

ALAN *(slowly, with building sadness).* It's true. My future is bleak. I'm a terrible student and everybody knows it. *(Pause)* I'm not an athlete. I don't debate. Or play chess. I'm funny looking. All my library books are overdue. I don't have any friends. I'm an orphan. *(Pause)* Well, I have

parents but they probably don't like me very much. I wouldn't either. *(Pause)* Wait a minute. Snap out of it. Quit feeling sorry for yourself. You have plenty of fine qualities. *(A long pause)* What about my singing? Just last week Mrs. Mandell said that my voice had great potential. "With a little training," she said, "you could have been a very fine tenor." Those were her exact words. "A very fine tenor." And that's something that makes me different. It's just one example of the many fine qualities that make me unique. I can always remember that no matter what happens, I have my music to make me just a little bit special.

PAT *(to the tune of Hallelujah).* Mr. Williams!

TEACHER. Yes, Pat?

PAT, CHRIS and LOIS *(strongly, in unison, to the tune of Hallelujah).* Mr. Williams!

TEACHER. Class?

PAT, CHRIS and LOIS *(to the tune of the line "And heav'n and nature sing" from* Joy to the World*).* May we have another blue . . . May we have another blue . . . May we ha-a-a-ave another bluebook, please? (ALAN *puts his head down on his desk.)*

TEACHER. Well, of course you may. That was lovely. Thank you very much. And I'll tell you what. Just for that, everyone who sang is going to get ten points extra credit. *(He makes a mark on* PAT*'s,* CHRIS*'s, and* LOIS*'s papers while handing them the bluebooks.)*

ALAN *(to himself).* Don't pay any atten-

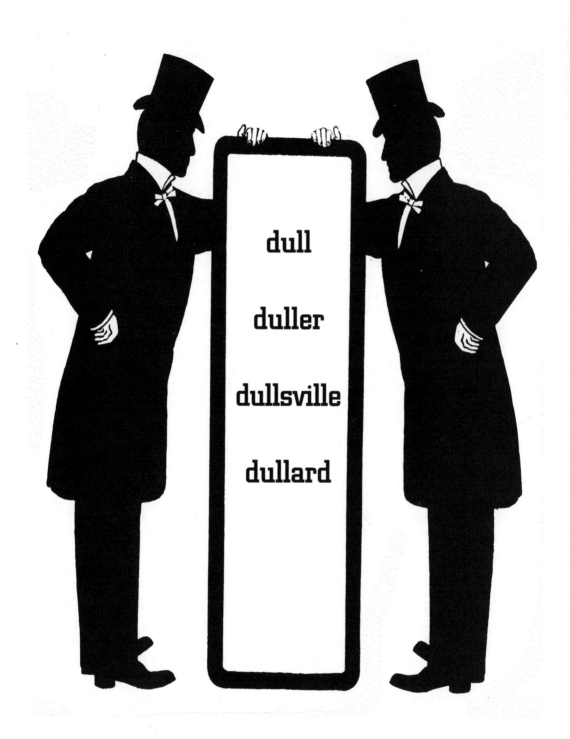

dull

duller

dullsville

dullard

This Is a Test by Stephen Gregg

tion to them. They are not your concern. Concentrate. What's the next question?

VOICE. Question Four. Essay question. Thirty points.

ALAN. Uh-oh.

VOICE. Opinion essay.

ALAN. Opinion essay! This is a breeze.

ONE. This is a breeze. (ALAN *shakes his head. The chorus members shake their heads.*)

TWO. This is a sneeze.

THREE. This is a cheese.

ONE. This is Louise.

TWO. This is Chinese.

ALAN. Stop it! (*He reads the test, looks puzzled, then panicked.*) Oh, no. (*He reads again.*) Oh, no. (*He calls over the teacher.*) Mr. Williams!

TEACHER. Yes?

ALAN. This essay question.

TEACHER. What about it?

ALAN. It's in Chinese.

TEACHER. Yes?

ALAN. I don't speak Chinese.

TEACHER. And why is that?

ALAN. I speak . . . English.

TEACHER. And why don't you speak Chinese?

ALAN. I've never learned it.

TEACHER. Never?

ALAN. No.

TEACHER. This may be something to take up with the Attendance Committee.

ALAN. Attendance! I'm never absent. You know that.

TEACHER (*opening the attendance book*).

Oh? What about last Tuesday?

ALAN. Tuesday . . . Oh, that's right. I missed this period. I had a dental appointment.

TEACHER. I thought so. (*Pause*) We learned Chinese on Tuesday.

ALAN. The only day I ever missed.

TEACHER. I am sorry. But you know the policy on making up work. (*He recites.*) "All students are responsible for all classwork missed for any reason including medical emergencies, family vacations and dental appointments." I'm very sorry about that, Alan. Or should I say, "Ning chok no quo, Alan."

PAT. Ni how fan shen kik? (May I have another bluebook, please?)

TEACHER (*handing a bluebook to* PAT). Tau.

CHRIS. Da lee hen wah? (How much time is left?)

TEACHER (*looking at his watch and holding up five fingers*). Nye ma.

ALAN. Wait! This can't be happening! This is a nightmare. (*He puts his head on his desk. The lights dim, except for a spot on* ALAN. *All, except* ALAN, *wobble back and forth, then crumple forward, motionless.*) This is a nightmare.

(MOTHER *enters from offstage as the ticking stops. She taps* ALAN *gently on the shoulder.*)

MOTHER. Alan?

ALAN. Mom?

MOTHER. You were dreaming.

ALAN. Was I?

MOTHER. You fell asleep at your desk.

ALAN (*still groggy*). I guess you're right.

MOTHER. What were you dreaming about?

ALAN. It's dumb. I was taking a test. I didn't know any of the answers.

MOTHER. Son, you worry too much.

ALAN. I know.

MOTHER. Are you still studying for that test tomorrow?

ALAN. Uh-huh.

MOTHER. I can't believe how hard you've been working.

ALAN. It's a huge test. I don't know the stuff at all.

MOTHER. You always say that and you always do fine.

ALAN (sarcastically). Yeah.

MOTHER. Don't you have the best grades in the class?

ALAN (shrugging it off). I don't know.

MOTHER (prodding). Alan?

ALAN. I guess. But Evan's pretty close.

MOTHER. Don't worry about it. Just do your best. That's all we ask. (She smiles.) Besides . . .

ALAN. What?

MOTHER. I have a surprise for you downstairs.

ALAN (sniffing). Cookies.

MOTHER. And something else.

ALAN. What?

MOTHER. It's downstairs.

ALAN. What is it?

MOTHER. An envelope.

ALAN. From who?

MOTHER. Majestica University.

ALAN. Yeah?

MOTHER. It's an awfully thick envelope.

ALAN (excitedly). Really?

MOTHER (kissing ALAN on the forehead). Congratulations. You got in, and we're very proud of you.

ALAN (dazed). Thanks.

MOTHER (walking to the side of the stage). How about those cookies? (The lights snap back up. MOTHER jumps offstage. all are instantly as they were before. The ticking resumes, even faster than it was before.)

TEACHER. How about some answers, Alan?

ALAN. What?

TEACHER. You'd better stop daydreaming if you want to have a chance of passing this. (The sound of a heartbeat comes up as ALAN begins to breathe hard.)

ALAN. Oh, no!

TEACHER. What's the matter?

ALAN. I'm almost done and I haven't answered anything!

TEACHER. Have you tried all the questions?

ALAN. No. I skipped some of them.

TEACHER. Why don't you go back and look at the ones you skipped.

ALAN (dejectedly). All right.

VOICE. Section one. Multiple choice. Question Two. Which of the following students . . .

ALAN. Students?

VOICE. . . . is most likely to be accepted to Majestica University? A: Lois Flan. B: Elizabeth Zimmerman. C: Carlos O'Neill. D: Anthony Montagu. E: Alan Lefenfeld.

ALAN. I don't know. (Pause) Elizabeth is

pretty smart, but her grades aren't as good as Carlos's. I think they're a little better than mine . . .

VOICE. Hint. It's not Alan Lefenfeld.

ALAN (*despondently*). Next question.

VOICE. Question Three. Which of Alan Lefenfeld's shortcomings do you find most annoying? (*Pause*) A: The way he shuffles when he walks. B: His poor posture. C: His bad breath. (*ALAN slaps his hand over his mouth.*) D: His irritating laugh. E: His sloppy attire. (*After a long pause, ALAN looks at the test, then turns to the next page.*) F: His whiny little voice. G: His bizarre sense of humor. H: His dismal standardized test scores. I: . . . (*Pause*) . . . The extremely embarrassing personal problem which Alan confided to the school counselor, Mrs. Fennelmeyer. (*Slight pause while ALAN looks up and then back down.*) Parentheses. Who is, by the way, a bit of a gossip but a wonderful cook.

ALAN. I hate this. I hate this test!

TEACHER. What's the matter now, Alan?

ALAN. I object to the third multiple choice question!

LOIS. Me, too.

CHRIS. I do, too.

ALAN. It's biased and it's mean.

LOIS. And it's too hard. (*To CHRIS*) I can't pick just one of these.

ALAN (*rattled*). And furthermore, It's subjective[6] . . .

PAT. And incomplete.

CHRIS. This must just be a partial list. (*LOIS, PAT and CHRIS ad lib agreement,*

along with suggestions for other possible answers.*)

TEACHER. All right, calm down. I'll tell you what. Let's strike the question and, to keep the number of points the same, why don't we say that Question . . . (*He looks through the test.*) . . . Nineteen is worth twice as much now. Okay?

ALAN (*thumbing through the pages*). Question Nineteen.

VOICE. Question Nineteen. Ten poi . . . (*The voice makes a squawking sound as ALAN scratches out the words "Ten Points" and writes "Twenty Points." Pause.*) Who was Saladin?

ALAN. Finally!

VOICE. What did his name mean?

ALAN. I know this!

VOICE. Where was he born?

ALAN (*throwing up his arms in joy*). Thank you! (*A bell rings and keeps ringing. The TEACHER, who was near ALAN's desk, snatches the test from his desk.*)

TEACHER. Kai foo len hee!

ALAN (*while the TEACHER grabs the other tests*). Wait!

TEACHER. Kai foo len hee which . . . (*He looks at ALAN.*) translated means what, Lois?

LOIS. Time's up. Kai foo len hee. (*The others begin to converse in Chinese as they gather up their books.*)

TEACHER (*He overlaps the STUDENTS and no matter where he is in the speech, he*

---

6. subjective (s-b jekåtiv) influenced by personal feelings; not objective

should stop talking when ALAN *shouts, "This is the end."*) Now I didn't want to tell you this earlier because I didn't want to make you nervous. I've decided it's too much work for me to make up these tests all the time so, instead of counting this as a midterm, I'm going to let it serve as your final. How you did on this test will determine your grade for this semester and, probably, for the entire year. It's just too much work for me to have to sit down and write out all these tests and then grade them and then hand them back so we'll just say that whatever grade you got here is the grade you get for the course.

VOICE (*This overlaps with the Chinese conversation and the* TEACHER *and should begin when the* TEACHER *says, "I've decided."*) This concludes our test of your emergency information retrieval system. The teachers in your area, in voluntary cooperation with parents, the School Board, and local authorities, have combined to bring you this test. We now resume our regularly scheduled life.

ALAN (*He overlaps with everything else and should overlap with the very end of the* VOICE*'s lines, shouting over the noise*). This is the end!

Instant Blackout

This Is a Test

Responding to the Play

1. Have you ever had an experience similar to Alan's? Compare what happened to you in this situation.
2. What do you think the Voice should sound like? Why?
3. Analyze Stephen Gregg's writing style. Use a chart to evaluate the language, sentence structure, characterization, and tone of the play.
4. With a partner, choose a scene involving the chorus, and discuss how you would handle the timing.
5. Write *Dull, Duller, Dullsville*, and *Dullard* as you think they should be written for display during the play. Share your calligraphy with the class.

More About Timing

There is a lot going on in this play, so discussion, planning, and practice will be necessary to work out the timing of each scene. The series of statements—*This is a test. Oh, a test.*—and the question—*A what?* —performed by the Chorus require cooperation, concentration, and exact timing. Since the middle person, Two, must both present and receive an object, his or her task is doubly difficult. And because only one object or idea is going through the line at a time, the first person, One, can control the pace. He or she may occasionally need to pause to let Alan finish what he's saying. On the other hand, Alan must be sure to time his lines so as not to interfere with those of the Chorus.

CREATING AND PERFORMING

1. In groups of four, practice the scene on pages 225–226 in which the Chorus passes along a shoe, a spoon, and other objects. Compare your version to those of others in the class.
2. With a partner, work out a scene between Alan and the Voice. Share it with the class.
3. Write a short scene about going to the dentist using a style similar to *This Is a Test*.

Before Reading

The Frog Prince

The Play as Literature: Dialogue

The *dialogue,* or conversation, between the people in a story is one way we learn what the story is about. In a novel or short story, we may learn less from the characters' dialogue than from the way the narrator describes their actions and way of speaking. In a play, however, the characters' own words reveal the meaning of the story. By paying attention to the dialogue and the way it is spoken, we learn about what is being discussed and the people who are speaking.

Considered a master of dialogue, David Mamet is noted for strong male characters who engage in highly charged verbal give and take. As you read *The Frog Prince*, be aware of the dialogue between the Prince and the other characters in the play.

The Play as Theatre: Voice

An actor's voice—the pitch, speed, rhythm, accents, and clarity of his or her speech—are very important in bringing a character to life. When trying to develop an idea for a character's voice, ask questions about the character. "What do the character's words tell me about the way he or she might speak?" "What instructions does the playwright give about the character's voice?" "Do other characters mention this character's voice or way of speaking?" Once you have gathered all your information, you can begin to investigate how voice captures a character's emotions. Then you can think about how your own voice might be made to suit a certain character.

Warm Up!

Your voice comes through the larynx, or voice box, but it is powered by your lungs and diaphragm. The diaphragm is a layer of muscles and tendons that separate the two cavities of the chest and abdomen. The more you use your diaphragm, the stronger your voice becomes. Practice breathing with the diaphragm by placing your hand just below your rib cage. Inhale slowly, to a count of eight, and feel your diaphragm expand. Exhale, and feel it contract.

THE FROG PRINCE

by David Mamet

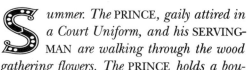

SETTING	CHARACTERS	TIME
A wood	**THE PRINCE** **A SERVINGMAN** (BILL) **PEASANT WOMAN** **A MILKMAID** (GRACE)	Long, long ago

SCENE ONE

Summer. *The* PRINCE, *gaily attired in a Court Uniform, and his* SERVINGMAN *are walking through the wood gathering flowers. The* PRINCE *holds a bouquet. The* SERVINGMAN *hurries about engaged in the actual picking of the flowers.*

PRINCE. Huh. I don't think I've ever been in this part of the Forest before. *(Pause)* It's nice . . .

SERVINGMAN. Yes, it is, Sire.

PRINCE. And what a *day*, huh . . . ?

SERVINGMAN. Absolutely, Sire.

PRINCE. A *day* . . . a *day* . . .

SERVINGMAN. . . . an exceptional day.

PRINCE. Yes. An exceptional day. And a *portentous*[1] day. Enough said about that! You know what I want? A blue flower. Something blue. A touch of blue. I want to tell you something, Bill: what we *need*, what we *need* in life (and *art* is a part of life—and flower arrangement is a part of art—the Japanese have a word for it. Which I've forgotten. It's a two-syllable word. Something like "Kamooka"[2] —a long discipline intended, no doubt, to get you in touch with yourself . . .) What you need in *art*, and what you need

in a *bouquet*, in short, is what you need in *life*.

SERVINGMAN. And what is that, Sire . . . ?

PRINCE. Thank you. *Contrast.* Eh? Contrast and balance. Call it Fire and Water. Call it, I don't know, call it *thrust* and equilibrium[3] . . . whatever you call it. You need both of 'em. You need 'em both.

SERVINGMAN *(handing him his blue flower)*. Your blue flower, Sire.

PRINCE. . . . who knew this stuff just grew wild . . .

SERVINGMAN. . . . for The Fair Patricia . . .

PRINCE. . . . I mean of course we all know they grow wild. How *else* would they grow . . . ? It's just, you know, you get them at the *florist's*, it's *one* thing. It's a mercantile transaction. You pick 'em out *here* and it's so *personal*.

(Pause)

---

1. portentous (pôr ten′təs), foreshadowing a coming event
2. Kamooka (kə mü kə), The Prince is probably referring to *Ikebana*, the Japanese art of flower arranging. *Ikebana* tries to represent elements of sky, earth, and mankind in a well-balanced relationship.
3. equilibrium (ē′kwə lib′rē əm), a state of adjustment between opposing forces

SERVINGMAN. It is, Sire.

PRINCE. And you know what *else?* I want to tell you something, Bill: It has an element of *fear* in it. Don't you feel that?

SERVINGMAN. I do.

PRINCE. Hey, you're a cheap date. You know that? But it *does* nonetheless . . . snuffing out a *life* . . . I mean, these things are *breeding* out here. Who knows *why* . . . ? It's awesome. *(Pause)* Huh? They're so *promiscuous* . . . all the time . . . *who* knows why? Who knows to what purpose they're put here, all the time, feast and famine, liberal, conservative, *they* don't care. They don't care. You know why they don't?

SERVINGMAN. Why, Sire?

PRINCE. 'Cause they're in tune with *Nature.*

(An OLD PEASANT WOMAN walks through the forest near them.)

Ah! An Old Peasant Woman! Gathering . . . who knows what, huh? Some . . . some *plants* for some herbal *remedy* . . . some, some long lost wisdom, I don't know . . . to cure an aching *tooth,* who knows, some *daffodils* to grace her grandson's *nuptial* bed . . . huh?

SERVINGMAN. Yes, Sire.

PRINCE. . . . for the upcoming day of his Happy Marriage. Just as in *whose* case . . . ? *Exactly.* So you see what's on my mind. *(He expatiates[4] on the bouquet he holds.)* A bouquet for my sweet Patricia. Flowers. Picked by Hand. Out of love. For you, My Fair Patricia. *(Pause)* May we . . . may we in our Married State be closely bound as the buds are in this bouquet: Individual, separate, each having its own life, and its *own* destiny . . . but each *united* into something *larger* than itself. By God, I *like* that. I'm going to tell her that when I give her these flowers. You got a pencil . . . ? I swear, walking outside brings out the best in you. *(The SERVINGMAN hands the PRINCE a pencil. The PRINCE starts writing down his encomium.[5])* I think it's something like a carburetor: You got to get the air in you to burn the fuel correctly.

SERVINGMAN. Sire—

PRINCE. What?

SERVINGMAN. Would Your Highness like someone to gather daffodils to grace Your Highness's Nuptial Sheets?

PRINCE. Yes, I would, Bill. I would. But it would have either to be a spontaneous *gesture,* eh? Arising out of an *impulse,* eh? *Unheralded* on someone's part . . . an, let's say, an *artistic impulse,* a spontaneous impulse on the part—excuse me here—but it would of necessity need be someone of my own *class,* don't you think? Or it would be puhrutty pre*sump*tive,[6] don't you think? *Or, or* . . . see what I'm saying, if someone in my own class, through an excess of *zeal* got thrown back to some, some atavistic[7]

---

4. expatiate (ek spā′shē āt), to speak at length
5. encomium (en kō′mē əm), enthusiastic praise
6. presumptive (prə zump′tiv), too bold or out of place, and thus unbecoming
7. atavistic (a/tə vis′tik), showing parts that are typical of ancestors more remote than parents; throwback

The Frog Prince by David Mamet   **243**

thing. Or, or it would have to be, say, if it were a *ritual* the *peasants* had. Do you know what I mean—which ones are the daffodils? (BILL *shows him.*) They're nice. I like them. Yes. If it were an old *ritual,* and, gosh, I don't know . . . if the *peasants,* out of *joy* at the Plighting of my Troth (whatever *that* may mean . . .) eh? To The Fair Patricia, out of jubilation at the uniting of our Kingdoms, and the implied *peace,* good *humor* and *prosperity,* so on, that that may bring; if they dug deep into their past and came up with this custom *just for us.* To make us feel a *part* of things . . . what do you think? Or out of raptures at her beauty. They could do that. That could happen . . .

SERVINGMAN. Sire; The Fair Patricia is possessed of beauty bordering on the Ideal . . . the more so for that it shines from within.

PRINCE. Yeah. And she's a good kid, too. Don't you think?

SERVINGMAN. Yes. I do, Sire.

PRINCE. No. Tell me seriously.

SERVINGMAN. No, I do.

PRINCE. You aren't just *saying* that . . . ? I mean, *you're* gonna have to live with her, too. *(Pause)* Bill . . . ? Well, *I* think she's exceptional. What do the *People* think?

SERVINGMAN. They love her as yourself.

PRINCE. They love her as myself, they do?

SERVINGMAN. They've taken her *completely* to their hearts.

PRINCE. Yeah? I couldn't get an honest opinion out of you with a Smith and Wesson . . . just kidding. You're a pal,

and I appreciate it.

(The PEASANT WOMAN *walks near to them.)*

Madam! *(What do they say . . . ?)* Mother! Good Mother . . . *(To* BILL*)* Oh! Oh! Oh! I got it! I got it! You don't know me. You don't know me. Okay . . . ? *(To* PEASANT WOMAN*)* Hola, Good Mother! And how doth the day find you? And what a *lovely* day it is! *(Pause)* I'm but a traveler from Across the Forest who's come here seeking to ply his trade and better his lot. What news is hereabouts? *(Pause)* What occurrences of note? *(Pause)* What's in the air, if you get my drift? Uh . . . rumors of the *Court* . . . *(Pause)* Royal *Marriages* . . . That sort of thing . . . didn't I hear the *Prince* was getting married? Which, as we all know, must needs affect us all . . . What sort of a guy is he? And how do the countryfolk take to his fiancée, who I have heard is called The Fair Patricia . . . ?

PEASANT. Are those flowers for me?

PRINCE. Um, *no.*

PEASANT. But you have picked them in my field.

PRINCE. I have?

PEASANT. Yes.

PRINCE. Well. Okay. It's actually not your field. It's part of the boundary of the Royal Wood, but if you feel I've trespassed on some land you, by "usage," have come to view as yours, I understand.

PEASANT. Are they for me?

PRINCE. No. I've *told* you.

PEASANT *(pause).* Who are they for?

PRINCE. A friend of mine, what's it to you?

PEASANT. I want them.

PRINCE. Tough.

PEASANT. Give them to me.

(Pause)

PRINCE *(to* SERVINGMAN). *She's* a rare old bird—*(To* PEASANT*)* Well, you know, I *would* give 'em to you, I would, but I made a *promise* over them. I, I made a sort of, they're for someone *close* to me. I made a sort of a little *prayer* over them. Now, if you like, my friend will *pick* you some? Would you like that? Bill . . . ? *(To* PEASANT*)* How is that?

PEASANT. Those flowers must be an offering.

PRINCE. Well, they are, sort of.

PEASANT. For me.

PRINCE. No, I can't do that. I've told you that. Bill! Give the Good Woman a coin. *(To* PEASANT*)* Go buy something nice.

PEASANT. Those flowers you must offer me, or you will dwell in misery.

SERVINGMAN. See here: You have just broken the law. You have Threatened and Insulted . . .

PRINCE. It's okay. Bill, Bill . . . Alright. *(To* PEASANT*)* Look. Look here: I've been kind of joking around. *Actually* I'm the Prince. It's alright. I'm not mad at you. I picked the flowers for my Betrothed. The Fair Patricia. Alright? And I said a sort of silly little *prayer* over them that the F.P. and I would be happy. *(Pause)* Now would you *really* want me to go and give these flowers to someone else? Now? Knowing who they're for? *(To* SERV-INGMAN*)* Give her the money . . .

PEASANT. Those flowers you must offer me, or you will dwell in misery.

PRINCE. Okay, now that's not funny anymore. I'm understandably all *full* of things these days and I'm very *suggestible* and susceptible. Alright? To all sorts of malevolent[8] *influences* and *suggestions* so you just take back what you said. Okay? I'm not *giving* you the flowers, and unless *you* retract your curse I'm going to throw your tush in jail. Can I make it more clear than that? *(Pause)* Eh? *(Pause)* Alright! Well, that's fine! No? *(Pause)* Bill? I think that I've had enough fresh *air* today . . . when we get back I want her taken *care* of. Get it? In fact, you hurry back and tell the Captain of the Guard I got an *errand* for him. He'll know what I mean. *(The* PRINCE *starts off with the* SERVING-MAN. *Sotto.*[9]*)* Just kidding. Thought I'd throw a little *scare* into her. *(To* PEASANT*)* And one last thought I'd like to leave you with: *Monarchy* . . .

PEASANT. Those flowers you must offer me, or you will dwell in misery.

PRINCE. You're pushing your luck, Babe. *(Pause)* You really are, and you just wait 'til these big *brawny* types get down here with their *pickaxes,* you're gonna be whistlin' a different *tune.* You see there's such a thing as *civility* . . .

PEASANT. Those flowers . . .

PRINCE. I'm not going to *give* you the flowers . . .

(A big flash. The PRINCE *is changed into a frog.)*

---

8. malevolent (ma lev′ə lent), showing ill will or hatred
9. sotto (sä tō), under the breath, softly

PEASANT. You shall remain in this vile form until a pure and honest woman of her own free will shall plant a selfless kiss upon your lips. At that time you shall be restored, but should you tell her of your former state you shall remain a frog forever. *Sic Transit Gloria Mundi.*[10] You should never have come into my part of the forest.

SCENE TWO

Fall. The PRINCE *(now a frog) and a* MILKMAID.

PRINCE. I really appreciate your spending this time with me.

MILKMAID. I like you.

PRINCE. Well, I like you, too, as a matter of fact I like you a lot. I like you more the more I *see* you and you tend to *grow* on me. I think you're smart. I think you're smart and pretty, now what do you think about that—are you susceptible to flattery? *(Pause)* I know, we all are, everybody likes to be told nice things about themselves, you know what *else* I like about you. You're *generous.* That's something in today's world. Isn't it? It's a *lot.* I think it's rather a *lot.* Not to be . . . *judgmental,* not to be "stuck-up" . . . to say, "However 'lowly' someone is, I'm going to see the *good* in them." *You* do that, and I think it's admirable. *(Pause)* I do.

MILKMAID. You're funny.

PRINCE. Ah, gedouddahere . . .

MILKMAID. No, you *are.*

PRINCE. Well, *thank* you.

MILKMAID. You say funny things.

PRINCE *(pause).* Gee, you're swell.

MILKMAID. You always *flatter* me . . .

PRINCE. It's just the truth. It's nothing but the *truth,* here you are, *working* every day, working so *hard,* carrying *milk* the whole time . . . uh, carrying *hay,* you look so *pretty* working in the sun . . . I see you walking *by* . . . you *do* something to me, and Grace . . . can I call you Grace?

MILKMAID. Yes.

PRINCE. *Grace,* you *do* something to me. Every day I see you going past a *feeling* has grown in my breast, and, Grace, I want to ask you something.

MILKMAID. What?

PRINCE *(sotto).* Okay, here it goes. I choose and elect this woman. And if she will give me all her selfless Love as evidenced by the physical evidence of her giving me a kiss I will be Free. And I choose her. *(To the* MILKMAID*)* Grace: I'd like to give you a kiss. Would you give me a kiss? *(Pause)* Grace . . . ? Would you do that?

(Mourning bells sound.)

MILKMAID. Aren't those bells sad . . . ?

PRINCE. Did you hear what I said . . . ?

MILKMAID. What? I'm sorry? Wait, I, when I hear those bells, I'm so . . . I suppose that we all have to die. *(Pause)* And I suppose it's good to be reminded of it. But it makes me sad. They say he was a good man. *(Pause)* Who's to know? It's hard to know what great people are, if they're real at all. What qualities they have. I'll

---

10. *sic transit gloria mundi* (sik tran′sit glôr′ē ə mŭn′dē), thus passes away the glory of this world

tell you what I know. It's sad he died when he was going to wed. *(Pause)* Life is such a mystery. What do you think happened to him?

(Pause)

PRINCE. I don't know what you mean.

MILKMAID. The *Prince*. Our Prince who disappeared on his *wedding day*.

PRINCE. What happened to him?

MILKMAID. Yes.

PRINCE. I'm sure that I don't know.

MILKMAID. Maybe it's better. *(Pause)* Maybe it is. Gone two months and his fiancée is marrying his cousin. *(Pause)* Life is so strange. I'm sure we love the trials of the great in that they save us from experiencing them ourselves. *(Pause)* I suppose that we think they're *more* than us. They can *bear* them. *(Pause)* That they are *stronger*, or *better (Pause)* or *worse* . . . *(Sighs)* I'll tell you what I think, though.

(Pause)

PRINCE. And what is that?

MILKMAID. It's *wrong* to hold a funeral for him today and for his fiancée to wed tomorrow. *(Pause)* I don't think that that's right.

PRINCE. You don't?

MILKMAID. Even if she did not love him. *(Pause)* She could be true to his memory. *(Pause)* Or she could show respect by being true to the appearance. *(Pause)* That's what I think. My father says she's doing it to keep the fortune. His cousin inherits today and tomorrow she will wed. I pity the new prince. I do. Life is so tenuous. You can't buy loyalty. It's so good to be loved for yourself. That's something that cannot fade.

PRINCE. I, look, look, look, I want you to . . . Will you give me a kiss, I really want to kiss you, would you do that?

MILKMAID. Oh, I couldn't.

(Pause)

PRINCE. You're disgusted, fine. I disgusted you. All you are is fine talk, when it comes down to *cases* you only care what's on the outside.

(Pause)

MILKMAID. I hurt you.

PRINCE. Huh . . .

MILKMAID. I'm sorry. No. Please understand.

PRINCE. I understand *completely*, you're like all the rest.

MILKMAID. I could only kiss a man I was pledged to marry.

PRINCE. Will you marry me?

MILKMAID. You're speaking so hastily.

PRINCE. No, I'm not. I mean it. I will *marry* you. I mean it. I've . . . from my soul . . . now. We'll get married today. I'll take care of you. You won't regret it, I promise you. Someday you're going to look back and remember I said this to you. Will you be mine?

(Pause)

MILKMAID. I am deeply touched.

PRINCE. Yeah. You aren't touched. I *know* this preamble. You're *hurt*. You're *appalled*, that I would *presume* on our *acquaintance* . . . a mere . . .

MILKMAID. I am *touched*. I never will forget this moment. *(Pause)* I never will forget it.

(Pause)

PRINCE. You could learn to love me.

MILKMAID. I love another.

PRINCE. . . . I have many qualities, and you bring them out *in* me, that *no* one has seen. I could *learn* from you, and you could learn to love *me* . . .

MILKMAID. I love another.

(Pause)

PRINCE. I'm sorry . . . ?

(Pause)

MILKMAID. I love another.

PRINCE. Oh. *(Pause)* Oh. *(Pause)* Oh. *(Pause)* Fine. That's fine. Getting there a little after the barn *door* was open, all the *horses* left, I'm shutting up to close the *door.* Ha. Ha.

(Pause)

MILKMAID. . . . you're hurt.

PRINCE. "You love another . . ." never mentioned *that* . . . some *other* guy . . . well, why don't you go marry him, *then,* if you're so "in love" the whole time. Why don't you do *that* . . . ?

MILKMAID. We have no money. *(Pause)* I'm going to go. I want to see the Prince's Funeral.

PRINCE. Oh, whattaya going to see his "body"? They don't even *have* a body . . . they don't have anything, just a bunch of cheap sentiment, cheap, tawdry, false emotions. Well, maybe that's where you belong . . .

MILKMAID. You're hurt.

PRINCE. No, I'm not hurt.

MILKMAID. We'll still be friends.

PRINCE. Oh. We will.

MILKMAID. This was hard for you. I'll always remember that you asked.

PRINCE. Swell. Tell your boyfriend, too. I'm sure that he'll be touched.

MILKMAID. I'll see you tomorrow.

PRINCE. Wait. Wait a second. Wait. Hold on. You can't get married 'cause you have no money?

(Pause)

MILKMAID. No.

PRINCE. If you *had,* if you could *find* the money you'd get married.

MILKMAID. Yes.

PRINCE. Okay now, okay now, okay, now, *great.* If someone could—what is it you need, a *dowry,* something like that . . . ? How much do you need?

MILKMAID. Twenty-five gold coins.

PRINCE. Twenty-five gold coins, great . . .

MILKMAID. . . . to buy my fiancé out of his apprenticeship.

PRINCE. Yeah. Yeah. Fine. If someone could *help* you to marry, if someone could *find* you that money, I don't mean to sound *crass,* but if someone *got* you that money, what would you *do* for that guy?

MILKMAID. I'd be eternally in his debt.

PRINCE. That's good enough for me. Okay! Go on, I'm not going to hold you up, you run along. I don't want you to worry about a thing.

MILKMAID. Oh, I'm not worried.

PRINCE. You aren't?

MILKMAID. No. I think that love will find a way. *(Pause)* See you tomorrow!

PRINCE. You bet your boots you will.

(PRINCE whistles. SERVINGMAN appears. Pause.)

SERVINGMAN. Sire? *(Pause)* Sire? Did she . . .*(Pause)*

PRINCE. What? Oh. No. No go. Not at all. She won't go for it.

SERVINGMAN. But did Your Highness elect her the one who must bestow the kiss?

PRINCE. Yes. Yes. I did. *(Pause)* We're committed. *(Pause)* We're in it, now . . . We're in a little bit of a *quandary.*[11] *(Pause)*, but I think I can pull it out.

SERVINGMAN. *Sire,* if we don't pull it out by tomorrow you will be pronounced dead, your fortune will devolve on your Cousin Charles, he will marry The Fair Patricia . . .

PRINCE. . . . and I'll be broke and friendless the rest of my life, yeah, I'm *talking* about fixing it before tomorrow, I'm talking about fixing it right *now,* can you believe the gall of this broad, dead two months, dead two months, dead two months, not *even* dead, what am I *talking* about, I'm right *here* . . . and she's marrying someone else.

(Pause)

SERVINGMAN. It must be very difficult for you.

(Pause)

PRINCE. Yeah. Yeah. *(Pause)* We're going to pull this one off yet. Here's what I want you to do. Go to the Palace. Alright? In the *library* of my *study* on the top *shelf* facing the *windows* there's a Big Blue Book. Alright? It's hollow. Now. We got a little *getaway* money in there, so be careful bringing it back. That was needless. I'm sorry. I know that you'd be careful. *(Pause)* Bring it back, *tonight* we'll go

to the *milkmaid's* house, we'll give her a dowry she'll never forget, she'll kiss me out of gratitude, we hop on back to the Castle, put the kibosh[12] on this whole affair, I save my *fortune,* put The Fair Patricia on a *bus* (you best believe it) and it's *business* as *usual* back at the Old Stand. *Okay.* Let's *do* it.

SERVINGMAN. I'm on my way, Sire . . .

PRINCE. And, hey, and how would you like to be the *Earl* of somewhere?

(Pause)

SERVINGMAN. I . . .

PRINCE. Let's not count our chickens, all I want to tell you, it hasn't gone unnoticed what you've done for me.

SERVINGMAN. I . . .

PRINCE. We'll celebrate later. Okay, you better hit the bricks.

SERVINGMAN *(exiting).* Your servant, Sire . . .

PRINCE. . . . I mean, you can't go around feeling *sorry* for yourself the whole time. The Going Gets Tough, The Tough Get Going. *(Pause)* Now I've stopped *moping* and we're gonna set a couple of things *straight* around this place.

SCENE ThREE

Winter. The SERVINGMAN *(in rags) and the* PRINCE *(as a frog) sitting around a campfire. The* PRINCE *reading a newspaper . . .*

---

11. quandary (kwan′drē), state of confusion or doubt
12. kibosh (kī′bash), stop: *She put the kibosh on our plans.*

PRINCE. Here's a good one. Woman about five miles from here arrested for not paying the Milk Tax. Five years in prison. "'What will happen to my babes,' Mom says." Well, that's The Fair Patricia for you . . .

SERVINGMAN. Yes, Sire . . .

PRINCE. Anything for a laugh. You warm enough?

SERVINGMAN. Yes. Thank you, Sire.

PRINCE. "Worst Winter in 200 years." Well, these things always seem to coincide. Don't you think? Hard times and hard weather? *(Pause)* You know what I think? I think it's sunspots. That's what I think it is. *(Pause)* You doing okay? Bill . . . ? You okay? I know it's easier for me. I don't eat much. I have cold blood. You got to keep *warm,* and you need a little *protein* once in a while.

SERVINGMAN. I'm okay, Sire.

PRINCE. Here's a good one, "Her Radiance The Fair Patricia and Prince Charles off for Extended Foreign Tour. Thousands Cheer . . ." And I don't blame them. Good Riddance to Bad Rubbish. Oh. Here's a happy note! "Parliament Endorses Emergency Discretionary Powers for Bailiffs." *(Sighs)* Whaddaya know about that . . . *(The* PRINCE *looks up from his paper.)* Yep. Looks like they're gonna make the *trains* run on time. You okay, Bill . . . ?

SERVINGMAN. Yes, Sire.

PRINCE. You don't look well.

SERVINGMAN. I'm fine, Sire.

PRINCE. You got a fever?

SERVINGMAN. No, Sire. Not at all.

PRINCE. Hey, look, Bill, I've been thinking, you don't have to call me "Sire" anymore. *(Pause)* Okay? *(Pause)* I mean, these are new times, we have to change with them.

SERVINGMAN. The old times will return, Sire.

PRINCE. Somehow I don't think so.

SERVINGMAN. I've never ceased to hope.

PRINCE. Well, Hope is a wonderful thing, but *reasonably* they've changed the locks on us at the Palace, Fair Patricia's issued a dictum anyone *resembling* The Late Prince was to be shot on sight for defamation of my sainted memory—*she* don't fool around—it's a crime to be seen wearing my *emblem,* and she's got the whole place pretty well cowtied. It looks like Under New Management. That's what *I'd* say.

(Pause)

SERVINGMAN. I've never ceased to hope.

PRINCE. Well, you hope, but keep it silent, 'cause if you hope out *loud* it's El Biggo Sleepo, if you follow me, and I'd rather have you around.

SERVINGMAN. Thank you, Sire.

PRINCE. No, it is I who thank *you,* Bill. *(Pause)* It's I who am in your debt constantly and I am never not mindful of that. You've cared for and protected me with everything at your disposal, and the only coin with which I can repay you is my constant thanks. *(Pause)* Thank you.

(Pause)

SERVINGMAN. Sire! Here she comes!

PRINCE. And *some*day, I'm gonna get that broad to *kiss* me, and then we're going to saddle up and *blow* this joint, and go down somewhere *warm!*

(MILKMAID *enters.*)

. . . And we're gonna start a *shoe store* or something. *(To* MILKMAID*)* Hi! *(Pause. To* SERVINGMAN*)* She doesn't look so good today. *(To* MILKMAID*)* Hi! Kiddo! Hi! How are you, why don't you sit *down* a spell. Hey, Grace . . . *(To* SERVINGMAN*)* Get her a *log* or something . . . (SERVINGMAN *does so. She sits.*)

That's better! *(To* SERVINGMAN*)* What have we got to eat? *(To* MILKMAID*)* You look pale as a sheet . . . (SERV-INGMAN *brings broth.*)

Some *broth* . . . *?* You want some nice *broth* . . . *? (They feed her.)* Yeesssss. *That's* better . . . *! That's* better . . . *!* Yesssssss. Now, what's the *matter* with you, letting yourself get so run *down* and all . . . ! And how come we don't *see* you anymore . . . you alright? You okay . . . ?

MILKMAID. They took everything.

PRINCE. Who took everything?

MILKMAID. The Bailiff.

PRINCE. What did they take? What?

MILKMAID. My fiancé . . .

PRINCE. . . . yes?

MILKMAID. Could I have some more broth . . . ?

SERVINGMAN *(serving her).* My pleasure.

MILKMAID. Thank you. *(Pause)* Thank you. My fiancé made a remark against The Fair Patricia. *(Pause)* He was turned in. They took his farm. They came to my farm and took my cow.

PRINCE. They took your cow?

MILKMAID. And, yes, and they, he's gone. They put a price on his head. Fifty golden coins. Dead or alive.

PRINCE. Where is he gone?

MILKMAID. Gone away. He left the country in the night. He left me a note. *(Hands note to the* PRINCE*)*

PRINCE *(reads).* "Don't worry."

MILKMAID. . . . and they took my cow.

PRINCE. Who took your cow . . . ?

MILKMAID. I'm basically not a political person . . . I'm going to town to plead my case before The Fair Patricia . . .

PRINCE. . . . she's out of town . . .

SERVINGMAN. Why did they take your cow?

MILKMAID. They said that I was an Accessory.

PRINCE. What is it that your boyfriend said that got them so ticked off?

MILKMAID. Someone was talking about The Fair Patricia and he said "Handsome is as Handsome Does." I'm going to ask them for my cow back. Do you think that's disloyal to him . . . ?

PRINCE. No. And I don't think it's gonna get you your *cow* back, either. As a matter of fact, I wouldn't go in there at all.

MILKMAID. . . . I have to eat . . .

PRINCE. They're going to ask you where he is.

MILKMAID. I won't tell them.

PRINCE. You won't tell them . . . you *know* where he is?

MILKMAID. No.

(Pause)

PRINCE. Somehow I don't believe you.

MILKMAID. I won't *tell* them, though. I'll say I don't know where he is. How will they know?

PRINCE. You've got a face like a transparent book, for starters. This is no good.

MILKMAID. It wasn't right of them to take my cow.

PRINCE. It certainly was not.

MILKMAID. What *right* do they have?

PRINCE. Only force.

MILKMAID. Isn't there any *law* anymore . . . ?

(SERVINGMAN *produces a golden sword from under his ragged cloak.*)

PRINCE. What's that?

(*Pause*)

MILKMAID. Is that *gold* . . . ?

PRINCE. Yeah. It's gold. But what is it *doing* here, if you get my meaning, when everything *like* it should have been buried *months* ago . . .

SERVINGMAN. This is my sword.

PRINCE. Now, Bill, don't be silly, how could that be *your* sword? When it's festooned all over with the blazonments of Our Late Prince, the ownership of which emblem is *Death?* I'm sure you must have *found* it somewhere, and are going to *bury* it. Immediately . . .

MILKMAID. . . . how did you get that sword?

SERVINGMAN. I'm taking it to town.

PRINCE. Now, that's the dumbest thing I ever heard . . . why would someone unless he didn't want to live anymore *do* a thing like that?

SERVINGMAN. I'm taking it to the Goldsmith to be melted down, and with the proceeds I am buying this Young Lady food. In fact I'm buying her a *cow* . . . and some new *clothes* . . .

MILKMAID. No, you can't do that, if they catch you on the *road* with it . . .

PRINCE. . . . have you been carrying that thing the whole time?

SERVINGMAN. It has been my great honor to.

MILKMAID. No, you can't do that. Thank you, no. It's much too dangerous . . .

SERVINGMAN. Farewell.

PRINCE. I forbid you to go.

SERVINGMAN. In what capacity?

(*Pause*)

PRINCE. As your *friend* . . .

SERVINGMAN. And as your friend I beg your understanding for my so precipitous[13] departure. Farewell. (*He exits; pause.*)

MILKMAID. I can't believe he's doing that for me. (*Pause*) I can't believe he's doing this.

PRINCE. Well, these are hard times, and I think he feels that we all have to stick together.

MILKMAID. Your friend is a very good man.

PRINCE. Yes. He is.

MILKMAID. What will we do if he doesn't come back?

PRINCE. I don't know.

MILKMAID. He's got a lot of pride, hasn't he?

PRINCE. Yes. He has.

MILKMAID. Is that a good thing?

PRINCE. I don't know. (*Pause*)

---

13. precipitous (pri si′pə təs), happening with no warning

SCENE FOUR

Spring. The PRINCE *(as a frog) is gathering flowers. He holds a bouquet.*

PRINCE.

"A Blue Flower's best for Spring.
A Blue Flower's best for Spring,
When Ground is raw. *(Pause)*
Red is the Color of Lust . . ."

(To himself) Well, that's true. Can blue be the Color of Lust? No, I don't think so. Perhaps some perverted blue, some *violet* midnight blue . . . some *midnight* blue, perhaps, it probably depends a great deal on what *surrounds* it. *(Pause)* Bill—I wish you were around to hear this. 'Cause I think you would appreciate it. *(He goes over to his journal and writes in it.)*

"A Blue Flower's Best for Spring,
When ground is raw . . .
Red is the Color of Lust . . ."

(The MILKMAID *appears, watches him.)*

"Red is the Color of Lust . . . of Saline Life, of blood . . ."
well, we know red is the color of blood . . . that's not very good . . . What other flowers do we have around here? *(He turns; sees* MILK-MAID.*)*

MILKMAID. Hello.

PRINCE. Oh, Hi! Oh, wait a minute, will you . . . *"Red* is the Color of Lust, of Saline Life . . . of Arrogance and Sloth; but *Blue* . . ."

MILKMAID. . . . are you writing a poem . . . ?

PRINCE. . . . hold on a second . . . "Red is the color of pride, and *blue* of loy-

alty." *(Pause)* Um . . .

(Pause)

MILKMAID. . . . did I break your train of thought?

PRINCE. It's alright. *(Pause)* It's alright. How are you? I'm sorry. My mind was somewhere else for a second. How are you? I haven't seen you in a while.

MILKMAID. No.

PRINCE. What have you been doing?

MILKMAID. I've been trying to farm.

PRINCE. You have.

MILKMAID. Yes. I was getting the farm ready for planting.

PRINCE. But they took your horse.

MILKMAID. I laid out a small patch behind the hut. *(Pause)* How have you been?

PRINCE. I've been okay. I was, you know, I was unwell for a time there . . .

MILKMAID. Yes, I know . . .

PRINCE. . . . since my . . .

MILKMAID. Yes, I know . . .

PRINCE. . . . since my *friend* died . . . *(Pause)* but I'm alright now, I think.

(Pause)

MILKMAID. What were you doing just now? You were writing a poem.

PRINCE. Just now. Yes.

MILKMAID. I didn't know that you could write.

PRINCE. Well, I've been working at it.

MILKMAID. You were writing it for *him?*

PRINCE. Yes. *(Pause)* Yes. I was. *(Pause)* I was picking some *flowers* to take over to his grave, and some thoughts came to me. *(Pause)* Well!

MILKMAID (*hands him a package*). I brought you this.

PRINCE. Thank you. What is it?

MILKMAID. My heavy shawl.

PRINCE. You brought me your shawl?

MILKMAID. Yes. I thought that you could make a little, you could make a *nest* for yourself.

PRINCE. But *you'll* need it. Next winter . . . You'll surely need it.

MILKMAID. I'm going away.

(*Pause*)

PRINCE. You're going away.

MILKMAID. Yes.

(*Pause*)

PRINCE. Where?

MILKMAID. I'm going South. I got a letter from my fiancé. He wants me to *join* him.

(*Pause*)

PRINCE. Then you must go.

MILKMAID. I (*pause*) I wanted to *ask* you if you would like to *come* with us.

(*Pause*)

PRINCE. To come with you to the South.

MILKMAID. Yes.

PRINCE (*pause*). That's very good of you.

MILKMAID. We would be glad to have you. There would be a place for you.

PRINCE. That's very good of you. That's very good of you, indeed.

MILKMAID. Will you come?

PRINCE (*pause*). You want me to come with you and live with you.

MILKMAID. Yes.

PRINCE. You know, you're a good woman. (*Pause*) I've wanted to tell you that for a long time. (*Pause*) And

your fiancé's a lucky man. A very lucky man to have someone as loyal as you. (*Pause*) And as good as you. (*Pause*) And there's something else, there's something that I'd like to say. I owe you an apology.

MILKMAID. You don't owe me.

PRINCE. Yes. I do, though. I've, uh, you know, when I *met* you . . . when I *met* you . . .

MILKMAID. That's, that's long ago . . .

PRINCE. Yes, I think that it is, and do you remember . . .

MILKMAID. You don't have to talk about that if . . .

PRINCE. No, I want to.

MILKMAID. I know that you were *hurt* that I *refused* you . . .

PRINCE. Yes, I was.

MILKMAID. If I were *free* . . .

PRINCE. I was hurt. More im*por*tantly . . .

MILKMAID. If I were *free* your offer would not have been *refused*. (*Pause*)

PRINCE (*pause*). Thank you. (*Pause*) Thank you very much. I . . . thank you very much. I . . . (*Pause*) You would have married me? (*Pause*)

MILKMAID. Yes.

PRINCE. I'm honored.

(*Pause*)

MILKMAID (*starting to go*). Well . . .

PRINCE. Wait, please, I wanted to *say* . . . I wanted to *say* when I first *knew* you I, I think, I wanted, there was something I *wanted*, I *wanted* to take advan . . .

MILKMAID. Shhh.

PRINCE. To, no, to take . . .

MILKMAID. . . . . it's alright.

PRINCE. . . . to take *advantage* of you. *(Pause)* There. *(Pause)* There. And *furthermore*, however I've *changed* has in large part been because of you, and Bill, of course, but because of you. Okay. I'm through. Enough. Okay. I've said it. There. I apologize. It came out a bit creepy but I mean it. *(Pause)*

MILKMAID. Will you come with me?

PRINCE. I . . .

MILKMAID. Will you come with me to the South? And live with us?

PRINCE. I . . . *(Pause)* I . . . *Thank* you. But I don't think that I can. *(Pause)* I think I'll stay here.

(Pause)

MILKMAID. It will be cold here.

PRINCE. Yes. *(Pause)* I . . . Yes, it will, but . . .

MILKMAID. . . . you have *ties* here.

PRINCE. Yes. *(Pause)* But thank you for asking me.

MILKMAID. I have to go. I want to cross the border before it gets dark. They close it down.

PRINCE. You have a safe trip.

MILKMAID. I'll think of you.

PRINCE. I'll think of you, too. I wish, I wish there was something I could *give* you . . . to *think* of me.

MILKMAID. Oh, I won't forget you.

PRINCE. I . . . isn't it funny; I was looking for a "jewel" or something to give you. Hah. Haha. I don't even have a *pocket!* Hah! Isn't it funny how some things take us back.

MILKMAID. What do you mean?

PRINCE. I was thinking of my Old Friend. I must have been thinking of him, and it took me back to another time. *(Pause)* Do you think we never know the good things 'til they've passed?

MILKMAID. I don't know.

PRINCE. I've been thinking that.

(Pause)

MILKMAID. You have a good heart.

PRINCE. Do I? Thank you. You do, too. Thank you. Oh. Oh. *(He starts writing.)* "Red for Pride, Blue for Loyalty . . . a good heart's *red* . . . a good heart's red . . ."

MILKMAID *(softly)*. Goodbye . . . *(She kisses him and slips quietly away.)*

PRINCE. "A Good Heart's Red . . ." Now we need *yellow*, we need some *contrast* . . . *yellow* . . . blue . . . *(He changes back into a PRINCE.)* Blue for Spring, Red for Saline Lust . . .

(The OLD PEASANT WOMAN appears.)

PEASANT. Hello. *(The PRINCE looks up; pause.)* Hello.

PRINCE. What are you doing here?

(Pause)

PEASANT. Hello.

PRINCE. Yes. Hello. It's been a long time.

PEASANT. Look at yourself.

PRINCE. I know what I look like.

PEASANT. Look at yourself.

(The PRINCE does so; pause.)

PRINCE. I seem to have changed. *(Pause)* Well. *(Pause)* Yes. *(Pause)* It's been a long time. Hasn't it? *(Pause)* Yes. And here you are again. *(Pause)* And now I have changed back. *(Pause)* How about that. *(Pause)* How about that. *(Pause)* How about that.

(Pause) May I ask you something? I'd like to understand. There's something that I've wanted to ask you for so long. The last time that we met . . . may I ask you . . . the last time that we met, I was about to get married. I ruled the kingdom. I refused a request that you made, at that time I thought that I was within my rights . . . I was on Royal Land . . . I was, let us say, on land I *knew* as Royal Land. Even if we were to say that possession of that land was in some form a usurpation.[14] I picked *flowers*. In a moment of exuberance. I felt no ill will toward you. None at all. And I was punished. My love proved false. My kingdom was taken from me. My friends were ruined. My comrade lost his life . . . *(Pause)* Don't you think I was unduly punished? *(Pause)* Or was it punishment for some . . . for some general *arrogance?* For my acceptance of the perquisites[15] of *rank?*

PEASANT. Are those for me?

PRINCE. I'm sorry?

PEASANT. Those flowers that you hold, are they for me?

PRINCE. No. *(Pause)* They're for my friend. *(Pause)* Who has died. I'm taking them to his grave.

PEASANT. You must offer them to me.

PRINCE. They're for my friend's grave.

PEASANT. Those flowers you must offer me, or you will dwell in misery.

(Pause)

PRINCE. They're somewhat *sacred.* *(Pause)* They're for my *friend. (Pause)* Here. Here they are. *(He gives her the bouquet.)* Take them. *(Pause)*

PEASANT. Thank you. *(Pause)* They're lovely.

PRINCE. Yes. They are.

PEASANT. I think that they're the loveliest thing in this part of the Wood.

PRINCE. *Yes.* I do, too.

PEASANT. Thank you for offering them to me.

(Pause)

PRINCE. That's perfectly alright.

(She exits. He puts the MILKMAID's *shawl over his uniform and starts out of the Wood.)*

_____

14. usurpation (yü sər pā′ shən), possession by force
15. perquisite (pər′kwə zet), something claimed as an exclusive right or possession

END

Responding to the Play

1. What do you think will happen to the Prince? Why?
2. Find dialogue that you believe characterizes the Servingman and the Prince. Tell why you chose these particular lines.
3. To help develop your ideas about character, write the name of a color, animal, and object that the following characters remind you of: Prince, Peasant Woman, Servingman, Milkmaid, Fair Patricia.
4. Say, "Those flowers you must offer me, or you will dwell in misery" in different ways to develop various vocal approaches.
5. Write a radio advertisement for a new production of *The Frog Prince*. Try to capture the tone of the play in your ad.

More About Royalty in Frog's Clothing

David Mamet loosely based his play on a fairy tale by the Brothers Grimm called *The Frog King*. In the Grimms' version, a princess loses her golden ball down a well. A frog appears and offers to retrieve her ball if she will promise to allow him to be her companion. She agrees, but when the frog returns her ball, she runs away. The frog follows her and the girl's father insists that she keep her promise, despite the fact that she finds the frog hideous. In the end, the frog is transformed into a king and weds the princess. They are escorted home by his servant, Faithful Henry. Henry has been so unhappy since his master's transformation into a frog, that he has been wearing iron bands around his heart to keep it from breaking. The bands spring free as Henry's heart swells with joy to once again be with his master.

CREATING AND PERFORMING

1. With a partner, read the first and the last encounter between the Prince and the Peasant. Discuss how the dialogue differs in each.
2. Look at the exchange between the Prince and the Servingman on page 249. How should the actors move and speak in this scene?
3. We never see the Fair Patricia, yet we learn a lot about her. Based on what you know, write an "Address to My Dear Subjects" by the Fair Patricia. Read it to the class.

The Frog Prince by David Mamet   **257**

THE LOVE OF THREE ORANGES

The Play as Literature: Archetypes

Written in 1761 by Carlo Gozzi, *The Love of Three Oranges* is based on one of the earliest known fairy tales. It is a *commedia dell'arte,* a form in which the actors must make up their own lines. (Read more about *commedia dell'arte* on page 269.)

Each character in this play is an *archetype*—a stock character who represents a certain kind of person. Because the actors have no written dialogue to follow, they must have a deep understanding of the characters they are portraying. Because each character exhibits his or her own standard traits, the actor knows what the character would say and do in any given situation.

The Play as Theatre: Improvisation

When actors don't have written dialogue to follow, they must improvise—or make up their own words and actions. Because improvisational actors do not have to memorize lines, they enjoy a freedom and spontaneity not available to scripted actors. On the other hand, they must be extremely alert, focused on their characters, and committed to the stories in which they are taking part. They must concentrate on the story line and the relationships between characters so that their words and actions seem natural.

Like all actors, improvisational actors must prepare. They must learn their character type and memorize the story line, paying particular attention to the beginning, middle and end of each scene. Within the scene, however, the actors can speak and act as they think appropriate for the character.

As you read *The Love of Three Oranges,* concentrate on the verbs. Think about the things the characters *do*.

Stuck in an Elevator
• a ten year old
• a pregnant woman
• a person who hates small spaces
• a businessperson late for an appointment

Watching a Basketball Game
•a five year old
•a visitor from the other team's town
•a grandfather
•a visitor from another planet

WARM UP!

In groups of four, choose a situation at left: Each participant develops a separate character. Then brainstorm a story line and improvise a scene.

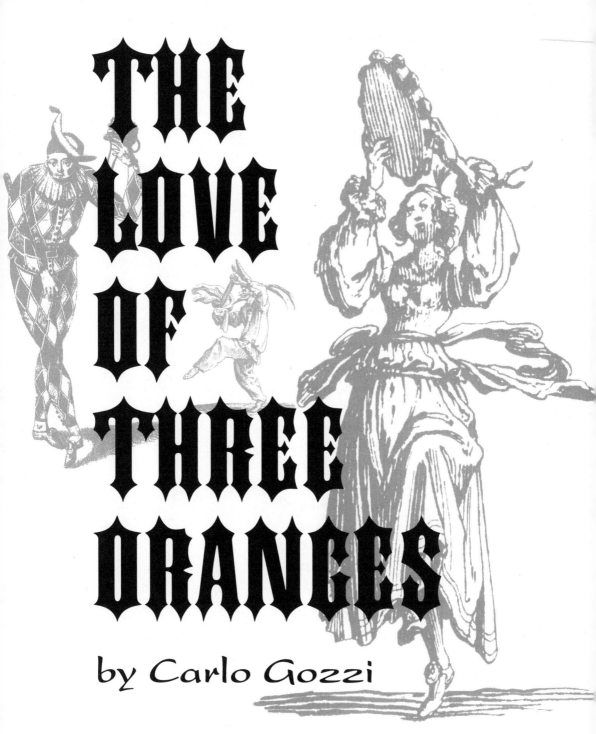

THE LOVE OF THREE ORANGES

by Carlo Gozzi

Adapted by Lowell Swortzell

A fairy tale kingdom

PRINCE TARTAGLIA a young man suffering from acute boredom

THE KING his father, determined to help his son

LEANDRO the Prime Minister, in love with CLARICE

CLARICE niece of the KING and a Princess who wants to be Queen

TRUFFALDINO a CLOWN in the tradition
of Harlequin

THREE DOCTORS

THE WITCH MORGANA Queen of Hypochondria

SMERALDINA servant of MORGANA

CELIO a magician and the protector of the PRINCE

THE BAKER'S WIFE

THREE MAIDENS who live inside the Oranges,
the third being . . .

NINETTA who turns into a dove

THE DEVIL OF THE BELLOWS

MEMBERS OF THE COURT

TOWNSFOLK AT THE LAUGHING FESTIVAL

COOKS

SERVANTS

WEDDING GUESTS

GUARDS

MUSICIANS

DANCERS

Long, long ago

ACT 1

SCENE 1
The Council Chamber in the Palace.

THREE DOCTORS examine the emaciated[1] PRINCE who sits
quietly, totally indifferent to their attention.

THE KING, expressing great concern over his son,
awaits their diagnosis.

THE DOCTORS confer among themselves, then, bowing
before the KING, announce that his son is dying of—
BOREDOM!

THE KING asks if there is any way to save the boy.

THE DOCTORS agree recovery can happen only if the PRINCE
laughs almost immediately: there is no
other cure.

THE KING orders LEANDRO, the Prime Minister, to
announce a Festival of Laughter and to offer a
reward to anyone who can move the PRINCE to mirth.

After the KING and DOCTORS exit, **LEANDRO** reveals he doesn't want the PRINCE to
recover because he hopes to gain the throne for himself. He is in love with
CLARICE, the niece of the KING, and they dream they will rule the Kingdom
together someday.

LEANDRO sings a sad song to the PRINCE, hoping to depress him even more. But
the PRINCE is too bored to listen and soon cuts him off.

CLARICE brings news that TRUFFALDINO has arrived at court, which alarms LEAN-
DRO, who fears that the clown's tricks and comic antics will amuse the PRINCE.

CLARICE proposes to be done with the PRINCE here and now, if not by poison then
by fire or sword. But LEANDRO is not yet ready to go this far.

Instead he departs to seek advice from the witch MORGANA to further his cause to
seize the throne.

---

1. emaciated (i mā′shē/āt id), so thin as to be unnatural; wasting away

SCENE 2

The PRINCE*'s Bedroom. Several days later.*

As the DOCTORS watch, **TRUFFALDINO** helps the PRINCE dress. He is going to attend the Festival of Laughter which the KING has arranged for his benefit. TRUFFALDINO tells him how much he will enjoy the celebration but the PRINCE shows no interest whatsoever.

TRUFFALDINO, hoping to get him to laugh, puts his jacket on backwards. The DOCTORS chuckle. The PRINCE is not amused.

TRUFFALDINO puts the boy's hat on upside down. The DOCTORS roar with laughter. The PRINCE is not amused.

THE CLOWN ties his shoe laces together and when the PRINCE tries to walk, he falls down. The DOCTORS become hysterical, rolling about on the floor. The PRINCE remains as solemn as before, if anything, feeling even sorrier for himself.

He begs not to go to the Festival and wants to go to bed.

Realizing there is no other way to get him there, **TRUFFALDINO,** pretending to be a horse, sweeps the PRINCE up and carries him on his back to the Festival.

Surprised at this strange treatment, the **PRINCE** waves goodbye to the DOCTORS but still doesn't see anything funny.

SCENE 3

The Festival of Laughter.

A mysterious **OLD WOMAN** is the center of attention as the crowd gathers in the town square.

She is overheard to say she is there to bring about the downfall of the PRINCE.

She draws water from the fountain and mixes a potion she plans to give the PRINCE.

As the festivities begin, **TRUFFALDINO** enters, still carrying the PRINCE. He dismounts while everyone gathers around the throne.

One by one, they bow before the PRINCE, each attempting to make him laugh.

They perform stunts, tricks, tell jokes, sing songs, but, alas, nothing amuses the young man.

In fact, with each act, the **PRINCE** grows more and more morose.[2]
Until . . .

THE OLD LADY comes forth with a flask, the contents of which she insists will cure the PRINCE.

Thinking the potion at least will put him to sleep and he no longer will have to endure the Festival, he agrees to take a spoonful of the medicine.

THE OLD WOMAN, excited that her plan is working, gleefully pours from the flask. But just as she projects the spoon forward to the PRINCE, TRUFFALDINO suddenly rises up in front of her, causing her to go splat in the street, spilling the potion.

The **CROWD** laughs at the awkward display of the lady sprawled before them.

EVERYONE, including, yes, you guessed it, the PRINCE himself, goes into spasms of laughter.

And each time he laughs, he becomes stronger and stronger, until he rises and soon is jumping up and down for joy.

THE KING, watching from the side, rushes forward and declares the PRINCE cured.

He names TRUFFALDINO the hero who wins the award. The CROWD praises the clown with a round of cheers. Confetti flies. Streamers stream. Music plays. They burst into dancing.

THE OLD WOMAN, helped to her feet by LEANDRO and CLARICE, who also have been watching attentively, becomes furious. She believes that because the PRINCE laughed at her, *she* should receive the reward.

THE KING refuses to consider her plea, giving full credit to the clown's cleverness.

LEANDRO and **CLARICE** pull the OLD WOMAN to the side and beg her to do something to prevent the PRINCE's complete recovery. Something to stop him from becoming the next King. *ANYTHING!*

THE OLD WOMAN steps forth and silences everyone; she throws off her wig and outer garments to reveal underneath that she is the evil witch MORGANA. Climbing upon a pedestal, she demands their attention.

So surprised is the **CROWD** to see her and, of course, also deeply

---

2. morose (mə rōs′), very sad; gloomy; ill-humored

frightened by her powers, they instantly freeze like statues made of stone.

In her rage, **MORGANA** places a curse upon the PRINCE: he will fall in love with three oranges and cannot be cured until he has procured[3] them.

That seems easy enough. But hold on, for she says the oranges grow two thousand miles away in a valley separated by mountains no one has crossed. Ever!

The only help she will allow him on his quest is to come from TRUFFALDINO, who is condemned to accompany the PRINCE.

THE KING is distraught and faints.

LEANDRO and **CLARICE** glow with happiness and thank MORGANA for the inspired doom that surely will fall upon the PRINCE and the CLOWN.

These two look at each other, and in a state of shock and uncertainty, stumble off in the direction of the oranges.

THE CROWD wishes them good luck but really believes they will never see them again. They wave a tearful farewell as the first act ends.

ACT 2

SCENE 1
Near the mountains.

THE PRINCE and **TRUFFALDINO** enter wearing iron boots they have been told they will need in order to climb the mountainside. They also carry weapons because they expect to meet many enemies.

Having followed them, the **KING**, accompanied by LEANDRO and CLARICE, begs his son not to continue.

THE PRINCE, however, is determined to dispel the curse of MORGANA by fetching the oranges for which he is already feeling considerable affection. But first, he and TRUFFALDINO must cross a great desert that separates them from the mountains.

After the KING returns to the palace, **LEANDRO** and **CLARICE** rejoice that their hopes to be King and Queen seem almost a reality. In telling each other how they plan to rule the country in the near future, they reveal how totally selfish they are.

---

3. procure, (prə kyür′) obtain by care or effort; secure

SCENE 2
A great desert.

THE MAGICIAN, CELIO, the Protector of the PRINCE, is looking for his charge, determined to save him at all costs. There is only one problem: he can't find the PRINCE.

Suddenly, the **PRINCE** and **TRUFFALDINO** bound onto the stage, chased by a DEVIL who pushes them forward with a pair of bellows.[4]

CELIO urges the PRINCE to turn around but, once again, the boy refuses to listen and insists that he and TRUFFALDINO will secure the oranges.

Giving up, the **MAGICIAN** presents the PRINCE with items he will need later in his travels: a jar of grease with which to open a rusty gate, a loaf of bread for a starved dog, and some brooms for the BAKER'S WIFE. He also warns the PRINCE not to cut open the oranges unless he is near a fountain.

THE DEVIL with the bellows returns and drives the two on their way again.

They arrive at the Court of Creonta where the oranges grow. First, they grease the gate, which immediately opens, and they enter.

They next encounter a barking dog, who blocks their way until given the bread and then lets them pass.

They meet the **BAKER'S WIFE**, who threatens to eat them for supper. But they give her the brooms she has longed for so she can sweep her kitchen.

She allows them to pass, and soon they stand before the three enormous oranges.

THE DEVIL with the bellows blows the PRINCE and TRUFFALDINO away once more. Grabbing the oranges, they put them in a bag and flee.

When they reappear, they pant from running and are thirsty and hungry. **TRUFFALDINO** suggests they eat one of the oranges and replace it with another later on.

Even though they realize there is no fountain nearby, the PRINCE cuts the orange open. Imagine his surprise when instead of juice

---

4. bellows (bel′ōz), a devise for producing a current of air that makes flames rise. The sides of a bellows are pulled apart, and air is forced out a nozzle at the end. The devil probably carries a bellows as an allusion to the fires of hell.

pouring forth out steps a beautiful MAIDEN dressed in white. She begs for something to drink or she will die.

TRUFFALDINO says they must cut open the second orange and give the MAIDEN the juice. But once they do, a SECOND MAIDEN appears, who is as thirsty and desperate as the first.

Neither orange produces a drop of juice and both MAIDENS quickly succumb[5] to their thirst.

THE PRINCE and **TRUFFALDINO** decide to cut open the third orange which by now has grown to the size of a pumpkin. And, again, a MAIDEN comes forth, saying she too is dying of thirst.

THE PRINCE, trying to save her, runs to the nearby lake and fills his iron boot with water.

Immediately upon drinking, the **MAIDEN** regains her strength. She introduces herself as the PRINCESS NINETTA, who along with her sisters, has been condemned by MORGANA to live forever within the oranges.

At first sight, the **PRINCE** falls in love with NINETTA. He vows to marry her at once, and along with TRUFFALDINO and NINETTA, rushes off to tell his father to make the necessary arrangements.

MORGANA arrives vowing to stop the marriage. She orders her servant Smeraldina to accompany her to the palace and to help her in her evil schemes. She gives her a charmed hairpin which she is to stick into NINETTA's head.

 # SCENE 3
Before the palace.

Elaborate preparations are underway for the wedding. Servants are decorating the palace with garlands.[6] Cooks cross with elaborate cakes and desserts. Musicians arrive.

SMERALDINA helps NINETTA prepare by fixing her hair. As she combs, she brings forth the magic pin and jabs it into NINETTA's head.

Immediately, **NINETTA** spins and twirls, turning into a beautiful white dove which, to the amazement of the CROWD, circles above the stage and flies away.

---

5. succumb (sə kum′), to give way, die of
6. garlands (gär′lənd), strings of flowers and leaves

SMERALDINA puts on the wedding gown left behind and takes
    NINETTA's place.

But when he arrives to discover SMERALDINA is his bride-to-be,
    the PRINCE is dumbfounded and brokenhearted.

SMERALDINA insists that he keep his word to marry her, and the
    court, not knowing that she is an impostor, agrees he
    must. Even the KING says so.

TRUFFALDINO, who has become the royal cook in charge of
    the wedding feast, enters from the kitchen wearing a
    large apron and pastry hat. He wheels in a large
    wedding cake which he proudly displays.

But just as he is about to place the figures of the bride and
    groom on top, the Dove returns and flutters about the cake
    preventing him from doing so.

Growing impatient and fearing something may go wrong, SMERALD-
INA insists the wedding begin.

THE KING orders TRUFFALDINO to get rid of the Dove so they can proceed.

He runs about and finally catching the Dove pulls out the hairpin
    from its head.

THE DOVE immediately turns into NINETTA.

THE PRINCE declares to everyone that she is his real
    bride.

THE KING asks SMERALDINA for an explanation of her actions.

She says she must obey the commands that LEANDRO and CLARICE
    give her. She reveals they are conspiring with MORGANA to over-
    throw the throne.

THE KING orders them arrested.

But as the guards come forth to take them away, MORGANA flies in.
    Everyone freezes in place.

She demands that the PRINCE produce the oranges.

He tells her they were cut open to release the maidens.

MORGANA orders him to marry SMERALDINA.

SMERALDINA says she doesn't wish to because it is clear the PRINCE
    really loves NINETTA.

THE PRINCE and NINETTA agree she is correct.

MORGANA says she must be obeyed: no oranges, no wedding.

TRUFFALDINO wheels his cake before MORGANA. He cuts a large slice.

MORGANA tries not to look at it. But she can't help herself.

TRUFFALDINO thrusts the cake closer and closer.

MORGANA sniffs it, weakening second by second. As she gives in, the CROWD progressively unfreezes.

TRUFFALDINO puts a fork into her hand.

MORGANA agrees to take just one bite, which she eats with the greatest of glee, completely absorbed in its sweet goodness.

TRUFFALDINO, seizing the moment, raises his arms behind her, revealing the hairpin in his hand.

As MORGANA dives deeper into the cake, TRUFFALDINO sticks the pin into her hair.

She instantly begins to twirl and spin, and before our eyes turns into a large rat.

Everyone cheers as THE WITCH sprouts whiskers and a long tail.

When MORGANA realizes what is happening, she is mortified and scurries about, looking even more like a rat.

Louder cheers.

Just as MORGANA is about to exit she stops and returns for another piece of cake. Then runs off.

TRUFFALDINO gives the KING the hairpin. He breaks it into small pieces so it can never be used again and declares they are now free of MORGANA's evil powers forever.

He thanks TRUFFALDINO, calling him the hero of the day whose inspired wit and instant action has saved them all.

He orders the wedding ceremony to begin.

And so it does, with the PRINCE and NINETTA embracing; LEANDRO, CLARICE and SMERALDINA being led away; and everyone else dancing happily as the curtain falls.

CURTAIN

THE LOVE OF THREE ORANGES

Responding to the Play

1. Which character would you like to play in *The Love of Three Oranges*? Why?
2. For the first two and one half scenes of the play, the actor who portrays Prince Tartaglia must appear to be bored. List ways the actor might convey boredom.
3. Make a chart that labels characteristics of Leandro, Morgana, and Smeraldina that make them archetypes.
4. Compare and contrast this play with either a well-known fairy tale or a contemporary romantic film.
5. Reread Act 2 Scene 3. Draw a picture of both Ninetta and Morgana before and after they encounter the magic pin.

More About *Commedia Dell'arte*

Commedia dell'arte was popular throughout Europe from before 1600 to the mid 1700s. By the time Carlo Gozzi wrote *The Love of Three Oranges* in 1761, the form was waning in popularity. Indeed, Gozzi wrote the play on a bet with another Italian playwright who felt Italian theatre needed a new, more realistic kind of play. Gozzi hoped to show his rival, Carlo Goldoni, that this form could still enthrall audiences. Gozzi won the bet and had audiences laughing louder than they had in years. *Commedia dell'arte* eventually gave way to scripted material, but Gozzi's plays are still performed and enjoyed all over the world.

CREATING AND PERFORMING

1. Think of a story that you and your friends would have no trouble improvising. What is the story and how would you present it?
2. Think of another fairy tale that could be cast as *commedia dell'arte*. Write a short outline for the actors.
3. Think about prominent figures in the national news. Do any of these people strike you as archetypes? Name one and list his or her characteristics.

MAGGIE MAGALITA

The Play as Literature: Foreshadowing

The term *foreshadowing* describes the clues or hints an author gives about what will happen next in the story. Foreshadowing helps prepare the reader for an important upcoming event.

In *Maggie Magalita,* the constraints of setting as well as the characters' movements and words foreshadow events. Look for gestures and statements that foreshadow how the relationship between Maggie, her grandmother, her mother, and her friend Eric will evolve. Also be aware of how the setting of the play influences this evolution.

The Play as Theatre: Costumes and Makeup

An actor's costume and makeup tell the audience a great deal about the character before a word is spoken. We can learn a character's age, social and economic position, and occupation; the time period and location of the events in the play; and even the time of year or time of day just by looking at the character. Costumes and makeup must be carefully chosen to fully complement the play.

Costumes are designed or selected by a costume designer who often has a crew to help with sewing, storage, and management. (See more about the costume crew on page 307.) The designer must keep in mind not only what the costume represents in the play but how the actor will wear it. Costumes must be comfortable and easy to move in—sometimes they must be easy to remove for quick changes. Costumes should be easy to make and inexpensive to buy.

WARM UP!

Look around your classroom. Find objects that you could use to help create a character of your choosing. Write the name of the object, the character who would use it, and how it would be used. List as many as you can. An example is shown below.

Object	Character	How Used
Two large books	Person working out	lift up & down in each hand

Maggie Magalita

by Wendy Kesselman

SETTING	CHARACTERS	TIME
New York City	MAGGIE ELENA, Maggie's Mother ABUELA, Maggie's Grandmother ERIC VOICE OF LITTLE MAGGIE VOICES OF SCHOOLCHILDREN	The Present

SCENE I

Opening music.

Light comes up dimly on MAGGIE, curled up on the couch in her nightgown, asleep.

MAGGIE *moves in her sleep. She is dreaming of herself as a small child,* LITTLE MAGGIE, *running after her grandmother,* ABUELA.

LITTLE MAGGIE *(V.O.; calling).* Abuela. Abuelita. ABUELITA!

ABUELA *(V.O.; laughing).* Magalita, ay mi niñita.

*(*LITTLE MAGGIE *laughs.)*

ABUELA *(cont'd.)* Quieres que te cargue?

*(*LITTLE MAGGIE *giggles delightedly.)*

ABUELA *(sings).* Dónde va la cojita.

LITTLE MAGGIE, ABUELA *(V.O.; sing).*

Que mi nauflí
Que mi nauflá
Voy al campo a buscar violetas
Que mi nauflí
Que mi nauflá

(Going up a half step)

Para quién son las violetas.

(There is the loud ring of a telephone. A light is switched on, revealing a small apartment, painted over many times, neat and clean, but shabby. The only touches of color come from things ELENA has made—pillows, an afghan, many winding plants. MAGGIE, half asleep, her hair in her face, stumbles to the telephone.)

MAGGIE. Ma? Ma, is she here?

ERIC *(on the telephone).* It's me.

*(*MAGGIE *is silent.)*

ERIC *(cont'd.)* Me. Eric. I've got this slight problem.

MAGGIE *(looking at her watch).* Eric, it's three o'clock in the morning.

ERIC. On page 98. You gotta help me, Maggie.

MAGGIE. I can't. Not tonight. I can't concentrate.

ERIC. You gotta concentrate, Mag. You gotta pull me through. Hey, who's got the scholarship to the dumb school anyway? *(Quickly)* Now listen: "The period of the pendulum is given by the equation T equals—"

(There is the sound of keys outside the apartment.)

MAGGIE *(interrupting ERIC).* Eric, oh

gosh, I gotta go. Don't worry—I'll call you in the morning, okay?

(The door to the apartment opens.)

ERIC *(going on).* Just tell me—fill in the blank.

MAGGIE *(hanging up quickly).* Bye-bye.

ERIC. Hey wait. Maggie—*(Looking at the phone in his hand)* Hey. *(He hangs up.)*

(ELENA bursts in, carrying a small battered suitcase.)

ELENA. She came, Maggie! She's here.

MAGGIE. Oh Mami—she's here?

ELENA. She's coming up the stairs.

(She goes out again to help ABUELA up the last stairs. ABUELA, small, frail, comes in. For a moment, she stands in the doorway, looking at MAGGIE. MAGGIE stands still, looking at her.)

ABUELA *(breathing heavily from climbing five flights of stairs; to ELENA).* Es ella?

(ELENA nods.)

ABUELA *(cont'd.)* No lo creo. Mi nieta. Mi niña. *(Reaching toward MAGGIE)* Mi Magalita.

ELENA *(moved).* Sí.

(MAGGIE doesn't move, gazing at ABUELA.)

ABUELA. Magalita. No puede ser. *(Coming closer to MAGGIE)* Pero qué grande estás. *(To ELENA)* Qué línda!

MAGGIE. Grandma . . .

ABUELA *(turning back to MAGGIE, puzzled).* Qué?

MAGGIE *(smiling).* Abuelita.

(She reaches forward and kisses ABUELA on the cheek.)

ABUELA *(embracing her).* Ay mi niña. Mi niña preciosa. Cuánto tiempo, cuán-

to tiempo sin verte. *(To ELENA)* Ella era tan chiquitita. *(Gesturing at MAGGIE's change of height)* Y ahora—mírala!

MAGGIE *(taking ABUELA's suitcase).* You're going to have my room, Abuela. *(To ELENA)* Don't you think she's tired, Mami? *(She puts the suitcase on the bed in her small room. She stands looking at ABUELA.)*

ELENA *(pulling ABUELA to the couch).* Siéntate, Mamá. Debes de estar agotada.

ABUELA *(pulling away).* Yo no me quiero sentar. Yo quiero mirar a mi nieta. Ven acá, Magalita. Déjame mirarte.

(MAGGIE comes forward a little, then stands still.)

ABUELA *(cont'd.)* Mmhm. Cabecidura como su abuelo.

ELENA *(laughing; to MAGGIE).* She says you're as stubborn as your grandfather.

MAGGIE. I hear her. *(After a pause)* Those stairs'll be hard for her, won't they, Ma?

ELENA. Ay, those stairs. Five flights. For me too they're hard.

(She takes off ABUELA's coat.)

ABUELA *(shivering).* Pero qué frío hace aquí. *(Hugging herself to get warm)* Uy, pero frío, frío, frío.

MAGGIE. You have to get used to it, Abuela. We had to.

ABUELA *(turning to ELENA).* Pero porqué ella no me habla en español?

MAGGIE. Because you have to speak English now, Abuelita. English, English, English. *(She laughs.)* From now on that's all you can speak.

ABUELA *(laughing too; then to* ELENA*)*. Qué dice? *(Worried)* No se le olvidó el español, Elena? No me digas que se le olvidó!

ELENA. No, Mamá. No te preocupes. *(Smiling, looking at* MAGGIE*)* She remembers her Spanish. Believe me.

MAGGIE. Look Abuela, I have something for you. *(From the bookcase dividing her room from the rest of the apartment, she takes a narrow flat box. It is wrapped in shiny paper and tied with a silver ribbon. She holds the box out to* ABUELA*.)*

ABUELA *(her face beaming)*. Para mí?

ELENA *(smiling)*. Para tí, Mamá.

*(*ABUELA *sinks into the couch, testing the cushions which seem strangely soft to her.)*

ABUELA *(taking off the ribbon and undoing the wrapping of the box)*. Ay, pero qué será?

MAGGIE. I made it.

ABUELA. Mmm?

ELENA. Ella lo hizo para tí.

ABUELA *(to* MAGGIE*)*. Tu lo hicistes para mí? Ay, qué bueno! *(She opens the box and takes out a very long green crocheted scarf.)* Ay pero qué cosa tan línda! *(*ABUELA *continues taking the scarf from the box. It goes on and on.)* Es para el frío?

*(*MAGGIE *nods.* ABUELA *continues pulling out the scarf. It is really very long.)*

ABUELA *(coming to the end)*. Ay Magalita.

(She stands up and kisses MAGGIE*.)*

ABUELA *(cont'd)* Gracias, mi niña. Qué mona tú eres. *(She holds out the scarf.)* Ahora, vamos a ver como va esto. *(She wraps the scarf around her head.)*

MAGGIE. No, no, Abuela. Like this.

(She flings the scarf around her neck, then hands it to ABUELA*.)*

ABUELA. Ah, sí. Ya veo. *(She flings the scarf around her neck, just as* MAGGIE *has done.)* Así está bien?

*(*MAGGIE *smiles.* ABUELA *steps forward, almost tripping on the long scarf. Wrapping the scarf around the other side.)*

ABUELA *(cont'd.)* Y así? *(Wrapping it back again)* Y otro más así? *(Wrapping it a final time)* Otrita más!

ELENA *(laughs)*. Mamá!

ABUELA *(perfectly serious)*. Qué línda. Qué bonita. *(She walks through the apartment, the scarf trailing on the ground.)* Y qué graande!

*(*ABUELA *walks into the small bedroom, trailing the scarf behind her.* ELENA *follows her, trying to pick up the scarf, but not succeeding.* MAGGIE, *smiling, starts to make up the couch in the living room, and then stops, remembering.)*

ABUELA *(V.O., sings)*.

Si te encuentras con la reina
Que mi nauflí
Que mi nauflá

LITTLE MAGGIE *(V.O., sings)*.

Yo le haré una reverencia
Que mi nauflí
Que mi nauflá

LITTLE MAGGIE, ABUELA *(V.O.; sing, going down a half step)*.

Si te encuentras con el guardia
Que mi nauflí
Que mi nauflá

(Laughing) Yo le haré un quiquiquo.

(They laugh wildly. MAGGIE *smiles to herself, as* ELENA *comes back into the living room.)*

MAGGIE. Is she comfortable, Mami?

ELENA. Very comfortable. *(Laughing)* She went to sleep with your scarf around her neck.

MAGGIE. She really liked that scarf, didn't she?

ELENA. She loved it. She could have stayed up all night. Just like in the old days.

(Together they continue making up the couch, where they will both sleep.)

ELENA *(cont'd.)* Ay Maggie, your Abuela. All night she would be cooking, cooking, cooking. Ay, what a cook she was! And how we ate. Ay, that food. *(After a moment)* She's thinner now. Much thinner.

MAGGIE. Yeah.

ELENA. Do you remember things about your grandmother?

MAGGIE *(looking away)*. Lots of things.

ELENA. You know what I remember? Her hair. When she got mad it filled the whole room. Black, black. Black like the water in the bottom of the well. And when she danced . . . *(She looks off.)* It was like a wild thing, that hair of hers. *(She pauses.)* It's so grey now.

MAGGIE. She's old, Ma.

ELENA. It's not just that. It's what she's been through. Ever since your grandfather died. *(Looking off)* The trying to get here. *(She pauses.)* The getting out.

MAGGIE. I'm tired, Ma.

ELENA. I was so scared she wouldn't be on that plane. That it would be like all the other times. All those times we went for her. Those lines. All of us waiting and waiting. And then the plane coming and everybody hugging and kissing and yelling at each other and then . . . then . . . *(She breaks off for a moment.)*

MAGGIE. Then she wouldn't come.

ELENA. Tú te acuerdas?

MAGGIE. I remember. *(After a moment)* You're not going to start speaking Spanish now, are you Mami?

ELENA. No, Maggie. Of course not, querida.

MAGGIE. Oh Ma, there you go.

ELENA. I can't believe she's here. I can't believe she finally got here. *(Hugging* **MAGGIE,** *half laughing, half serious)* And how's she ever going to get used to it here?

MAGGIE. It'll be fine, Ma.

ELENA. You should have heard her about that plane. When your Abuela gets started, ay, olvidate.

MAGGIE *(laughing)*. When you get started, you mean.

ELENA. She said—listen to this—she said it was like being inside the stomach of . . . un pájaro blanco y grande . . . like being in the stomach of a big white bird. She sure can say things.

MAGGIE *(turning toward* **ELENA***)*. How long do you think it'll take her to say something in English?

ELENA. I don't know. It may take her awhile. Remember how long it took me?

MAGGIE. Yeah, but I want her to learn fast.

ELENA. It's very hard for a person her age to learn a new language.

MAGGIE. What's so hard about it?

ELENA. It's not like when you learned. You were little. It was easy for you.

MAGGIE. No. It wasn't. (*Looking at* ELENA) Ma, she's got to—

ELENA. Don't try to change her, Maggie.

MAGGIE. I know, Ma. But she's here now. And she's gonna get—

ELENA (*breaking in*). We'll talk about it in the morning. (*She pulls back the blankets of the couch and begins to tuck* MAGGIE *in.*)

MAGGIE. Ma, do you—do you think she remembers me? I mean, do you—

ELENA (*interrupting and kissing her*). Don't worry, pumpkin. Your Abuela remembers every little thing about you. I can promise you that.

(*She turns out the light, takes a last look at* ABUELA, *and goes into the kitchen. The moment* ELENA *goes out,* MAGGIE *sits up in bed. She clasps her knees to her chest, thinking back.*)

LITTLE MAGGIE (*V.O.*) Uno, dos, tres, cuatro, cinco, seis, siete, ocho, nueve, diez!

(MAGGIE *smiles.*)

LITTLE MAGGIE (*V.O., cont'd.*) Ronda, ronda, que el que no se haya escondido se esconda!

(ABUELA *laughs softly.*)

LITTLE MAGGIE (*V.O., finding her*). Te veo!

ABUELA (*V.O.*) Ah! Ahora, niña!

(*She laughs.* LITTLE MAGGIE *giggles rapturously.[1])*

ABUELA, LITTLE MAGGIE (*V.O.; sing joyfully.*)

Arroz con leche
Se quiere casar
Con una viudita
De la capital.

(MAGGIE *hums aloud.*)

ABUELA, LITTLE MAGGIE (*V.O.; sing*).

Que sepa coser
Que sepa bordar
Que ponga la aguja
En su canevá.

(*Softly,* MAGGIE *sings along with* LITTLE MAGGIE.)

LITTLE MAGGIE (*V.O.; sings*).

Ti-lin
Ti-lan
Copita de pan
Haya viene juan
Allá
Comiendo el pan
Si no se lo dan.

(*The light dims.*)

SCENE 2

In the small bedroom, light comes up on ELENA *and* ABUELA, *going through a few old photographs.*

MAGGIE *stands facing the audience, in front of an imaginary mirror in the living room. She is trying on different sweaters, each one wilder than the next.*

ELENA (*Holding up a photograph and laughing*). Ay Mamá, no es verdad! (*Calling to* MAGGIE) Maggie, come look at this picture of me—eating cake with a pig when I was six years old!

---

1. rapturously (rap′chə rəs lē′), being carried away by overwhelming emotion

(ELENA *and* ABUELA *laugh.*)

ELENA *(Cont'd. Picking up another photograph.)* Y mira ésta Mamá—ay, qué línda luces aquí.

ABUELA. Ah sí, ésa era la favorita de tu papá.

MAGGIE *(calling in from the mirror).* Hey Ma, can you come in for a sec?

ELENA. In a minute, Maggie. I'm talking with your grandmother.

ABUELA *(holding up another photograph).* Y mira ésta, Elena.

MAGGIE. Ma-a. I have to ask you something.

ELENA. I'll be right there. *(Looking at the photographs; to* ABUELA, *sadly)* Ah sí.

MAGGIE. Ma, I'm waiting.

ELENA. I'm coming.

ABUELA. Mira tu papá, aquí.

MAGGIE. Ma, I'm gonna be late for school.

ABUELA. Hace dos años. La última foto de él.

ELENA. Ay Mami.

MAGGIE. Ma-a.

ELENA. Shhh, Maggie. I'm looking at a photograph of your grandfather.

ABUELA. La única.

(MAGGIE, *having found just the right combination, comes into the small bedroom wearing a bright red sweater covered with huge buttons [I Love New York, etc.], a glittering scarf and a silver hat.*)

MAGGIE *(twirling around in her outfit).* Look, Ma!

ABUELA *(almost doing a double take).* Ay, pero qué es eso?

MAGGIE *(laughing).* What?

ABUELA. Elena, tú no las vas a dejar salir así!

MAGGIE. What's she talking about? This is my favorite outfit.

ELENA *(smiling).* I know, I know. *(To* ABUELA*)* Mamá, aquí las niñas—

ABUELA *(interrupting, pulling at the sweater).* Pero Elena, no estamos en un carnaval!

(MAGGIE *goes back into the living room and starts putting on a pair of bright red roller skates.*)

ABUELA *(cont'd.)* Está loca?

(ELENA *laughs.*)

MAGGIE *(fastening her skates).* Tell her I'm going skating after school, Mami. Then she'll understand.

ELENA. Understand? A woman's who's lived in the mountains all her life? *(Laughing)* She's never even seen a pair of skates.

ABUELA *(standing up).* Elena, no te rías. Dile que se los quite.

MAGGIE *(watching them).* Boy, does she boss you around. *(She stands up on the skates.)*

ABUELA *(crossing herself).* Jesús, María y José.

ELENA. Mamá, las cosas son diferentes aquí.

ABUELA. Las cosas son diferentes pero—

(MAGGIE *bursts in on the roller skates. She glides right up to* ABUELA. ABUELA *shrieks in surprise.*)

ABUELA (cont'd.) Ay, pero Elena!

ELENA *(laughing).* No tengas miedo, Mamá. Esos son patines. *(To*

MAGGIE) Maggie, take those skates off right now.

(Laughing, MAGGIE pulls ABUELA out into the living room.)

ABUELA *(moaning, as MAGGIE pulls her along).* Ay, ay, ay.

ELENA *(following them).* Come on, Maggie. You're upsetting your grandmother.

(ABUELA plops down onto the couch, her moans gradually turning into laughter, as she shakes her finger at MAGGIE.)

MAGGIE *(watching ABUELA).* She doesn't look so upset to me.

ELENA. You know she is. She's not used to you. *(After a moment)* Yet.

MAGGIE. A-bue-la! *(On tiptoes on the roller skates, half clowning, she does a ballet step.)*

ELENA. Stop it.

(MAGGIE gracefully skates forward.)

ABUELA. Magalita.

(MAGGIE stops skating.)

ABUELA *(cont'd.)* Ven acá.

(MAGGIE is still.)

ABUELA *(cont'd.)* Ven acá, Magalita. Siéntate conmigo. Magalita.

MAGGIE *(taking off her skates).* Ma, tell her not to call me that.

(ELENA is silent.)

MAGGIE *(cont'd.)* Tell her to call me Maggie.

ELENA. Give her a day, pumpkin. Just one day. She won't understand.

MAGGIE. She's got to understand. She's got to get used to it.

ELENA. She will. Believe me.

ABUELA. Cállate, Elena. *(To MAGGIE)* Magalita—

MAGGIE. Please tell her, Ma.

ELENA. All right, all right. *(To ABUELA)* Óyeme Mamá, no la llames Magalita—llámala Maggie.

ABUELA. Cómo?

ELENA. Maggie.

ABUELA. Cómo? No te entiendo.

ELENA *(to MAGGIE).* You see? She doesn't understand.

MAGGIE. Okay, okay, I'll write it down for her. *(She tears open her schoolbag and rips a piece of paper out of her notebook. She scrawls her name in large letters across the page. Sitting down on the couch opposite ABUELA, she holds the piece of paper across her chest.)*

ABUELA. Ah sí. *(Pronouncing it with difficulty)* Maghi-e.

MAGGIE. No! Maggie. *(Spelling her name out loud in Spanish)* EME-A-GE-GE-I-E.

ABUELA. Pero por qué? Magalita es un nombre tan precioso.

MAGGIE. Porque I like it. That's why.

ABUELA *(to ELENA).* Por qué?

ELENA. Porque a ella—

MAGGIE *(overlapping).* Porque Magalita no fit here at all. I hate that name, okay? *(Crushing the paper into a ball, she throws it on the floor.)*

ABUELA *(anxiously, to ELENA).* Qué me dice?

MAGGIE. Tell her it sounds strange here. It sounds weird. Abuela— nobody's got that name here.

ELENA *(trying to explain it to ABUELA).* Mira, Mamá—es que . . .

ABUELA *(interrupting).* Pero por qué ella usa otro nombre aquí?

ELENA. Mamá, escuchame—

ABUELA (loudly). Yo te escucho.

ELENA. No te excites.

ABUELA. No me digas que no me excite. Yo quiero saber por que no le gusta su propio nombre.

MAGGIE. It is my name. MAGGIE is my name.

ABUELA. Pero qué clase de nombre es ése? Elena, cómo la dejaste—

MAGGIE (interrupting). It's a perfectly good name. Maggie is a perfectly good name. And it's my name now. (She sits down in the rocking chair.) Ay, she just doesn't understand anything.

ELENA. Speak to her in Spanish, Maggie.

MAGGIE. I won't. So forget it.

ELENA. Don't talk to me like that.

MAGGIE. I'm sorry, Ma, but—

ABUELA (overlapping). Elena, qué pasa? Qué pasa?

MAGGIE (tears coming to her eyes). You've got to explain it to her, Mami.

ELENA. I'm trying, Maggie.

ABUELA (going over to MAGGIE in the rocking chair). Cálmate, mi niña. Cálmate. (Stroking MAGGIE's hair, rocking her a little, she croons, singsong.) Mi nieta Magalita—(She stops, realizing what she has said, and looks nervously at ELENA. With an effort.) Ma-gee? Es así? (Half whispering) Ma-gee?

ELENA (half laughing). Sí. Casi, Mamá.

ABUELA (looking at MAGGIE, singsong). Mi nieta Ma-gee.

(She rocks MAGGIE in the rocking chair, nearly tipping it over, then smiles innocently when MAGGIE swings around to look at her.)

MAGGIE (unable to stop from laughing). Ay Abuelita. You're crazy—you know that?

ABUELA (smiling happily, because MAGGIE is smiling). Sí?

MAGGIE. You're a real nut.

ABUELA. Sí?

MAGGIE. Sí.

ELENA. Seguro que sí.

ABUELA. Ay sí. (ELENA laughs.)

MAGGIE. Don't worry, Tata. You don't have to worry. (Touching ABUELA's hand) I'll teach you.

(As ELENA and ABUELA go into the kitchen, MAGGIE rocks back and forth in the rocking chair, remembering.)

A SCHOOLCHILD (V.O.) Say "Stupid."

LITTLE MAGGIE (V.O.) Estupid.

(There is a muffled giggle.)

ANOTHER SCHOOLCHILD (V.O.) Say "Students."

LITTLE MAGGIE (V.O.) Estudents.

(There is another giggle.)

ANOTHER SCHOOLCHILD (V.O.) "Always stammer."

LITTLE MAGGIE (V.O.) Always—estammer.

(Another giggle)

ANOTHER SCHOOLCHILD (V.O.) "So stupid students shouldn't speak."

LITTLE MAGGIE (V.O.) So estupid estudents shouldn't espeak.

(Giggles again)

FIRST SCHOOLCHILD (V.O.) Now say the whole thing.

(LITTLE MAGGIE is silent.)

FIRST SCHOOLCHILD (V.O., cont'd.) Go

ahead. Go on. It's easy—"Stupid students always stammer, so stupid students shouldn't speak."

(In the rocking chair, MAGGIE mouths the words.)

LITTLE MAGGIE *(V.O.; starting).* Estu—

(There is a laugh. She stops.)

ANOTHER SCHOOLCHILD *(V.O.)* Good, good. Go on. You can do it.

LITTLE MAGGIE *(V.O.; haltingly).* Estupid estudents always estammer, so estupid estudents shouldn't espeak.

(The SCHOOLCHILDREN try not to laugh.)

FIRST SCHOOLCHILD *(V.O.)* Very, very good. Now do it faster.

(MAGGIE sighs, leans forward in the rocking chair.)

SCHOOLCHILDREN *(V.O.; very quickly).* Stupid students always stammer, so stupid students shouldn't speak.

(In the rocking chair, MAGGIE closes her eyes. She says the words aloud.)

LITTLE MAGGIE *(V.O.; trying to go fast).* Estupid-estudents-always-estammer-so-estupid-estudents-shouldn't-espeak.

(She gets all caught up in the s's, as the SCHOOLCHILDREN, unable to hold themselves back, burst into laughter. MAGGIE leans back in the rocking chair, and begins rocking desperately, back and forth, back and forth.)

SCENE 3

Before light comes up, the SCHOOLCHILDREN's laughter blends into the clatter of a cafeteria and the piercing sound of a school bell. Light comes up on

MAGGIE *and* ERIC, *sitting in study hall.*

MAGGIE, *concentrating intensely, writes rapidly, neatly filling the pages of her notebook. She has a collection of long, finely sharpened pencils before her. Next to her,* ERIC, *chewing on the end of an already chewed up pencil, is completely stumped. On his desk is an assortment of chewed pencil stubs with no points. From time to time, he glances surreptitiously[2] at* MAGGIE. *For just an instant,* MAGGIE *turns to look at him. He immediately bends over, scribbling furiously away. He turns a page hurriedly, tears it, pulls wildly at his already disheveled hair, and stops, his head in his hands. He turns and watches* MAGGIE, *overwhelmed with admiration. He leans closer, knocking all his pencil stubs on the floor. Silently, without even looking at him, and without stopping writing,* MAGGIE *hands him one of her perfectly sharpened pencils. He takes it, starts scribbling again, and breaks it. Wordlessly,* MAGGIE *hands him another. He takes it, breaks it also, and holds it silently to him, gazing at her. He is watching her face, her beauty, her amazing concentration.*

MAGGIE *(whispering).* What are you looking at? Do the problem.

ERIC. You're so organized. I've never seen anyone so organized. Even your pencils are organized. *(Moving closer)* Isn't there any room in your life for a little disorganization? *(He pauses, kicking her lightly under the table.)* Like me?

MAGGIE *(smiling).* Shhh. I've gotta finish this problem.

ERIC. Yeah, well me too.

(They work side by side for a few moments,

---

2. surreptitiously (sər/əp tish/əs lē), secretly; done with stealth

ERIC *clearly not getting any further ahead.*)

ERIC *(cont'd.)* So uh, can you help me out after study hall today?

(MAGGIE is silent.)

ERIC *(cont'd.)* I thought you were coming over to my house.

MAGGIE. Oh, Eric, I wish I could, but my grandmother's waiting for me.

ERIC. Well, what am I gonna do? I'm practically flunking math without you. *(Gently tapping MAGGIE's arm with his pencil)* Can't your grandmother be alone for just one day?

MAGGIE. She's alone every day.

ERIC. Yeah. But I mean—

MAGGIE *(overlapping).* Eric, you know my mother's in night school—she's taking this awful statistics course. She never gets back till—

ERIC *(breaking in).* I know, I know. But—

MAGGIE *(interrupting).* You don't understand. My grandmother. She's just—

ERIC. I've gotta meet this grandmother of yours. Why don't we go over there right after school?

MAGGIE. No! *(Glancing around; softer)* I mean—not today. *(She goes back to her notebook.)*

ERIC. You say that every day. *(Suddenly putting his hand over the page MAGGIE is working on)* Maggie. When am I gonna see you?

MAGGIE *(moving his hand away; laughing).* Soon. *(Gently)* I promise.

ERIC. Well, you just pick the day and I'll be there.

MAGGIE. O-ka-ay.

ERIC *(after a moment).* When? *(Another moment)* Tomorrow?

MAGGIE. I can't. I'm taking my grandmother to the zoo.

ERIC *(excited).* The zoo! Oh neat! That's my favorite.

MAGGIE *(looking around).* Shhh.

ERIC. Hey, why don't all three of us go? *(Looking at her)* What do you think?

MAGGIE. I don't know. We'll see. *(Softer)* Maybe.

(ERIC leans even closer to her. The bell rings.)

ERIC. Ooh—

(MAGGIE gathers her books together.)

ERIC *(cont'd.)* You know—

(MAGGIE looks at him.)

ERIC *(cont'd.)* This is the only time I get to talk to you anymore—during study hall.

MAGGIE. Yeah, well, maybe you shouldn't have talked so much.

ERIC *(looking at the clock on the wall ahead).* Don't worry. I got a couple of minutes till math.

MAGGIE *(also looking at the clock).* One minute. To be exact.

ERIC. Yeah well—one minute. Mmm. That's life.

(MAGGIE starts to go, turns back.)

MAGGIE. You know something.

(ERIC looks at her.)

MAGGIE *(cont'd.)* You can call me anytime. I mean anytime. *(Half whispering)* You can call me at four o'clock in the morning . . . if you want. Just—well—*(Looking at the clock)* Anyway . . . *(Hardly audible)* I miss you. *(Loud)* Bye.

Maggie Magalita by Wendy Kesselman   **281**

ERIC *(stunned).* Hey, yeah, well—me too—I uh—I—Maggie, I—*(He whirls around, once again dropping all his pencil stubs and notebook on the floor, but she is gone. He looks down at the fallen notebook and pencils.)* Oops.

(He looks up and smiles, as light comes up on ABUELA, *a dignified figure, dressed all in black, sitting on the bed in her tiny bedroom. There is a very small window. She is looking down at the floor. After a few moments, she gets up and walks to the dividing bookcase. She seems listless, tired. She picks up a large conch shell, puts it to her ear, listens to the ocean, smiles. She puts it down again. She walks into the living room, hesitates, goes to the window. She struggles to open it, finally succeeding. From the street comes the blasting sound of a police siren. She hurriedly closes the window. As she moves away, she finds that her scarf is caught outside the window. She opens the window for an instant and pulls the scarf out again. Exhausted from the effort, shivering from the cold, she moves away from the window. She walks to the television set. She fiddles with the knobs, finally switches it on. The sound of an afternoon soap opera blares forth. She switches it off. She picks up* MAGGIE's *silver hat and walks back into the tiny room. She sits down on the bed, cradling the hat in her hands. Then she looks down at the floor again. The door to the apartment opens.* ABUELA *looks up.* MAGGIE *bursts in, breathing heavily from having rushed up the stairs.)*

MAGGIE. I'm home, Tata.

ABUELA. Magalita! *(A huge smile breaks across her face.)*

SCENE 4

In the living room, ELENA *is working on her statistics course.*

MAGGIE *is sprawled out on the floor with her homework.*

ABUELA *comes in and, after a few moments, begins humming to herself, wandering around the apartment, picking things up, putting them down, studying things. After a while, she begins rearranging the apartment. She starts with small things—a pillow here, a pillow there, gradually moving on to bigger and bigger things.*

ELENA *(suddenly breaking into Spanish over the survey she is working on).* Ocho y nueve, diesisiete, llevo una, dos y una, tres, y una cuatro. Cuatro y—

MAGGIE *(interrupting).* Mami—what are you doing?

ELENA. Qué?

MAGGIE. You never count in Spanish.

ELENA. Shhh. I always count in Spanish.

MAGGIE. Not anymore, Ma. Not for years.

ELENA. Okay, okay. Four and eight are twelve, carry the one—*(She whispers to herself, continuing the counting in Spanish.)* Una y dos, tres, y una cuatro. Cuatro y cinco, nueve—

MAGGIE. Ma, I can hear you.

ELENA. Maggie, do you want to do these statistics?

(There is silence for a while, with ELENA *counting quietly in Spanish under her breath, and* MAGGIE *doing her homework.* ABUELA, *who has been quietly moving things around all along, starts moving the rocking chair in front of the television set.*

MAGGIE *looks at her, but doesn't say anything.* ABUELA *goes on moving things. Now she is on to the table.)*

MAGGIE. Abuela.

(ABUELA *drags the table along the floor.)*

MAGGIE. Ma, would you tell her not to make so much noise. I can't concentrate.

ELENA. Shhh, Maggie. Leave her alone.

MAGGIE. Just look at her. She's going nuts.

(ELENA *keeps counting.)*

MAGGIE *(cont'd.)* Mami.

ELENA. I'll be done in a minute. You tell her to stop.

MAGGIE. She won't listen to me.

ELENA. That's because you won't speak to her in any way she can understand.

MAGGIE. She understands me when she wants to. *(Suddenly)* Abuela!

(ABUELA *jumps. Then she goes on moving the small television set in its squeaking movable stand across the floor.)*

MAGGIE *(annoyed).* Abuela.

(ABUELA *fixes the television set in front of the rocking chair.)*

MAGGIE *(cont'd.)* Ma, she's changing the whole house around.

ELENA. So let her change it. *(Glancing at* ABUELA*)* She's enjoying herself.

(ABUELA *plugs in the television set.)*

MAGGIE. She sure is. It doesn't even look like our house anymore.

ELENA. Cuatro y dos, seis—What's the difference? You never cared how it looked before.

MAGGIE. Okay, let her. It doesn't matter to me.

ELENA *(looking up).* What's wrong with it? It looks fine.

MAGGIE. Really? You like it?

ELENA. Try and be more casual. You're such a worrier. Your grandmother isn't going to—

(ABUELA *moves a long hanging plant from the window.* ELENA *jumps up.)*

ELENA *(cont'd.)* Pero qué tú haces, Mamá?

MAGGIE *(laughing).* Aha!

(ABUELA *continues to walk away with the plant.)*

ELENA. Mamá!

ABUELA *(deciding where to put the plant).* Y ésta—déjame ver—dónde va . . .? *(Finding a place, pleased)* Aquí!

ELENA *(standing in front of her).* Mamá, qué estás haciendo?

ABUELA. Estoy poniendola donde haya más luz.

ELENA. Better light? The light is terrible there. *(She tries to get the plant away from* ABUELA.)*

ABUELA *(hanging onto it).* Pero Elena, mírala aquí.

(MAGGIE *gets up to watch them.)*

ELENA. La cuestión no es mirarla, la cuestión es que tenga luz. *(To* MAGGIE*)* Isn't it, Maggie?

MAGGIE *(smiling).* Oh definitely, Mami—it's definitely a question of the best light.

ABUELA *(pulling fiercely on the top of the plant hanger).* Espérate, Elena.

ELENA *(pulling back).* Yo sé, Mamá, el mejor lugar.

(MAGGIE *laughs as* ELENA *finally pulls the*

plant away from ABUELA *and puts it back where it was.* ABUELA *watches* ELENA. *She is not happy.* ELENA *goes back to her work. On tiptoes,* ABUELA *moves toward another plant. Without looking, reaching for her.)*

ELENA *(cont'd.)* Ay no, Mamá! No toques ésa!

ABUELA *(carrying the plant away).* Déjame, Elena. Tú no sabes nada de plantas.

ELENA *(to Maggie).* I don't know anything about plants. Who knows about plants if I don't? Look at the plants in this house. *(To* ABUELA, *who has somehow managed to climb on top of the radiator below the small window in the little room.)* Mira las plantas en esta casa.

ABUELA *(examining the plant in her hand contemptuously[3]).* Sí. Ya las veo. *(She tries to hang the plant in the small window.)*

ELENA *(climbing up on top of the radiator with* ABUELA *). There's not enough sun there. (Cutting herself off, to* ABUELA *)* No hay suficiente sol ahí.

*(*ABUELA *laughs.)*

ABUELA. Sol? Qué sol? Aquí no hay sol.

ELENA. No sun? What is she saying? The sun comes in every afternoon.

ABUELA. Y a eso tú le llamas sol? *(A small disdainful[4] giggle)* Tú no te acuerdas del sol, mi hija.

ELENA. She still treats me like a child.

(Taking the plant from ABUELA *)*

ELENA *(cont'd.)* I remember el sol, Mamá. *(To* MAGGIE *)* Where have you been taking her all these days?

MAGGIE. Out.

ELENA. And has she seen the sun?

MAGGIE. I don't think that's what she's talking about, Mami.

ELENA *(putting the plant back where it was).* Well, next time take her to the real sun.

(On top of the radiator, ABUELA *struggles to get down.)*

MAGGIE *(going to help her).* If you'd just let her go, Mami—I'm taking her to the zoo today.

ELENA. Ay—the zoo—good, I forgot about that. *(Pleased; to* ABUELA *)* Van al zoológico, Mamá.

MAGGIE. And then we're going shopping.

ELENA. Mmhm.

(Trying to distract ABUELA *from the plants, she brings over* ABUELA*'s long black coat and* MAGGIE*'s jacket. But* ABUELA *has hurried on to another plant.)*

ELENA *(cont'd. Rushing forward, throwing the coats toward* MAGGIE.*)* Ay no, Mamá—por favor!

(She runs toward ABUELA, *who runs on, clutching the small plant to her.)*

ELENA *(cont'd.)* Mamá—no!

ABUELA *(pointing toward the small window).* Allí sí hay sol! Allí sí hay sol!

MAGGIE *(the coats over her arm, turning from one to the other).* Mami! Abuela!

SCENE 5

Music under, as MAGGIE pulls ABUELA along to the zoo. MAGGIE and ABUELA are walking in the direction of the audience.

---

3. contemptuously (kən temp′chü was lē), showing intense dislike
4. disdainful (dis dān′fəl), showing scorn or disapproval

MAGGIE (running ahead). Come on, Tata. You'll see. You're going to love it. Look—(She points in the direction of the audience.) There's the lion's cage.

(ABUELA comes forward, dressed in her black coat and trailing her long green scarf.)

ABUELA (tired). Espérate, Magalita. Despacio.

MAGGIE (coming back to ABUELA). I'll go as slow as you want. But today you have to promise to speak English. You promise?

ABUELA. Sí, sí. (Raising one hand) I prometto.

(Slowly they walk forward and face the audience.)

MAGGIE (pointing straight ahead). You see, Tata—that's a lion. A big lion.

(The lion roars.)

ABUELA (jumping back). Ah sí. Un león.

MAGGIE No. (Slowly) LI-ON.

ABUELA (trying). LI-O.

MAGGIE. Good. LI-ON.

(They move to the next cage.)

ABUELA. LI-0.

(MAGGIE looks back for an instant, then goes on.)

MAGGIE. See, Tata. That's an elephant. EL-E-PHANT.

ABUELA. ELE- (Pointing suddenly) Ay mira, Magalita!

(She covers her nose with her scarf. MAGGIE and ABUELA laugh.)

MAGGIE. Yeah. Now listen. EL-E-PHANT. ELEPHANT.

ABUELA (proudly, with emphasis). ELE-FANTE.

(The elephant trumpets loudly. ABUELA steps forward and gazes, awed, delighted, at the elephant. MAGGIE takes ABUELA's hand and pulls her along to the next cage.)

MAGGIE (reading the sign). You see, Tata. This is where they have the polar bears. (She looks around for the usually absent polar bears.)

ABUELA (her eyes searching the cage). Dónde? Dónde está?

MAGGIE. I don't know. It doesn't matter. Just say BEAR—POLAR BEAR.

ABUELA (still looking). Pero dónde. dónde?

MAGGIE. I don't know where. Maybe it's behind that rock over there.

ABUELA. Pero qué cosa es?

MAGGIE. Abuela, it's a polar bear. (Making bear motions with her arms) A BEAR. (She advances on ABUELA, the bear motions getting bigger.) PO-LAR BEAR.

(ABUELA backs up, as MAGGIE advances.)

ABUELA (stopping). Aah-ha-ah! (Loudly, with accent, and huge bear motions) PO-LA BE-A

(MAGGIE, startled, jumps back. Then, as ABUELA advances on her, the bear motions growing bigger and bigger, she laughs.)

SCENE 6

The sixth floor of a department store. MAGGIE and ABUELA are walking toward the down escalator. They are both carrying packages.

MAGGIE. C'mon, Tata, we're going down this way.

(ABUELA follows MAGGIE cheerfully, but backs up when she sees the escalator.)

ABUELA. Ay no—

MAGGIE (*gently taking her arm*). C'mon. You don't have to be scared. It's an escalator. A moving staircase.

ABUELA (*staring at it*). Yo no—yo no me voy en eso.

MAGGIE. Sure you are. It's not going to bite you.

(ABUELA *moves closer to the escalator, stands with her feet just at the edge, but doesn't get on it.*)

MAGGIE (*cont'd.*) Just put your foot on it.

(ABUELA *lifts her foot, hesitatingly puts it on the escalator, then quickly removes it.*)

ABUELA. No, Magalita. Yo no puedo.

MAGGIE. Of course you can. Don't be frightened. Just go. (*She holds out her hand to* ABUELA.)

ABUELA (*holding* MAGGIE*'s hand for an instant, then dropping it*). No—

(*She moves away.* MAGGIE, *coming up from behind* ABUELA, *smiles at the nearby shoppers, then pushes* ABUELA *back toward the escalator.*)

MAGGIE (*half whispering*). Go ahead. Vamos!

(ABUELA *leans back against* MAGGIE, *who continues to push her toward the escalator. At the last moment,* ABUELA *slips out of* MAGGIE*'s grasp.*)

ABUELA. Ay no, Magalita.

MAGGIE. Would you come with me.

ABUELA (*fiercely standing her ground*). No!

MAGGIE (*stepping onto the escalator*). Well I'm going.

ABUELA (*panic-stricken*). Espérate, Magalita. No bajes!

MAGGIE (*offstage, from the escalator*). Just follow me.

ABUELA. Magalita, ven acá! MAGALITA!

MAGGIE (*offstage, turning back, embarrassed*). Shhh! Cálmate.

ABUELA (*crying now*). Magalita, no me dejes sola.

(MAGGIE *makes her way up the down escalator.*)

MAGGIE (*furious, between clenched teeth*). Cálmate. I'm coming. I'm coming. Espérate. God. (*Looking at* ABUELA *in a rage*) C'mon, we'll take the elevator down. (*She walks ahead.*)

ABUELA (*following* MAGGIE). Tengo miedo, Magalita.

MAGGIE. Shhh! Oh God, everybody's looking.

ABUELA. Ay Magalita. Perdoname.

MAGGIE. Forget it. Olvidate. (*Cold as ice*) We are taking the elevator—I told you.

(*She walks on.* ABUELA *follows her, her long green scarf trailing, as light comes up on* ELENA, *holding a small can of paint in one hand and a paintbrush in the other, retouching the peeling doors of the apartment.* MAGGIE *and* ABUELA, *almost knocking the can of paint out of* ELENA*'s hand, come through the front door. It is obvious they are not speaking.* ABUELA *walks right past* ELENA *and goes into her small room. She sits down on the bed in her coat.* MAGGIE *slumps down on the couch with her packages.*)

MAGGIE (*cont'd.*) Why can't she leave? Why can't she go back?

(ELENA *is silent.*)

MAGGIE (*cont'd.*) But why not? That's where she belongs, isn't it?

ELENA. Shhh. Stop shouting, Maggie.

MAGGIE. Why should I?

ELENA. She'll hear you.

MAGGIE. So what? She can't understand me anyway.

(In the other room, ABUELA *turns away.)*

ELENA. What happened, Maggie? What's going on?

MAGGIE *(breaking into tears).* I don't want her here anymore.

ELENA. Ay please, Maggie. Don't say that. I know you don't mean what you're saying.

MAGGIE. But I do. You just don't understand.

ELENA. I understand that you're tired and upset—

MAGGIE *(interrupting and jumping up).* I am not tired. And I am not upset.

ELENA *(going on).* And that it's been hard for you with Abuela. I do understand.

MAGGIE. It's not just that.

ELENA. Then what is it? Hmmm—tell me.

*(*MAGGIE *is silent.)*

ELENA *(cont'd.)* You can tell me, Maggie.

MAGGIE. I can't talk to her, Mami. I don't know what to say. I hate it when she calls me Magalita, and speaks Spanish all the time. And then she doesn't say anything for hours. What is she thinking about?

ELENA. Why don't you ask her?

MAGGIE. I don't want to ask her. She's changed. I don't remember her that way.

ELENA. Ay Maggie, I thought maybe she'd be happy here. I prayed she would be. She left so much behind. *(Quiet)* We all did. She's old, Maggie.

She doesn't have anyone else.

MAGGIE. What are you saying—she can't be happy because of me?

ELENA. Abuela is tired. Coming here has worn her out.

MAGGIE. Well, me too. I'm tired too. I'm tired of her being here. *(She starts to open her packages. In* MAGGIE's *packages are a pair of flashy red plastic glasses, a huge baggy T-shirt with a photograph of The Police, a fluffy red headband, a pair of red heart-shaped earrings, two huge strips of black licorice. Throughout the rest of the scene, she takes these out and tries them on.)*

ELENA. She can't get used to this city.

MAGGIE *(pulling on the baggy T-shirt).* She never will.

ELENA *(quietly).* Maybe not. You were too little. When we—

MAGGIE *(breaking in).* I know, I know what it was like. *(She sits down on the couch and opens another package.)*

ELENA. She hasn't changed. You have changed, Maggie.

MAGGIE *(putting on the fluffy red headband).* But what's the matter with her? Why can't she do something. She doesn't do *anything.*

ELENA. She's trying. I know she is.

MAGGIE *(putting on the red heart-shaped earrings). How?* I am sick of having her around. I can't bring my friends here anymore. I can't bring Eric.

ELENA. Why not? I think Eric would like Abuela.

MAGGIE. Ma. She is so embarrassing.

ELENA *(coming closer).* I want to tell you something.

Maggie Magalita by Wendy Kesselman   **287**

MAGGIE. What? *(She starts chewing the licorice.)*

ELENA *(her voice rising)*. Your Abuela is not someone to be ashamed of.

MAGGIE. I know, I know.

ELENA. Do you hear me?

MAGGIE. I hear you, I hear you.

ELENA. Think about it.

MAGGIE *(standing up)*. I don't want to think about anything anymore. I just want her to go.

ELENA *(quiet)*. You're so like her.

(MAGGIE turns away.)

ELENA *(cont'd.)* Don't turn away like that. When we first came here, I wanted to bring your grandfather and Abuela with us. But they didn't want to come. And you wouldn't go without them. You cried and cried. For days you begged her to come with us. She practically brought you up. I was so young when I had you.

(She looks at MAGGIE, who is silent.)

ELENA *(cont'd.)* And then after we got here, and things began to go better, we wrote asking them to come. We wrote many times. And it was always you who wrote the letter. It was always you. *(She pauses.)* But they had lived their whole lives there. No matter what happened, she never wanted to leave. She told me. She wanted to die there.

MAGGIE. Then why did she come? Why didn't she die there? *(Turning away, stunned at her own words)* Oh, God.

ELENA. Ay Maggie, you've forgotten. I think you have forgotten everything.

(Brushing away her tears, MAGGIE puts on the flashy red plastic glasses.)

ELENA *(cont'd.)* But I can't make you remember. I can't expect you to remember anything about our country.

MAGGIE *(facing ELENA in all her full regalia—red plastic glasses, heart-shaped earrings, fluffy headband, T-shirt, her lips stained with black licorice)*. This is our country, Mami.

ELENA. Is it? This may be your country, Maggie. But don't speak for anyone else. And don't try to force it on her. She'll never accept it. Believe me.

(She walks out of the room, into the small division, and sits down beside ABUELA on the bed. MAGGIE paces back and forth, her hands clenched. There is the sound of a jump rope rhythmically hitting the pavement.)

SCHOOLCHILDREN *(V.O.; starting slow and quiet)*.
Magaleeta
Is a freaka
Every time she talk a leeta
She begin to speeta speeta

(Growing in force and intensity)
Magaleeta
Magaleeta
She's a cheat
And she's a sneaka
She can't ever join our cleeka
Just a leetle freakareeka

(They giggle.)

LITTLE MAGGIE *(V.O.; pleading with them)*. No, no, no, no!

SCHOOLCHILDREN *(V.O.; in a whisper)*.
Magaleeta
Magaleeta
Is a leetle Spanish freaka

(The jump rope smacks the pavement faster and faster.)

Magaleeta
Leetle freaka
Magaleeta
Leetle freaka

(Their chanting grows to a crescendo.[5] MAG-GIE pulls off her flashy red glasses, stares out. She puts her hands over her ears.)

SCHOOLCHILDREN *(cont'd.)*

Leetle freak, leetle freaka
Leetle freak, leetle freaka
Leetle freaka
Leetle freaka
Leetle freaka
MAGALEETA!

LITTLE MAGGIE *(V.O.; crying).* Cállate, cállate.

MAGGIE *(her head in her hands; overlapping).* Cállate!

SCENE 7

Before light comes up, the sound of a *Spanish television program blends with* **LITTLE MAGGIE***'s last words.*

Light comes up on **ABUELA** *rocking in the rocking chair before the television set. She is watching a Spanish program.*

MAGGIE *walks into the apartment, her heavy schoolbag slung across her back. She is wearing the flashy, red plastic glasses. The moment* **MAGGIE** *enters,* **ABUELA** *is still in the rocking chair.* **MAGGIE** *goes into the kitchen and walks straight to the refrigerator. She opens it, takes out a can of Coca-Cola, slams the refrigerator door.*

MAGGIE. How long have you been watching?

*(***ABUELA** *is silent.)*

MAGGIE *(cont'd.)* All day, I bet. *(Looking at the television)* At least you could try

watching something in English.

(She pauses, waiting for **ABUELA** *to switch the channel.* **ABUELA** *doesn't move.)*

MAGGIE *(cont'd.)* Okay—suit yourself. *(She sits down on the couch and uncaps the can of soda. Suddenly shouting above the sound of the television.)* Could you turn that down a little bit, please?

*(***ABUELA** *doesn't budge. The television continues just as loud.)*

MAGGIE *(Cont'd.)* Bájalo. *(With irony)* Por favor.

(Slowly **ABUELA** *reaches forward and turns down the volume of the television.)*

MAGGIE *(coldly).* Gracias.

(She sits still for several moments, drinking her Coke, listening to the sound of the Spanish television program, watching **ABUELA***. Suddenly she jumps up and flicks on a radio next to the couch. Wild rock music blares forth. Startled,* **ABUELA** *looks up. Moving slightly to the beat,* **MAGGIE** *folds her arms, stands glaring at* **ABUELA***. Slowly,* **ABUELA** *moves forward in the rocking chair, turns the television volume back up. She leans back, folds her arms.* **MAGGIE** *and* **ABUELA** *stare at each other.)*

SCENE 8

Light comes up on **ABUELA** *peering into the living room from the kitchen. She slips in quietly, a small watering can in her hand. Smiling to herself, humming, she begins watering the plants. Suddenly there is a loud ring.* **ABUELA** *jumps. There is another ring. It is the telephone. It rings and rings, over and over again.* **ABUELA***, undecided,*

---

5. crescendo (krə shen′dō), an increase in volume; getting louder and louder

finally walks over to it. The telephone rings again. She stands looking at it. It rings again. Tentatively, ABUELA *lifts the receiver.*

ERIC *(on the telephone).* Hello?

(ABUELA *is silent.*)

ERIC *(cont'd.)* Hello?

(He waits. ABUELA *stands looking at the receiver in her hand.)*

ERIC. Hello?

ABUELA *(holding the receiver to her ear).* Sí?

ERIC. Uh—can I speak to Maggie, please?

ABUELA. Cómo dice?

ERIC. Is Maggie there?

ABUELA *(catching on, smiling).* Ah sí—Magalita. Sí. *(Flat)* Ella no está.

ERIC. What?

ABUELA *(slowly).* Magalita. Ella—She no está. *(Remembering, slow)* She no here.

ERIC. Oh—okay. Could you tell her to call me?

ABUELA. Qué?

ERIC. Tell her it's Eric. ERIC.

ABUELA *(trying to imitate him).* ERR-UC. Err—*(Realizing who this is; smiling)* Mmmm-hmm. Erruc.

ERIC *(laughing).* You must be her grandmother.

ABUELA. No. No comprendo.

ERIC. Grandmother—you must be Maggie's grandmother.

ABUELA *(finally figuring it out).* Ah sí, sí. Granmother. I granmother Magalita.

ERIC. I thought so.

ABUELA *(pleased).* Sí. I granmother.

ERIC. Maggie talks about you a lot.

ABUELA. Cómo?

ERIC. Maggie. She likes you very much.

ABUELA. No, no. No entiendo.

ERIC *(almost shouting).* MAGGIE LIKES YOU VERY MUCH.

(ABUELA *holds the phone away from her, rubs her ear.*)

ERIC *(cont'd.)* I know. She told me.

(MAGGIE *and* ELENA *come into the apartment, carrying bags of groceries.*)

ABUELA. Ah—Magalita. *(Holding out the phone)* Teléfono.

(MAGGIE *rushes forward and takes the telephone from* ABUELA.)

MAGGIE. Hello?

(ABUELA *takes the packages from her, and goes into the kitchen with* ELENA.)

ERIC. Guess who?

MAGGIE *(smiling).* Oh hi. I was just going to call you.

ERIC. Uh huh. Hey, put your grandmother back on the phone.

MAGGIE. What for?

ERIC. I didn't finish talking to her.

MAGGIE. What were you talking about?

ERIC. As a matter of fact, we were talking about you.

MAGGIE *(a little nervous).* Oh yea? What'd she say?

ERIC. What's that name she calls you? Maleeter?

MAGGIE. Magalita. It's what they used to call me.

ERIC. Ma-ga-li-ta.

MAGGIE *(overlapping).* Don't call me that.

ERIC. Why? I like it.

MAGGIE. Well, I hate it.

ERIC. Let me speak to your grandmother again.

MAGGIE. She's not going to understand

a word you say.

ERIC. That's not true. She understands me perfectly.

MAGGIE (*after a moment; turning toward the kitchen*) Tata!

ABUELA (*appearing at the kitchen door*). Mmmm?

MAGGIE (*waving the phone*). Eric.

(ABUELA *smiles, fixes her hair and straightens her scarf as she walks to the phone.*)

ABUELA (*pleased*). Ay Dios mío. Y qué me querrá decir Erruc ahora? (*Taking the phone from* MAGGIE) Dígame, Erruc.

ERIC. I just wanted to repeat what I said before. Maggie likes you very much.

ABUELA (*nervously watching* MAGGIE, *who is watching her, filled with curiosity*). Sí, sí.

ERIC. And I—I would like to meet you.

ABUELA. Ah—sí?

ERIC (*hesitant*). Si. (*Pleased*) I really would.

ABUELA. Ah sí. Sí.

(ELENA, *smiling, tiptoes in with a box of dominoes and puts it on the top shelf of the low dividing bookcase.*)

ERIC (*firmly*). I'm sure I will meet you. (*He pauses.*) One of these days.

ABUELA (*smiling*). Sí. Gracias, Erruc. (*With emphasis*) Bye-bye.

ERIC (*trying to capture her inflection*). Bye-bye.

(*Smiling, he hangs up. Tossing her scarf over one shoulder,* ABUELA *proudly walks past* MAGGIE *into the small room and sits down on the bed.* MAGGIE *follows her.*)

MAGGIE. What did he say, Tata? What did he tell you?

(ABUELA *smiles secretly.*)

MAGGIE (*cont'd.*) Did you understand him?

(ABUELA *is silent, smiling to herself, smoothing the folds in her skirt.*)

MAGGIE (*cont'd.*) "Bye-bye"—where'd you pick that up?

ABUELA. I pick. (*She notices the box of dominoes on the bookshelf, unbelievingly looks again. Rising to pick up the box.*) Dominós! Y qué hacen estos dominós aquí?

ELENA (*looking in from the kitchen*). Los compré para tí, Mamá.

MAGGIE (*overlapping*). We got them for you.

ABUELA (*opening the box, delighted*). Dominós. Qué bueno! (*Calling into the kitchen*) Elena, vamos a jugar. (*Turning the box over and smacking the dominoes down on the table*) Elena!

MAGGIE (*pulling a chair up and sitting down opposite* ABUELA). No, I want to play. Conmigo, Tata.

ABUELA. Tú? Pero tú no sabes. (*Calling to* ELENA) Ella no sabe, Elena, verdad?

MAGGIE. Sí, sí. I know.

ABUELA. Ajá. Seguro.

MAGGIE. Sure.

ABUELA. Bueno. Vamos. Revuélvelos.

(MAGGIE *casually spreads the dominoes around the table.*)

ABUELA (*cont'd.*) Revuélvelos bien! (*She stirs the dominoes noisily on the table.*)

MAGGIE (*stirring them up also, laughing*). Okay, Tata. Okay.

(*During the course of the game,* ABUELA *plays rapidly, smacking down the dominoes with the utmost seriousness and ferocity. She is an expert player.*)

ABUELA. Ahora coje siete. *(Picking and setting up her seven dominoes)* Uno . . . Dos . . . Tres . . . cuatro, cinco, seis, siete. *(Rapidly checking* MAGGIE's *dominoes also)* Uno, dos, tres, cuatro, cinco, seis, siete. Muy bien. *(She pauses.)* Quién tiene el doble seis? *(Waving her arms, delighted)* Ajá! Yo lo tengo! *(She smacks down the double six.)*

MAGGIE. Hey! Well, I've got a six. *(She puts it down.)*

ABUELA *(moving* MAGGIE's *domino to the correct place)*. Así, no niña—en el centro.

MAGGIE. Oh yeah, I forgot.

(ABUELA looks at her.)

ABUELA. Mmm-hmm. *(Going on with the game)* Seis cinco, seis cinco. *(Smacking down a domino)* Cuatro seis.

(Waiting for MAGGIE *who is looking through her dominoes)*

ABUELA *(cont'd.)* Vamos, niña. No te duermas.

(MAGGIE, who doesn't have either a four or a six, starts picking from the pile.)

ABUELA *(pleased).* Ahh-ha.

(As MAGGIE *picks)*

ABUELA *(cont'd.)* Coje. Coje. Coje más. Sigue cojiendo.

MAGGIE *(picking and getting annoyed).* Shhh Tata, would you be quiet. *(Putting down a domino)* Look, I got it.

(ABUELA immediately slaps down another, looks at MAGGIE. MAGGIE *finds another and puts it down.* ABUELA *slaps down another.)*

MAGGIE *(cont'd.)* I don't have that one either.

ABUELA *(smiling).* Yo sé. Yo sé que tú no tienes.

(MAGGIE starts to pick again.)

ABUELA *(cont'd.)* Bueno, bueno, que bueno! Coje más. Coje otro. *(Pushing the dominoes toward* MAGGIE.) Otro. Anda!

MAGGIE. Stop it.

ABUELA. Pero juega, niña.

MAGGIE. I am playing. *(Finding the domino she needs and putting it down)* See— there's one.

ABUELA *(upset).* Ay, ay, ay. Yo no tengo ése.

MAGGIE. Aah-hah. Oh good. Why don't you take one? Go ahead. Take it, take it! Why don't you take another? *(Pushing the dominoes toward* ABUELA) Why don't you take the whole thing?

(ABUELA stops the push of dominoes toward her, glares at MAGGIE. *Taking her time, she stirs the dominoes, raises her eyes upward, lets her hand fall gently on a domino, slowly peeks at it.)*

ABUELA. Ay mira, qué suerte! *(Immediately slapping it down)* Me doblé! Cuatro y cuatro. *(Looking at* MAGGIE) Y tú no tienes cuatro. *(Pointing to* MAGGIE's *dominoes)* No four.

MAGGIE. Again? You're just lucky, that's all. *(She starts picking again.)*

ABUELA *(As* MAGGIE *picks).* Nada.

(MAGGIE picks again.)

ABUELA *(cont'd.)* Nada.

(MAGGIE picks another.)

ABUELA *(cont'd.)* Nada.

(MAGGIE picks yet another.)

ABUELA *(singsong).* Tú no tienes nada!

(MAGGIE picks faster and faster, stretching her hand all around the table for the dominoes.)

ABUELA *(looking at the mass of dominoes* MAGGIE *has collected).* Ay, mira eso!

(*Laughing and rubbing her hands together*) Esta la gano yo! (*She presses her two last dominoes to her cheeks.*)

MAGGIE. Did you fix this?

(ABUELA *laughs, hums to herself.*)

MAGGIE (*cont'd.*) I bet you did. (*As she picks another domino with her left hand, with her right she quietly tries to slip several dominoes into her lap. They fall, clattering to the floor.*)

ABUELA (*hearing them fall*). Ay, pero mira eso! No lo creo.

(*She stands up, leans over* MAGGIE, *who, trying to conceal what has happened, folds her arms, resting her chin in her hand.*)

ABUELA (*cont'd.*) Magalita, ésa es una trampa! (*Sitting down again*) Recójelos y ponlos en la mesa.

MAGGIE (*leaning down to pick up the dominoes*). I got confused.

ABUELA. Ah sí—(*Mimicking* MAGGIE) I got confused. Tú crees qué no tengo ojos? Vamos.

MAGGIE (*picking*). Shoot!

(*She picks and picks, finally putting one down.* ABUELA *smacks down her next to last domino.* MAGGIE, *searching through her mass of dominoes, puts another one down.*)

MAGGIE (*cont'd.*) There.

(ABUELA's *face breaks into a triumphant smile.*)

ABUELA. Ay! Justo lo qué quería. (*Holding up her last domino*) Mira, Magalita. (*Joyfully putting it down*) DOMINÓ!

MAGGIE (*leaning back in her chair, with unconcealed admiration*). Tata!

(*Music under, as the light dims*)

SCENE 9

Light comes up on ELENA *setting the table for four.* ABUELA *is humming in the kitchen.* ELENA *goes into the kitchen.* MAGGIE *rushes into the apartment.*

MAGGIE (*excited*). Ma?

(*She stops, sniffing the air. She takes another step, sniffs again.* ELENA *comes in with four plates for the table.*)

MAGGIE (*cont'd.*) Ma, I thought you were cooking dinner tonight. It was all arranged.

ELENA. I couldn't.

MAGGIE (*smiling anxiously*). Don't tell me Abuela's cooking. Don't tell me that. Not tonight.

(ELENA *is silent.*)

MAGGIE (*cont'd.*) She is, isn't she?

ELENA. I'm sorry, pumpkin. When I got back from the hospital, Abuela was in the kitchen. She'd been in there all day. I couldn't say no.

MAGGIE. Why not? Why couldn't you?

ELENA. She was so excited about Eric coming tonight.

MAGGIE. Mami, you can't let her make dinner. You have to cook. You have to.

ELENA. What your grandmother cooks is delicious. You're just not used to that kind of food anymore.

MAGGIE. Ma, please stop her.

ELENA. Stop her? Are you kidding? You know your Abuela.

MAGGIE (*running to the telephone and starting to dial*). I'm going to call Eric and tell him to come another night.

ELENA. Eric just called to say he's on his way.

MAGGIE (putting down the phone). Oh, God.

ELENA. Maggie, calm down. You're acting like a three-year-old.

MAGGIE. Couldn't we just have hamburgers? Please. Just this once. Just tonight.

(ELENA is silent. MAGGIE peers into the kitchen and comes back.)

MAGGIE (cont'd.) It's Mondongo. (She pauses, looking at ELENA.) Mondongo, Ma. I don't believe it.

ELENA (laughing). Okay, so it's Mondongo. So?

MAGGIE. He can't eat that. Eric can't eat that. Ma—he'll die.

ELENA. He won't die, Maggie. No one's ever died from Mondongo.

MAGGIE. He will, Ma. Eric will. You don't know him. He's got a very delicate stomach.

ELENA. And you've got una imaginacion fantastica.

MAGGIE. You know something? You know what Eric's going to do when he sees that? He doesn't even have to eat it. He just has to look at it—and he's gonna throw up all over this apartment. I know it, Ma.

ELENA. Ay Maggie, exagerada.

MAGGIE. Listen—(Grabbing her bag and going to the door) I'll go down to MacDonald's and get us four Big Macs. It won't take long. Eric won't even be here by the time I get back. (She starts to open the door.)

ELENA. And what are we going to do with all the food your grandmother cooked? Throw it out?

MAGGIE (turning back). I'll eat it tomorrow. I promise. Every bit.

ELENA (quiet but intense). She spent the whole day preparing this meal. The whole day she was in the kitchen. Do you hear me?

MAGGIE (coming back and throwing herself down on the couch). Well, why did she? Nobody asked her to.

(ABUELA comes in with a large wooden spoon for ELENA to taste the Mondongo. MAGGIE doesn't notice her.)

MAGGIE (cont'd.) Every night. Every night. I hate that stuff she cooks.

(ABUELA stands still, looking at MAGGIE.)

ELENA (seeing ABUELA). Maggie, shhh. (Warningly, low) Cállate.

MAGGIE (turning away). I hate that she did it.

ELENA. Maggie.

MAGGIE (starting to get up). I hate—

(She stops suddenly, seeing ABUELA. ABUELA turns and goes into her room. She sits down on the bed.)

ELENA. She heard you, Maggie.

(MAGGIE is silent.)

ELENA (cont'd.) She understood. Go in and talk to her.

(MAGGIE looks at her.)

ELENA (cont'd.) Tell her you're sorry.

(MAGGIE is still.)

ELENA. Tell her, Maggie. (She looks at MAGGIE.) Go on. (Insistent) Go on.

MAGGIE. Okay, okay, I'll go. (She goes into ABUELA's room, stands at the entrance. After a moment.) I'm sorry, Abuela.

(ABUELA is silent.)

MAGGIE *(cont'd.)* I'm sorry.

ABUELA. No es necesario, Magalita. Yo entiendo.

MAGGIE. But I am. I really am.

(ABUELA is still.)

MAGGIE *(cont'd.)* Really. I mean it.

ABUELA. Sí. Sí.

MAGGIE. You don't understand. I really am sorry. Really. Please, Abuela. I didn't mean to hurt your feelings.

(ABUELA turns away.)

MAGGIE *(cont'd.)* Oh, Abuela, listen to me.

(ABUELA doesn't move.)

MAGGIE. Abuela, please. *(Moving in front of ABUELA)* Please.

(ABUELA doesn't respond.)

MAGGIE *(cont'd.)* Abuela.

(ABUELA turns the other way. MAGGIE again moves to face her.)

MAGGIE. Listen to me. Why won't you listen to me? *(Looking at ABUELA, suddenly)* Because I don't speak Spanish to you? Is that it? Is that why?

ABUELA. No importa.

MAGGIE *(shouting)*. Oh yes it is important.

ELENA *(coming in from the kitchen)*. What's all the screaming about?

MAGGIE *(going on; to ABUELA)*. Do I have to speak Spanish to make you listen?

ABUELA. No.

MAGGIE. Do I? Do I? Is that what I have to do? *(Watching ABUELA)* I do, don't I? Don't I? *(Turning away, very upset)* I give up. *(She starts to leave.)*

ELENA *(stopping her)*. No, Maggie. *(Turning to ABUELA)* Dile, Mami. Dile algo.

(ABUELA remains silent. Turning to MAGGIE.)

ELENA *(cont'd.)* Make it up with her, Maggie.

(MAGGIE is still. ELENA turns from one to the other. To ABUELA.)

ELENA *(cont'd.)* Mamá, contéstale. Está enfadada. *(To MAGGIE)* Maggie, please. *(To ABUELA)* Ay Mami, por favor.

(She takes both of them by the arm. They both pull away.)

ELENA *(helpless)*. Oh, God, I can't take this. *(She turns away from them.)*

ERIC *(coming into the apartment through the door MAGGIE has left open)*. Hello? *(He is carrying a long skinny plant with a single drooping flower.)*

ELENA *(turning back to MAGGIE and ABUELA)*. And what do you think it's been like for me?

ERIC. Anybody home?

MAGGIE *(to ABUELA, not hearing ERIC)*. Why won't you talk? Talk!

ERIC *(hearing their voices and going into the small room)*. Hi!

(They are silent, all three staring at him.)

ERIC *(cont'd.)* Hey, I hope I'm not late or something.

(They are still silent.)

ERIC *(cont'd.)* I'm not early, am I? *(He hands the plant to ELENA.)*

ELENA *(laughing and taking the plant from him)*. Of course not, Eric. You're just in time. *(Pointedly)* Thank you.

(ERIC stands smiling at all of them.)

Maggie Magalita by Wendy Kesselman   **295**

ABUELA (coming forward and shaking his hand). Ahhh, Erruc. Erruc. Qué bueno!

(She follows ELENA into the kitchen. ERIC takes off his jacket and triumphantly waves a small Spanish phrase book at MAGGIE.)

MAGGIE (taking his jacket; ironic). Oh, great.

ERIC (following her into the living room). Tell me one thing in Spanish before they come back.

MAGGIE. Listen. I am sick of Spanish. I didn't come to this country to speak Spanish.

ERIC. Oh yeah? Well, I'll tell you something then.

MAGGIE. What?

ERIC. When you get mad, you've got the prettiest—the greenest eyes I've ever—

(Breaking off as ABUELA brings in the bowl of steaming Mondongo)

ERIC (cont'd.) Ahh-hah!

ABUELA (overlapping; smiling happily). Ajá!

(She and ELENA sit down at the table.)

ERIC (looking at the Mondongo which ABUELA has placed in the center of the table). Aah. (Fainter) Mmm. (He looks more closely.) What is that exactly?

(ABUELA smiles peacefully.)

MAGGIE (sitting down). Exactly?

ERIC. Looks good. (To MAGGIE.) What's it called?

MAGGIE. Don't ask.

ELENA (laughing). It's called Mondongo, Eric.

ERIC. Mon—what?

ABUELA (passing ERIC the Mondongo).

Usted primero, Erruc. Sírvase.

ERIC (smiling broadly, happy). She's nice. (Taking the small Spanish phrase book out of his pocket) I've been waiting for this moment. (Slowly, with terrible pronunciation) Kee-er-ro ko-mer.

ABUELA (puzzled). Qué?

ERIC (repeating). Kee-er-ro komer.

ELENA (smiling, to ABUELA). Quiere comer, Mamá.

ABUELA. Ah sí—comer. Sí, sí. (She spoons a healthy portion of Mondongo onto his plate.) Coma Erruc, coma.

MAGGIE (low). You don't have to eat it if you don't want to. No one's going to care. We're very casual around here.

ERIC. You—casual?

MAGGIE (quiet). I told them about your stomach.

ERIC. What about it?

MAGGIE. How delicate it is.

ERIC. Delicate? Are you kidding? (To ELENA) You should hear what my mother says about my stomach. (To ABUELA, patting his stomach) Estommajoe graaandee. (Looking at his plate) Boy this looks . . . good. Real good.

MAGGIE. Eric . . . don't rush into anything.

ELENA. Let him eat, Maggie. He's hungry.

(Taking the serving spoon, ERIC starts spooning more Mondongo onto his plate.)

ABUELA (pleased). Coje más. Más. No tenga pena.

ERIC (looking in his phrase book again). I can't find that.

ELENA. She wants you to take more.

ERIC. Oh. Oh yeah. I see. *(Smiling at* ABUELA*)* Grashas.

(He spoons a little more Mondongo onto his plate. ABUELA *grins widely.)*

ABUELA *(correcting Eric).* No gra-shas, Erruc. Gracias.

MAGGIE. Tata, leave him alone.

ERIC. No, I want to learn.

*(*ELENA, ABUELA, *and* MAGGIE *sit watching* ERIC, *who has started to put his spoon to his mouth. He looks up, sensing them watching him. He stops with the spoonful of Mondongo just at his mouth.)*

ABUELA. Vamos, Erruc.

ELENA. Go ahead.

*(*ERIC *takes a bite. He chews hesitantly, then reflectively, as they all watch. He looks up.)*

MAGGIE *(whispering).* You don't have to say anything. Really.

ERIC *(overlapping).* Hey I like this.

*(*ABUELA *smiles.)*

MAGGIE. You don't have to be polite.

ERIC *(his mouth stuffed).* I'm not being polite. This is really good. *(He looks in his phrase book.)* Mee gusto.

*(*ABUELA*'s smile grows bigger.)*

ERIC *(cont'd.)* Mee gusto mucha.

ELENA *(explaining to* ABUELA*).* Le gustó, Mamá.

ABUELA *(overlapping).* Sí, sí, yo entiendo.

MAGGIE. Blaachh.

ELENA. Maggie, stop it. Now.

*(*ERIC *keeps on eating, wolfing down the Mondongo.)*

ABUELA *(laughing).* Pero mira como come!

ERIC *(between mouthfuls).* What's she saying?

ELENA. She's happy you're eating so much.

ERIC. Oh yeah. Kom-er. Ko-miendo. *(Munching away)* I've never eaten anything like this. This is great. *(In an ecstasy of eating; to* ABUELA*)* Buena! *(Kissing his hand to her)* Buena!

*(*ABUELA *laughs.)*

ERIC *(suddenly looking up).* Hey, how come nobody else is eating?

*(*ELENA *and* ABUELA *begin eating, as* ERIC *goes back to the Mondongo.* MAGGIE *sits silently pushing her food around her plate.)*

ELENA. Ay Eric, it's nice you're here. I haven't seen you in . . .

ERIC. Nice? Are you kidding? You know how long I've waited to come?

ELENA. Then why didn't—

ERIC *(looking at* MAGGIE, *who turns away).* Well . . . *(To* ABUELA, *holding out his plate)* Can I have some more? *(Smiling)* Por favor.

ABUELA. Ah sí, sí. Seguro que sí.

(She smiles at him and piles his plate high with Mondongo. MAGGIE *sits brooding, watching them.* ABUELA *hands the plate back to* ERIC, *who begins to eat.)*

ABUELA *(cont'd.)* Coma más, Erruc. Anda.

MAGGIE *(suddenly, to* ERIC*).* How can you like it? It's awful.

ERIC. What are you talking about?

MAGGIE. Want me to tell you what's in it?

ERIC *(looking up for a moment from his eating).* Uh—No.

(He smiles at ABUELA, *who smiles back.)*

MAGGIE. Don't you think you ought to know before you eat any more?

ERIC. I don't care what's in it. I like it.

MAGGIE. You wanted to know before. Don't you want to know now?

ELENA *(warningly)*. Maggie.

ERIC *(looking at* ABUELA*)*. Okay. Sure. Go ahead. Tell me.

ELENA. Maggie, don't go too far.

ABUELA. Qué dice, Elena?

ELENA *(smiling at* ABUELA*)*. There's no reason to ruin the meal.

*(*ABUELA *continues eating the Mondongo contentedly.)*

MAGGIE *(to* ERIC*)*. Listen, it's got—

*(*ERIC *starts to take a bite of the Mondongo.* ELENA *glares at* MAGGIE.*)*

MAGGIE *(smiling)*. Sausages, potatoes, green peppers—

ERIC *(eating, relaxed)*. Yeah.

MAGGIE. Onions, garlic—

ERIC *(continuing to eat)*. Yeah—and?

MAGGIE *(still smiling)*. Cow's stomach—

ERIC *(looking up)*. Cow's—what?

MAGGIE *(her voice growing more ominous)*. Cow's stomach.

ERIC *(slowing down on the Mondongo)*. Uh-huh. *(He peeks into the serving bowl.)*

MAGGIE. Cow's intestines.

ERIC. Hmmm. *(He stops eating.)*

MAGGIE. Pig's feet.

ERIC. I see.

MAGGIE. Pig's shoulder blades.

ERIC. Yeah.

MAGGIE *(building to a crescendo)*. Pig's muscles. *(Darker yet)* Pig's eyeballs. *(Even darker)* Pig's—

ELENA *(breaking in)*. Maggie, I think he heard you.

ERIC. You got it, Mag. I heard you. And now—*(Looking at* ABUELA, *smiling)* Kee-er-ro komer.

(Happily, ABUELA *pushes the bowl of Mondongo toward* ERIC. MAGGIE *deliberately pushes it back.* ABUELA *stands up and again pushes it toward him.* MAGGIE *again pushes it away.* ABUELA *and* MAGGIE *struggle over the bowl.* ELENA *jumps up and pulls the bowl away from both of them.)*

ELENA *(banging the bowl down on the table)*. Enough! Basta ya!

ABUELA. Elena!

ELENA *(to* ABUELA*)*. Y tú tambien. *(To* ERIC*)* Is it like this in your family, Eric? Is it? Because this family is driving me crazy. Loca! *(To* MAGGIE*)* You want to go out for the Big Macs, Maggie? Go out for the Big Macs. Here, I'll give you the money.

(Quickly getting her purse and throwing the money down on the table) If you don't want your guest to eat the food that's cooked for him, forget it!

MAGGIE. Ma, I didn't—

ELENA. You didn't what?

MAGGIE. I didn't mean—

ELENA. Ay Maggie, Maggie, eres imposible. Malcriada!

MAGGIE. Ma, don't—

ELENA *(interrupting)*. Y porqué no?

MAGGIE. Ma—

ELENA *(going on)*. Even Eric is trying to speak the language. And you . . . you've known it since the day you were born.

*(*MAGGIE *jumps up.)*

MAGGIE *(in an outburst of anguished Spanish and English)*. You want me to speak Spanish? Is that what you want? Ustedes quieren que yo hable español? Esta bien. Okay. Muy bien. Tú crees que yo me he olvidado, right? But I haven't. I haven't forgotten. Yo me acuerdo de todo. Todo. Pero yo no me quiero acordar. *(More and more upset)* Sometimes, God, sometimes I remember one thing y despues otra y otra y despues vienen tan ligero—tan ligero—faster and faster they come, más y más, and I can't stop them. *(Like a caged animal,* MAGGIE *paces the small apartment.)* Y yo no me quiero acordar de nada, nada. I don't want to remember. Qué no. And none of you understand. Ustedes no entienden. Ninguna de ustedes. *(She runs into* ABUELA*'s small room, throws herself on the bed.)*

ELENA *(calling after her)*. Maggie.

ABUELA. Magalita.

Maggie Magalita by Wendy Kesselman   **299**

ERIC. Gosh.

(*Light dims on the living room and comes up on* MAGGIE*'s tearstained face.*

Light comes up on ABUELA*'s face. She is still sitting at the table. There is the sound of a train pulling in.*)

LITTLE MAGGIE (*V.O.*) Tata, Tata! Tu vienes conmigo, no?

ABUELA (*V.O.*) No, mi niñita.

LITTLE MAGGIE (*V.O.*) Tu vienes?

ABUELA. Ay, no, mi Magalita. No puedo.

LITTLE MAGGIE (*V.O.*) Por qué?

ABUELA (*V.O.*) Por qué—Adios, mi niña. (*Her voice rising*) Adios Magalita!

LITTLE MAGGIE (*V.O.*) Adios Tata.

(*There is the sound of a train pulling away.*)

LITTLE MAGGIE (*cont'd.*) Tata! Tata! Dejame quedarme contigo. No quiero ir. No quiero ir. No quiero ir sin tí.

MAGGIE (*calling out*). TATA!

ABUELA (*rising and turning toward her*). Magalita!

(*Music under, as the light dims*)

SCENE 10

L ight comes up on ABUELA in her room, getting dressed slowly, carefully, taking her time.

Light comes up on MAGGIE, *brushing her hair before the mirror.*

MAGGIE. Come on, Tata. You know how long it takes you to get down those stairs.

(ABUELA *continues just as slowly.*)

MAGGIE (*cont'd.*) It's a great movie, really Tata. This time I promise you'll like it.

ABUELA. Yo no te creo. Qué—movie?

MAGGIE (*getting their coats from the closet*). The Beast From the Deep.

(ABUELA *looks at her.*)

ABUELA. Hmm.

MAGGIE. You're gonna love it. You won't want to miss a minute.

(ABUELA *puts on her black shoes, ties the laces, stands up. She is, as usual, dressed entirely in black.*)

ABUELA. Ahora I ready.

MAGGIE (*holding out* ABUELA*'s black coat; suddenly*). Wait a minute. You always wear black. That's all you ever wear. (*She runs to the closet and brings* ABUELA *a bright red wraparound skirt.*) Here. Try this on.

ABUELA. Qué?

MAGGIE. Go ahead. Just put it on.

(MAGGIE *holds out the skirt to* ABUELA, *who shakes her head.*)

MAGGIE (*cont'd.*) See—you wear it like this. (*She wraps the skirt around her, then takes it off and hands it to* ABUELA.)

ABUELA. Pero no, Magalita. Yo no puedo.

MAGGIE. Sure you can.

ABUELA (*running away*). No Magalita, no.

MAGGIE (*following her*). Qué sí Abuelita, sí.

ABUELA. No.

MAGGIE. Sí.

ABUELA. No

MAGGIE. Sí.

ABUELA. Pero—

MAGGIE (*breaking in*). Póntelo.

ABUELA. No.

MAGGIE. Pón-te-lo.

(Finally catching ABUELA *in front of the mirror, she wraps the bright red skirt around* ABUELA*'s black one. Together they face the mirror,* MAGGIE *standing behind* ABUELA *and tying the red skirt.* ABUELA*'s head is bent, watching* MAGGIE *tie the skirt.* MAGGIE, *her head over* ABUELA*'s shoulder, smiling.)*

MAGGIE. You see? It looks beautiful on you.

(Slowly, ABUELA *lifts her head.)*

MAGGIE *(cont'd.)* It looks fantastic.

ABUELA *(looking in the mirror, giggling delightedly).* Sí?

MAGGIE. I told you. You have to wear it. You have to.

*(*ABUELA *turns around. The skirt swings out from her.)*

MAGGIE *(cont'd.)* Remember when you used to dance for me?

ABUELA *(excited).* Yo tenía una saya más roja que ésta. Roja, roja, roja. Roja como un fuego! Y cuando me iba a bailar, bailaba toda la noche!

(She breaks into the waltz step of "Ramona," sings the first few bars. Holding out her hands to MAGGIE, *she continues humming the song.* MAGGIE *tries to follow her in the waltz. Remembering.)*

ABUELA *(cont'd.)* No . . .

(Grabbing MAGGIE *by the shoulders)*

ABUELA *(cont'd.)* Esta, ésta, ésta. *(She sings and dances.)*

Dónde va la cojita

*(*MAGGIE *laughs and joins in.)*

MAGGIE, ABUELA *(sing and dance together).*

Que mi nauflí
Que mi nauflá

Voy al campo a buscar violetas
Que mi nauflí
Que mi nauflá

MAGGIE *(sings).*

Para quién son las violetas
Que mi nauflí
Que mi nauflá

ABUELA *(sings).*

Para la virgen de mi patrona
Que mi nauflí
Que mi nauflá

(Going up a half step)

Si te encuentras con la reina
Que mi nauflí
Que mi nauflá

MAGGIE *(sings).*

Yo le haré una reverencia
Que mi nauflí
Que mi nauflá

MAGGIE, ABUELA *(sing, going down a step).*

Si te encuentras con el guardia
Que mi nauflí
Que mi nauflá

(Laughing)

Yo le haré, un quiquiquo.

(They make a gesture of spreading the fingers of both hands, the thumb of the left hand touching the nose, the thumb of the right hand touching the little finger of the left. They laugh wildly.)

MAGGIE *(stopping suddenly).* Wait . . .
(She runs to the radio, switches it on. Rock music blasts forth.) Watch, Abuelita. Want me to teach you? *(She runs up to* ABUELA.*)* Mírame.

(But ABUELA *has already begun dancing, rocking back and forth, with some difficulty, but with her own rhythm and at her own pace. She is not just a good dancer, she is terrific.)*

ABUELA. Yo sé, yo sé.

(She beckons to MAGGIE to dance with her. MAGGIE watches her, astonished.)

MAGGIE. Abuela . . . tú . . .

ABUELA (tossing away her scarf). Ven acá, Magalita. (Holding out her hands) Baila conmigo.

(MAGGIE, laughing, joins in. They dance, faster and faster, all around the apartment, until finally they collapse together on the small trunk in front of the mirror.)

MAGGIE (out of breath). Ay Abuela, you can really dance. (She switches off the radio. After a pause.) Wait, I . . . I want to show you something. (Taking a looseleaf notebook from the bookshelf, she comes back to ABUELA.) It's something I made up for school. (She opens the notebook.) I want you to hear it. It's a poem. Un poema.

ABUELA (smiling). Ah sí.

MAGGIE. Listen. It begins like this. (Sitting down on the floor, she begins reading from the notebook.) When I (Pointing to herself) came here

ABUELA (mimicking with a heavy accent). When I (Pointing to herself) come here

MAGGIE. Hey, that's right! Come on Tata. Say it with me. (She goes back to the beginning of the poem.) When I came here

ABUELA. When I come here

MAGGIE. I didn't like it very much

ABUELA. Very much

MAGGIE. I didn't like the buildings

ABUELA. Buildings

MAGGIE. I didn't like the noise

ABUELA. Noise

MAGGIE. The way it got dark so early

ABUELA. So early

MAGGIE. And so cold

ABUELA. Col

MAGGIE. People scared me here

ABUELA. People scare me

MAGGIE. Made me feel small

ABUELA. Small

MAGGIE. And lost

ABUELA. Los

MAGGIE. And like I was all alone

ABUELA. Alone

MAGGIE. If I ever got used to it

ABUELA. If

MAGGIE. It was because of a friend of mine

ABUELA. Friend of mine

MAGGIE. He has funny lopsided hair

ABUELA. Funny hair

MAGGIE. And a lot of freckles

ABUELA. Freck-less

MAGGIE. Freckles

ABUELA. Freck-less

MAGGIE. Freckles, Tata

ABUELA. (definite). Freckless

MAGGIE. But it took me a long, long time

ABUELA. Long time

MAGGIE. And even now

ABUELA. Now

MAGGIE. I still don't know what to expect.

ABUELA. Spect.

MAGGIE. If I ever go back to where I was born (Looking at ABUELA). If I ever go back to the ocean again

ABUELA. If I ever go back

MAGGIE. I will know just what to expect

ABUELA. Spect

MAGGIE. For even though I left when I was very little

ABUELA. Very little

MAGGIE. There is nothing I have forgotten

ABUELA. Nothing

MAGGIE. And some things I remember as if they happened yesterday.

ABUELA. Yesterday.

(MAGGIE is silent, looking at ABUELA. ABUELA stares wordlessly out.)

MAGGIE *(closing the notebook).* Well, what do you think? Qué tú piensas? *(After a pause)* Do you think she'll like it? *(She waits.)* You don't know how strict that teacher is. *(Watching ABUELA, nervous)* Tata, do you think it's good enough?

(ABUELA smiles.)

ABUELA. Is good.

MAGGIE. Do you really think so?

ABUELA. Is good, is good. She like it. I know. Yo sé.

MAGGIE. Tata—did you understand it?

(ABUELA is silent. MAGGIE looks at her intently.)

MAGGIE *(cont'd.)* You did, didn't you? *(Smiling up at ABUELA)* Didn't you, Abuela? Tell me. Dime.

ABUELA *(after a pause, quietly).* Sí, Magalita. I understan. And I do like it. Very much.

(They smile at each other. There is a pause.)

MAGGIE *(suddenly).* Tata, listen. Listen to me, Tata. Let's go to the ocean. Now! Come on. *(She leaps up and grabs their coats.)* We'll take the subway right out to Coney Island.

ABUELA. Subway? No. *(Looking at MAGGIE)* Pero movie. Beast.

MAGGIE *(laughing).* Forget about the Beast—olvidate! *(Wrapping the long green scarf around ABUELA's head)* I want you to see that—even from here—the ocean isn't so far away.

(The light dims as they go out and comes up on the beach. The sound of the ocean. Light comes up on MAGGIE and ABUELA. Over her coat, ABUELA wears the crocheted green scarf MAGGIE gave her on her arrival. Wrapped several times around her head and neck, it still trails on the ground.)

MAGGIE *(reaching her arms out toward the audience).* Look, Tata—the ocean! *(She breaks away from ABUELA and runs forward.)* Just look at it! *(She turns back to ABUELA.)* Ven aquí conmigo. Ven.

(ABUELA follows, her long scarf trailing. She moves haltingly, but her face expresses a tremendous joy.)

ABUELA. I coming.

(MAGGIE runs back to ABUELA and walks with her.)

MAGGIE. Look at those waves. God—they're huge.

(They both take a few steps even closer to the audience. They are standing right at the edge of the water.)

MAGGIE *(cont'd).* Tata, tú te acuerdas—remember our house with the blue windows? Where the mountains went right down to the waves.

ABUELA. Ah sí. La casa con las ventanas azules. Sure. Sure. Yo me acuerdo. Azules como . . .

MAGGIE *(breaking in).* I know. Blue like the windows of the sea.

ABUELA (*smiling*). Como las ventanas del mar.

MAGGIE. Qúe líndo está el mar, eh Tata?

ABUELA. Beautiful, Magalita. Ver-y beautiful.

MAGGIE. The ocean is beautiful everywhere.

ABUELA. Every-where.

MAGGIE (*reaching her foot out over the edge*). I wish we could go in. Don't you wish we could go swimming?

ABUELA (*making swimming gestures with her arms*). Ah sí—Swi-mming. (*Frowning*) Ay no. Mucho frio.

MAGGIE. Yeah, I bet it's freezing. Not like at ho—(*Her eyes bright*) I haven't forgotten anything, Abuela.

ABUELA. No?

MAGGIE. I'll never forget.

ABUELA (*bundling* MAGGIE*'s jacket close around her*). No.

MAGGIE (*slowly*). Do you think you'll get to like it here, Tata? Do you think you ever will?

(ABUELA *puts her arm through* MAGGIE*'s.*)

ABUELA (*smiling*). Sí, Maggie. Sí, mi niñita. I will.

(*They walk off together, leaving the empty stage.*)

ABUELA (*V.O.; after laughing deeply, calls*). Uno, dos, tres, cuatro, cinco, seis, siete, ocho, nueve, diez!

LITTLE MAGGIE (*V.O.; out of breath, singsong*). Yo me escondo, yo me escondo. No me encuentras, no me encuentras.

ABUELA (*V.O.*) Ronda, ronda, que el que no se haya escondido se esconda!

LITTLE MAGGIE (*V.O.*) Ven, Tat, ven! Apúrate, apúrate! Sí tú no vienes, más nunca me encontrarás!

(*The light dims.*)

SCENE II

Before light comes up, there is the sound of static coming from the television.

Light comes up on ABUELA *sitting in her rocking chair in front of the television set.*

MAGGIE *comes running into the apartment.*

MAGGIE. Tata! She loved it! Can you believe it? (*She stops to catch her breath.*) She read it out loud to the whole class! (*Excitedly she rummages in her schoolbag.*) I brought something home for you. I bet you'll never guess what it is. (*She takes a mango out of the schoolbag.*) Look. A mango! (ABUELA *is silent.*) Watcha watching? (*She sees the image of the television flickering.*) Hey, what's the matter with the T.V.? (*She taps the television set, fixes the antenna.*) Abuela? (*Turning to* ABUELA) Abuelita? (*There is no answer. The sound of the television static is the only sound in the room.* MAGGIE *turns the television off. Smiling.*) Tata, despiértate. (*She tiptoes over to* ABUELA.) Hey, what's the matter? Qué te pasa, Abuela? (*She touches* ABUELA*'s shoulder.*) Abuela. (*Bending over her*) Wait a minute. Abuelita. (*Stepping back*) Oh no. (*Moaning*) No. No, Abuela. (*She moves closer.*) Don't be dead, Tata. Don't die. Abuela, please. (*Kneeling before* ABUELA) No te mueras. (*Clutching* ABUELA*'s knees*) Esperame. (*Pleading*) Tata, no me dejes so—(*She touches* ABUELA's *hand. It falls.*) Oh, my God. (MAGGIE *draws back.*) Tata. (*She stands up, still for a moment. Then she races to the telephone. She lifts the receiver and starts to dial.*) Um . . . uh . . . what's her number? Seven two—Oh God, I can't remember her number. (*Frantic*) Seven three two . . . No, that's not it. (*She starts again.*) Oh please, I've got to remember it. Seven . . . wait . . . wait . . . (*With an immense effort at concentration*) Siete dos tres—zero siete—yeah that's it—siete seis. (*Shakily, but carefully, she dials the number.*) Answer. Come on. Somebody answer. (*Desperate*) Oh, please, please. Somebody. Please. (*Sobbing*) MAMI!

(*Blackout*)

SCENE 12

Before light comes up, there is the sound of a haunting guitar solo.

Light comes up on ELENA *and* MAGGIE, *standing at a diagonal on opposite sides of the living room, folding* ABUELA's *long green scarf.* ELENA *walks toward* MAGGIE, *folding as she goes. When she reaches* MAGGIE, *they look at each other for a moment. They embrace.*

MAGGIE (*holding the scarf*). Can I keep this in my room, Mami? (*Looking at* ELENA) And the dominoes?

(*There is a knock on the door.*)

ELENA. You keep them, pumpkin.

(MAGGIE *goes to the door.* ERIC *is standing there.* MAGGIE *smiles.*)

ERIC. Hi. (*To* ELENA) I wanted to come.

ELENA. Come in, Eric.

ERIC (*awkwardly coming into the apartment*). I wanted to—but I uh—now I—I don't know what to say.

ELENA. It doesn't matter, Eric. It's good you've come.

ERIC. I'm sorry. I mean—I'm really sorry. I didn't know her very well, but . . . well . . . I liked her. She—she was—(*Gesturing with his hands*) I don't know—she—

ELENA. I know.

MAGGIE. Yeah.

ERIC. Yeah, I guess she was.

ELENA (*taking his hands*). Thank you.

(*Brushing her tears away, she goes into the kitchen.* MAGGIE *moves to pick up the box of dominoes from the table.*)

ERIC. Hey, are those the famous dominoes you told me about?

MAGGIE (*nodding*). That's them.

(*She takes the box into the small room,* ERIC *following her. After a pause.*)

MAGGIE (*cont'd.*) She was a great domino player.

ERIC. Yeah, I remember.

MAGGIE (*picking up the bright red wraparound skirt from the bed*). And she sure could dance. (*Smiling; enthusiastic*) There was this time when—(*She pauses, reflective.*) There were so many times. (*She sits down on the corner of the bed.*)

ERIC (*sitting down cattycorner to her*). I'll never forget that meal she made.

MAGGIE. Me neither.

ERIC. I mean, that stuff was—really—great. It was—so—

MAGGIE (*laughing*). I know. (*She is silent. After a pause.*) You know something?

(She hesitates.) I miss her. I miss her, Eric. And . . . I don't know. I feel scared now sometimes. I don't think she ever knew.

ERIC *(putting his hands over hers).* I think she did.

MAGGIE. I can't stop thinking about her.

ERIC. Yeah.

MAGGIE. It's like I remember every little thing. I mean—every little detail. And—

ERIC. What?

MAGGIE. I keep thinking about that day we went to the ocean. We should have gone there more often.

ERIC. I'll take you there, Maggie. *(Nervously playing with the afghan at the bottom of the bed)* You know something? *(Looking at MAGGIE)* I never knew anybody who died before.

(MAGGIE looks at him, stands up. She fingers the bright red skirt. She walks into the living room. Getting up and following her.)

ERIC *(cont'd.)* Hey . . .

(MAGGIE stands in front of the mirror.)

MAGGIE *(starting to wrap the skirt around her).* What?

ERIC. You know that name she called you? That um—uh—Ma-ga-li-*(He breaks off and is silent.)*

MAGGIE *(after a pause).* What about it?

ERIC. I liked it.

(Slowly, MAGGIE ties the skirt around her waist.)

ERIC *(cont'd.)* I mean—sort of. *(After a moment)* It was nice.

(Looking in the mirror, MAGGIE, remembering, hums the first bars of "Ramona." She turns to the side. The skirt swings out from her.)

ERIC *(watching her).* Kind of.

MAGGIE *(after a pause).* Yeah, I know you liked it.

ERIC. Do you think I could call you that sometimes?

(MAGGIE sits down on the small trunk at the edge of the stage.)

ERIC *(cont'd.)* I mean, like it's no big deal, but uh—

MAGGIE *(smiling).* Come on, Eric. *(She drapes the skirt about her legs.)*

ERIC. What do you think?

MAGGIE. I don't know. *(Thoughtful)* We'll see.

ERIC *(looking at her).* Do you think I could?

MAGGIE *(facing out).* Maybe. *(Turning and looking up at him, she smiles.)* Sometimes.

CURTAIN

MAGGIE MAGALITA

Responding to the Play

1. What would you say is the major struggle in this play?
2. Do you agree with Elena that Maggie is like her grandmother? Give examples from the play to support your opinion.
3. How does Eric's phone conversation with Abuela foreshadow his reaction to eating Mondongo?
4. Use a graphic organizer and create a list of costume items for Maggie, Elena, and Abuela.
5. Write a poem based on this play.

More About the Costume Crew

Costume crews vary in size depending on how many costumes are needed. Costumes may need to be created from scratch, reconstructed, bought, rented, or borrowed. The following people are usually members of the costume crew:

The Costume Designer Decides what each actor wears, draws sketches, provides patterns and fabric (or instructs others in these activities).

The Wardrobe Mistress/Master Takes care of the costumes, stores them, cleans and repairs them, etc.

Seamstress/Tailor Sews costumes and makes alterations.

Dresser Helps actors change clothes, especially quick changes.

CREATING AND PERFORMING

1. With a partner, block out how you would move and gesture during either the escalator scene, the dominoes scene, or the last scene between Maggie and Eric.
2. In groups of four, practice reading the Mondongo dinner table scene. Be prepared to share your scene with the class.
3. Choose any character from the play and draw two costumes for that character. Include indications for necessary makeup.

THE DRUMMER
THE BIG BLACK BOX

The Play as Literature: Beginning, Middle, and End

All stories have to start somewhere, and most start right at the beginning of things. Then they move along toward an ending. The ending usually presents the audience with a resolution of the events. That's the way most literature works. The two plays you are about to read work that way to a certain extent, but not entirely. In *The Drummer*, the playwright designates the end of the play as the beginning. In *The Big Black Box*, the playwright has written a beginning and an ending that are exactly the same (although much happens in between).

As you read, notice how the action builds in both plays and pay particular attention to how each play ends.

The Play as Theatre: Lighting

Lighting draws the viewer toward the stage. It illuminates the actors and the sets in a way that conveys the director's interpretation of the playwright's theme. Lighting creates mood and establishes a sense of time and place.

Bright light can create a mood of sunlight, warmth, and good feeling, but overdo it and the scene will seem intense and oppressive. Dim lighting can create an aura of mystery, romance, or sadness. Use cool colors if you want to create a strange or alien atmosphere. A red spotlight will make a character look cruel or aggressive, while warm colors such as yellow or orange can have a comic effect. Purple creates a regal or dreamy effect, while white creates the look of peacefulness and honesty. Whether a scene is lit from overhead, from the side, or from below will also influence the mood of the scene.

color wheel

WARM UP!

To get the effect of different lightening on your face, use a flashlight. Look in a mirror and aim the light at the top of your head, pointing it downward. How do you look? Next, position the light below your chin. What do you look like now? Compare the differences created by the different lighting.

THE DRUMMER

by Athol Fugard

THE BIG BLACK BOX

by Cleve Haubold

THE DRUMMER

by Athol Fugard

SETTING

A city pavement

CHARACTER

THE MAN

TIME

The present

SCENE

A pile of rubbish on a pavement, waiting to be cleared away. This consists of an over-filled trash-can and a battered old chair with torn upholstery on which is piled an assortment of cardboard boxes and plastic bags full of discarded junk. Distant and intermittent city noises. These will increase in volume and frequency as the action demands.

AT RISE: A BUM *Enters. He walks over to the pile of rubbish and starts to work his way through it . . . looking for something useful in terms of that day's survival. He has obviously just woken up and yawns from time to time. After a few seconds he clears the chair, sits down, makes himself comfortable and continues his search. One of the boxes produces a drumstick. He examines it and then abandons it. A little later he finds a second drumstick. He examines it. Remembers! He scratches around in the pile of rubbish at his feet and retrieves the first. Two drumsticks! His find intrigues[1] him. Another dip into the rubbish but it produces nothing further of interest. Two drumsticks! He settles back in his chair and surveys the world.*

An ambulance siren approaches and recedes stage right. He observes indifferently. A fire engine approaches and recedes stage left. He observes. While this is going on he taps idly[2] on the lid of the trash-can with one of the drumsticks. He becomes aware of this little action. Two drumsticks and a trash-can! It takes him a few seconds to realize the potential. He straightens up in his chair and with

a measure of caution, attempts a little tattoo[3] on the lid of the can. The result is not very impressive. He makes a second attempt, with the same result. Problem. Solution! He gets up and empties the trash-can of its contents, replaces the lid and makes a third attempt. The combination of a serious intention and the now resonant bin produces a decided effect. He develops it and in doing so starts to enjoy himself. His excitement gets him onto his feet. He has one last flash of inspiration. He removes the lid from the can, up-ends it, and with great bravura[4] drums out a final tattoo . . . virtually an accompaniment to the now very loud and urgent city noises all around him. Embellishing his appearance with some item from the rubbish . . . a cape? . . . and holding his drumsticks ready, he chooses a direction and sets off to take on the city. He has discovered it is full of drums . . . and he has got drumsticks.

THE BEGINNING

1. intrigue (in trēg′), arouse interest or curiosity
2. idly (īd′lē), lazily, without much thought; not busy
3. tattoo (ta tü′), a series of taps or raps
4. bravura (brə vyùr′ə), show of spirit or brilliance; dash

The Drummer by Athol Fugard   **311**

THE BIG BLACK BOX

by Cleve Haubold

SETTING	CHARACTERS	TIME
A street	ARNOLD THE BOX	The present

The only setting necessary is THE BOX *itself. Street signs, hydrants and such may be added to suggest a street.*

At Rise: The big black BOX *is sitting there, chuckling and singing to itself.*

BOX. Merrily we roll along, roll along, roll along,
Merrily we roll along, o'er the deep blue sea . . .

(It laughs and belches heartily. ARNOLD *enters and crosses the stage.)*

BOX. Nice day.

ARNOLD. Huh?

BOX. I just said it's a nice day.

ARNOLD. Is it?

BOX. I just said it. You don't have to agree if you don't want to.

ARNOLD. It's a nice day.

BOX. Thank you. Oh, don't run off.

ARNOLD. What?

BOX. I mean . . . what's your hurry?

ARNOLD. I do not speak to strange boxes. So long. See you.

BOX. Merrily we roll along, roll along, roll along,
Merrily we roll along—

ARNOLD. You're singing.

BOX. You noticed!

ARNOLD. I don't miss much. Why are you singing?

BOX. I thought you didn't talk to strange boxes.

ARNOLD. I make that a very firm rule.

BOX. That's very wise of you.

ARNOLD. Why are you singing?

BOX. Oh . . . no reason.

ARNOLD. I have never found a box to sing with no reason.

BOX. How perceptive[1] you are, sir.

ARNOLD. So, why are you singing?

BOX. You'll find out.

ARNOLD. I'm not that interested.

BOX. Naturally. Of course not. Naturally. Merrily we roll along, roll along, roll along—

ARNOLD. Just sing your lid off. I don't care.

BOX. Naturally not. Merrily we roll along . . . Ha, ha, hah.

ARNOLD. Now what are you laughing about? What?

BOX. Same thing I was singing about. But you wouldn't care. Ha, ha, hah.

ARNOLD. No, I wouldn't. I wouldn't, would not, wouldn't. Couldn't care less. Absolutely with effort could not care less. Good-bye.

BOX. Before you go . . .

ARNOLD. Yes?

BOX. Have you got a light?

ARNOLD. Yes. Here.

BOX. Say, that's a nice lighter you've got there. Very nice indeed.

ARNOLD. Don't you want a light?

BOX. Don't be silly. Boxes don't smoke. I just wondered . . . say, what is your name?

ARNOLD. Arnold. What's yours?

BOX. Boxes don't have names, Arnold.

ARNOLD. Oh.

BOX. I mean . . . you've noticed that. Haven't you noticed that?

ARNOLD. I have. Now that you mention it.

BOX. Arnold. That's a good upstanding name. A name with something to it. Ar-nold!

ARNOLD. That's my name.

BOX. How lucky you are, Arnold, to have a name like that. How lucky you are. I wish I had a name like that.

ARNOLD. It's handy. People can call you by it.

BOX. Can they now?

ARNOLD. Oh, yes. Everyone does.

BOX. Fancy that. Everyone calls you by it?

ARNOLD. Everyone that knows it.

BOX. You are downright fortunate. Put down your umbrella and come here, Arnold.

ARNOLD. No.

BOX. Why not, Arnold? Just around in front so I can have a look at Arnold.

ARNOLD. What's inside?

BOX. I beg pardon?

ARNOLD. I said, "What's inside?"

BOX. I don't know you that well, Arnold. But if you look honest, well . . . I might let you in on it.

ARNOLD. I look honest.

BOX. How do I know that?

ARNOLD. I have an honest name.

BOX. How do I know it's your name?

ARNOLD. I told you.

BOX. But if you look dishonest, that may not be your name. May not be your name at all. No I just don't know you at all, Arnold.

ARNOLD. Can you see me now?

---

1 perceptive (pər sep′tiv), having keen understanding or insight

BOX. A bit to the left. Now a bit closer.

ARNOLD. Closer?

BOX. Not much. Just a step.

ARNOLD. No.

BOX. Just half a step. What can that hurt?

ARNOLD. How do I know what's inside?

BOX. How're you ever going to find out?

ARNOLD. You don't look like much from here.

BOX. Appearances, Arnold. Only appearances. Arnold, you *don't* look dishonest.

ARNOLD. I'm not.

BOX. And I believe you. Now come a bit closer.

ARNOLD. How do I know you're trustworthy?

BOX. I'm trustworthy.

ARNOLD. How do I know?

BOX. Arnold, have I ever lied to you?

ARNOLD. You don't look unkind.

BOX. Down deep inside, I'm pure velvet.

ARNOLD. What color?

BOX. Oh, ho. Wouldn't you just like to know? Wouldn't you just!

ARNOLD. No. And I've got a bus to catch.

BOX. I'm fuchsia.[2]

ARNOLD. Fuchsia? Really, pure fuchsia?

BOX. Pure, pure, oh pure. What else would it be?

ARNOLD. Pure fuchsia! I would like to see that!

BOX. I thought you would.

ARNOLD. Show me.

BOX. Come a little closer.

ARNOLD. Poke a little out the keyhole.

BOX. Oh, come now, Arnold. You couldn't expect me to do that!

ARNOLD. Are you sure it's pure fuchsia?

BOX. Who would know better than I?

ARNOLD. Well . . . here I am. Let's see it. Come on . . . please. I've always had a more than passing interest in fuchsia.

BOX. You're sincere?

ARNOLD. And trustworthy.

BOX. Admirable. Put a dollar through the keyhole.

ARNOLD. A dollar?

BOX. Then I'll open up. Just roll up a dollar and put it through the keyhole. You are sincere, aren't you?

ARNOLD. I'm sincere, but—

BOX. What are you worried about? It isn't as if you wouldn't know where your money is. And, of course, you'll get it right back. I just want to be sure you're sincere.

ARNOLD. I'll get it back?

BOX. What could happen to it, Arnold? I'm not a big spender.

ARNOLD. Well . . . all right. Here.

BOX. . . . And another.

ARNOLD. Another?

BOX. You either trust me or you don't.

ARNOLD. I'm not sure.

BOX. Arnold, do you place a price on your sincerity? Shame on you, Arnold. Go catch your bus.

ARNOLD. You've got my dollar.

---

2 fuchsia (fyü′shə), a vivid purplish-red color

BOX. I want your faith and confidence.

ARNOLD. Come on. Open up. You promised.

BOX. Did I? Put in another dollar, and I will.

ARNOLD. Are you sure?

BOX. Do I look deceitful?

ARNOLD. Well . . . here.

BOX. You are a jewel, Arnold. A real jewel.

ARNOLD. So, open.

BOX. Oh, I will. I will. Come up real close, so you can get a good look.

ARNOLD. How much closer?

BOX. And . . . you'll want your two dollars back, won't you? Real close. Right up to the front. Very, very close. And lean over so you can see good.

ARNOLD. I knew you couldn't be trusted. There's my bus. I am going. Keep the two dollars. Dirty old box!

(ARNOLD *starts to go. The* BOX *opens a crack.*)

BOX. If you're going to be that way about it . . . here! You take your money. But don't you dare look at the fuchsia velvet!

ARNOLD. Keep the two dollars, I'll miss my bus.

BOX. For two dollars you could take a taxi.

(ARNOLD *comes toward the* BOX.)

ARNOLD. You're not mad?

BOX. Mad? Why should I be mad? I'm hurt, I confess. A little hurt, but not mad. Take your two dollars and go. Put down your umbrella. Don't rumple the velvet. Just take your two dollars.

ARNOLD. You bet I will. I can't get my hand out. Your lid is closed on my hand.

BOX. How about that!

ARNOLD. I can't get my hand out. And I can't reach my two dollars.

BOX. Really now! That's odd.

ARNOLD. If you're as trustworthy and sincere as I am, you'll let go my hand.

BOX. Yes, I bet I would.

ARNOLD. I want my two dollars.

BOX. But, Arnold, it's down at the bottom. Just reach in a little farther, and you'll have it.

ARNOLD. No.

BOX. Oh, come on, Arnold! What are people going to say? "Look at Arnold. He's afraid to reach in and get his two dollars." Is that what you want them to say about you?

ARNOLD. Let go my hand. You can keep the two dollars.

BOX. No, no. I wouldn't hear of it that way. You've got to have your money back. Oh, while you're in, you might as well feel the velvet. That should show that I'm sincere.

ARNOLD. I want my hand.

BOX. Well, of course you do, Arnold. And you shall have it back just as soon as we can figure out how to do it. Why not reach your other hand down and lift the lid?

ARNOLD. No.

BOX. Arnold, sometimes your lack of trust distresses me. Let me think. I have it! Stick your hat in and wriggle it around. That should convince you.

Go on. You're not going anywhere.

ARNOLD. It's my good hat.

BOX. I'll take that as a sign of your trust and confidence.

ARNOLD. There . . . Something's got my hat!

BOX. Must be caught on the latch. Do you have a fountain pen?

ARNOLD. Yes.

BOX. Just the very thing. Just the right size and shape to poke the hat off the latch.

ARNOLD. You think so?

BOX. I am absolutely certain of it. Give it a try.

ARNOLD. Now something's got my fountain pen.

BOX. Arnold, you are a clumsy one! Is that a watch and chain you have on?

ARNOLD. It was my father's.

BOX. Then I'm sure it's a good one. Just slide the watch through the crack and let it swing around on the chain. It can't miss picking up everything.

ARNOLD. Something would get it.

BOX. What's this talk about "something"? There's nobody here but you and me. What would get it?

ARNOLD. I don't know.

BOX. See? A groundless fear.

ARNOLD. You would get it.

BOX. What would I want with a watch? I've got all the time in the world. But you're going to miss the next bus. Desperate situations demand desperate measures. I'm trying to help you. Try the watch.

ARNOLD. You're sure that something won't get it?

BOX. Positive.

ARNOLD. I've already lost my hat and fountain pen.

BOX. You haven't lost them, Arnold. You know precisely where they are.

ARNOLD. But you'll guarantee the watch and chain?

BOX. I guarantee them.

ARNOLD. There's no doubt in your mind?

BOX. Not a bit.

ARNOLD. Well . . . I'll try.

BOX. That's the boy.

ARNOLD. Something got my watch.

BOX. Son-of-a-gun!

ARNOLD. I am beginning to suspect something.

BOX. How 'bout that!

ARNOLD. I am beginning to suspect that you are deceitful. Deceitful and conniving. That is what I am beginning to suspect.

BOX. Oh, come off it, Arnold. Say, boy, if you lean down real close you can see the fuchsia velvet. Want to give that a try?

ARNOLD. No. I want you to let go.

BOX. Just a peek? You ought to get something for your money.

ARNOLD. You are greedy. Oh, how I hate a greedy box!

BOX. Don't kick.

ARNOLD. Let go. You want something else. What else you want?

BOX. Guess.

ARNOLD. Here is my neatly folded pocket handkerchief. You want my neatly folded pocket handkerchief? Is that what you want?

BOX. It's a start.

ARNOLD. Here's my whole entire wallet.

BOX. Keep on.

ARNOLD. How about a shoe?

BOX. Let's have it. And the other one, too.

ARNOLD. Now will you let go?

BOX. No.

ARNOLD. Take my coat and I'll tell you a secret about this coat. Sewn into the lining is a tinker-toy that I have carried for years as a talisman against evil. That's a real good thing to have on you.

BOX. That's the best yet.

ARNOLD. And you can have it.

BOX. Don't just flap your sleeves. Put it in.

ARNOLD. I can't get my coat off.

BOX. You can't?

ARNOLD. Can't get it off over my hand. You've got my hand. Let up for a minute and you've got the coat.

BOX. Now, Arnold, really! What do you think I am?

ARNOLD. I trusted you. Now you trust me.

BOX. Arnold, Arnold, Arnold. Shame.

ARNOLD. You don't think I'd run off, do you?

BOX. Well . . .

ARNOLD. You don't sincerely think I'd run off and leave my two dollars, my good hat, my fountain pen, my father's watch and chain, my neatly folded pocket handkerchief, my whole entire wallet, my shoes, and my coat with my entire tinker-toy talisman against evil, do you?

BOX. I'll risk it. Put in all but the sleeve. Now, quick! The sleeve!

(ARNOLD *snatches his hand out of the box.*)

ARNOLD. Ha! You are a silly greedy box. Let that be a lesson to you. Trick, trick, trick . . . and I win! Now you don't have me, or my umbrella! Dirty, silly, greedy box!

BOX. Don't talk smart.

ARNOLD. He who laughs last, laughs best! Ho. Ho. Hee. Hee.

BOX. Oh, boy.

ARNOLD. I grant you that I shall have difficulty walking to the bus-stop without my shoes, and I shall miss my coat a great deal. But that really wasn't my good hat you got. And the fountain pen writes only with great difficulty. And it will leak, leak, leak on your fuchsia velvet. So there!

BOX. When's the next bus?

ARNOLD. It should be here in . . . I shall miss my watch.

BOX. Want to peek at it?

ARNOLD. Definitely not. Don't you worry about me. I can get along without that watch. Of course, walking around without one's talisman is risky . . . But I'm out of reach now, and I intend to stay that way. Do you hear that? Do you hear that? I'm on my way. I am going. I am going to the bus-stop, and you'll never see me again. Good-bye!

BOX. Arnold . . .

(*The lid of the* BOX *opens fully.*)

ARNOLD. It is fuchsia velvet!

BOX. All the way.

ARNOLD. No tricks now.

BOX. Arnold, you are too smart for me.

ARNOLD. You bet.

BOX. And look at all the goodies inside . . .

ARNOLD. I still don't trust you. Here. You want my umbrella? Take it.

BOX. What would I do with an umbrella?

ARNOLD. Then I can have it back?

BOX. Naturally.

ARNOLD. I've got it! You didn't get the umbrella! Here it is again. Can I have it back?

BOX. Take it. What do I care?

ARNOLD. I've got it now. I've got it back now. That really makes you mad, doesn't it! Just hopping mad!

BOX. Not particularly.

ARNOLD. Just to show you what I think of you . . . here it is. For keeps! *(He props the lid open with the umbrella.)* Boy, you're in a mess now. I hope it rains on your fuchsia velvet. What's the matter? Can't you talk with your lid open? Hey? Hello? What's the matter? Look, look, look. Here's my hand. Can't do anything about it, can you? Look. Here's the whole arm. Missed it that time, didn't you! Look here. I'm going to get my two dollars. Got 'em! See? One. Two. And my good hat. How about that? And my fountain pen. And my father's watch and chain. And my neatly folded pocket handkerchief. And my whole entire wallet. And my shoes. Both of 'em! Oh, boy! And my coat with the tinker-toy sewn into the lining as a talisman against . . .

(The umbrella falls into the box. The lid slams shut, enclosing ARNOLD *in the* BOX. *He begins to shout and struggle, but the sounds die out shortly.)*

BOX. Merrily we roll along, roll along, roll along,
Merrily we roll along, o'er the deep blue sea . . .

(It belches with soul-satisfying resonance. And just sits there. Curtain.)

END OF PLAY

THE DRUMMER
THE BIG BLACK BOX

Responding to the Play

1. Compare these two plays in terms of their beginnings and their endings.
2. Arnold in *The Big Black Box* and The Man in *The Drummer* both make important discoveries. In one sentence, tell what they are.
3. Which of these plays would be more interesting to light? Why?
4. Make a list of props you would need to acquire to produce *The Drummer*. Notice that the stage directions indicate only that the set should contain "rubbish." What would that rubbish include?
5. Write the copy for a news release about either play. Include information as to the theme, the playwright, the cast, and the location of the play.

About Lighting Plots and Cue Sheets

Most lights are moveable and can thus be hung in many different spots. The lighting engineer or designer makes a lighting plot to show where the lights are and the range of their illumination. The plot identifies the location of each light. It is drawn to scale.

The cue sheet explains every change in lighting from the beginning of the play to the end. It includes information on which lights are involved, the settings to use, and the length of time each change takes.

CREATING AND PERFORMING

1. Draw a stage set of either play. Include as many details as you can, such as characters, props, and lighting.
2.. With a partner, choose the role of Arnold or The Box. Experiment with different voices for your characters. Try to come up with a voice that captures your character's personality. Read a few lines together for the class.
3. You are a reporter at the scene of the mysterious disappearance of Arnold. Tell the viewing audience the details of the case— describe Arnold, where he was going, where he was last seen, etc.

The Hitch Hiker

The Play as Literature: Suspense

Have you ever read a mystery that had you turning on all the lights and locking all the doors? How does an author create a story so full of suspense that it gives you goosebumps? Often the author starts with a plot line in which the main character faces a fear of impending doom. This fear is magnified by uncertainty about the future and mystery about how and why events are occuring. Evidence of the dreaded person or event mounts throughout the story. Finally, the character must face the evidence—or the dreaded person or event. For better or worse, the mystery is solved.

Two common elements of suspense are:

- a mystery that has to be solved
- a potential for dire consequences

As you read *The Hitch Hiker*, be aware of how the mystery deepens and the suspense builds.

The Play as Theatre: The Radio Play

Creating a play for a radio audience has it's own unique demands. Because radio speaks exclusively to our sense of hearing, authors who write radio scripts must always keep that in mind. The audience cannot see movement or facial expression, so the actors' emotions must come from the voice. And each actor must have a distinctive voice so that the audience knows immediately who is speaking. Sound effects and music play a vital part in informing the listener as to what is happening. Notice how SOUND and MUSIC are indicated in this script—just as though they too were characters in the play.

WARM UP!

Practice varying your voice, tone, articulation, and speed while saying the lines below as the characters indicated.

16-year-old Midwest sales clerk: I'm sorry, that item is out of stock.
20-year-old California surfer: Dude, those waves are awesome!
70-year old Bostonian: You just can't find good help these days, my dear.

The Hitch Hiker

by Lucille Fletcher

SOUND. *Automobile wheels humming over concrete road.*

MUSIC. *Something weird and shuddery.*

ADAMS. I am in an auto camp on Route Sixty-six just west of Gallup, New Mexico. If I tell it perhaps it will help me. It will keep me from going mad. But I must tell this quickly. I am not mad now. I feel perfectly well, except that I am running a slight temperature. My name is Ronald Adams. I am thirty-six years of age, unmarried, tall, dark, with a black mustache. I drive a 1940 Ford V-8, license number 6V-7989. I was born in Brooklyn. All this I know. I know that I am at this moment perfectly sane. That it is not I who has gone mad—but something else—something utterly beyond my control. But I must speak quickly. At any moment the link with life may break. This may be the last thing I ever tell on earth . . . the last night I ever see the stars. . . .

MUSIC. *In.*

ADAMS. Six days ago I left Brooklyn, to drive to California. . . .

MOTHER. Goodbye, Son. Good luck to you, my boy. . . .

ADAMS. Goodbye, Mother. Here—give me a kiss, and then I'll go. . . .

MOTHER. I'll come out with you to the car.

ADAMS. No. It's raining. Stay here at the door. Hey—what is this? Tears? I thought you promised me you wouldn't cry.

MOTHER. I know, dear. I'm sorry. But I —do hate to see you go.

ADAMS. I'll be back. I'll only be on the coast three months.

MOTHER. Oh—it isn't that. It's just—the trip. Ronald—I wish you weren't driving.

ADAMS. Oh—Mother. There you go again. People do it every day.

MOTHER. I know. But you'll be careful, won't you? Promise me you'll be extra careful. Don't fall asleep—or drive fast—or pick up any strangers on the road. . . .

ADAMS. Lord, no. You'd think I was still seventeen to hear you talk—

MOTHER. And wire me as soon as you get to Hollywood, won't you, son?

ADAMS. Of course I will. Now don't you worry. There isn't anything going to happen. It's just eight days of perfectly simple driving on smooth, decent, civilized roads, with a hot dog or a hamburger stand every ten miles. . . . *(Fade)*

SOUND. *Auto hum.*

MUSIC. *In.*

ADAMS. I was in excellent spirits. The drive ahead of me, even the loneliness, seemed like a lark.[1] But I reckoned without *him.*

MUSIC. *Changes to something weird and empty.*

Crossing Brooklyn Bridge that morning in the rain, I saw a man leaning against the cables. He seemed to be waiting for a lift. There were spots of fresh rain on his shoulders. He was carrying a cheap overnight bag in one hand. He was thin, nondescript, with a cap pulled down over his eyes. He stepped off the walk and if I hadn't swerved, I'd have hit him.

SOUND. *Terrific skidding.*

MUSIC. *In.*

ADAMS. I would have forgotten him completely, except that just an hour later, while crossing the Pulaski Skyway over the Jersey flats, I saw him again. At least, he looked like the same person. He was standing now, with one thumb pointing west. I couldn't figure out how he'd got there, but I thought probably one of those fast trucks had picked him up, beaten me to the Skyway, and let him off. I didn't stop for him. Then—late that night, I saw him again.

MUSIC. *Changing.*

ADAMS. It was on the new Pennsylvania Turnpike between Harrisburg and Pittsburgh. It's two hundred and sixty-five miles long, with a very high speed limit. I was just slowing down for one of the tunnels—when I saw him—standing under an arc light by the side of the road. I could see him quite distinctly. The bag, the cap, even the spots of fresh rain spattered over his shoulders. He hailed me this time. . . .

VOICE *(very spooky and faint).* Hall-ooo. . . .

(Echo as through tunnel) Hall-ooo. . . .

ADAMS. I stepped on the gas like a shot. That's lonely country through the Alleghenies, and I had no intention of stopping. Besides, the coincidence, or whatever it was, gave me the willies.[2] I stopped at the next gas station.

SOUND. *Auto tires screeching to stop . . . horn honk.*

MECHANIC. Yes, sir.

ADAMS. Fill her up.

MECHANIC. Certainly, sir. Check your oil, sir?

ADAMS. No, thanks.

----

1. lark (lärk), something done for fun or adventure
2. willies (wil′ēz), fit of nervousness; jitters

The Hitch Hiker by Lucille Fletcher   **323**

SOUND. *Gas being put into car . . . bell tinkle, et cetera.*

MECHANIC. Nice night, isn't it?

ADAMS. Yes. It—hasn't been raining here recently, has it?

MECHANIC. Not a drop of rain all week.

ADAMS. Hm. I suppose that hasn't done your business any harm.

MECHANIC. Oh—people drive through here all kinds of weather. Mostly business, you know. There aren't many pleasure cars out on the Turnpike this season of the year.

ADAMS. I suppose not. *(Casually)* What about hitch hikers?

MECHANIC *(half laughing).* Hitch hikers *here?*

ADAMS. What's the matter? Don't you ever see any?

MECHANIC. Not much. If we did, it'd be a sight for sore eyes.

ADAMS. Why?

MECHANIC. A guy'd be a fool who started out to hitch rides on this road. Look at it. It's two hundred and sixty-five miles long, there's practically no speed limit, and it's a straightaway. Now what car is going to stop to pick up a guy under those conditions? Would you stop?

ADAMS. No. *(Slowly, with puzzled emphasis)* Then you've never seen anybody?

MECHANIC. Nope. Mebbe they get the lift before the Turnpike starts—I mean, you know—just before the toll house—but then it'd be a mighty long ride. Most cars wouldn't want to pick up a guy for that long a ride. And you know—this is pretty lonesome country here—mountains, and

woods. . . . You ain't seen anybody like that, have you?

ADAMS. No. *(Quickly)* Oh no, not at all. It was—just a—technical question.

MECHANIC. I see. Well—that'll be just a dollar forty-nine—with the tax. . . . *(Fade)*

SOUND. *Auto hum up.*

MUSIC. *Changing.*

ADAMS. The thing gradually passed from my mind, as sheer coincidence. I had a good night's sleep in Pittsburgh. I did not think about the man all next day—until just outside of Zanesville, Ohio, I saw him again.

MUSIC. *Dark, ominous note.*

ADAMS. It was a bright sunshiny afternoon. The peaceful Ohio fields, brown with the autumn stubble, lay dreaming in the golden light. I was driving slowly, drinking it in, when the road suddenly ended in a detour. In front of the barrier, *he* was standing.

MUSIC. *In.*

ADAMS. Let me explain about his appearance before I go on. I repeat. There was nothing sinister about him. He was as drab as a mud fence. Nor was his attitude menacing. He merely stood there, waiting, almost drooping a little, the cheap overnight bag in his hand. He looked as though he had been waiting there for hours. Then he looked up. He hailed me. He started to walk forward.

VOICE *(far off).* Hall-ooo . . . Hall-ooo. . . .

ADAMS. I had stopped the car, of

course, for the detour. And for a few moments, I couldn't seem to find the new road. I knew he must be thinking that I had stopped for him.

VOICE (*closer*). Hall-ooo . . .
Hallll . . . ooo. . . .

SOUND. *Gears jamming . . . sound of motor turning over hard . . . nervous accelerator.*

VOICE (*closer*). Halll . . . oooo. . . .

ADAMS (*panicky*). No. Not just now. Sorry. . . .

VOICE (*closer*). Going to California?

SOUND. *Starter starting . . . gears jamming.*

ADAMS (*as though sweating blood*). No. Not today. The other way. Going to New York. Sorry . . . sorry . . .

SOUND. *Car starts with squeal of wheels on dirt . . . into auto hum.*

MUSIC. *In.*

ADAMS. After I got the car back onto the road again, I felt like a fool. Yet the thought of picking him up, of having him sit beside me was somehow unbearable. Yet, at the same time, I felt, more than ever, unspeakably alone.

SOUND. *Auto hum up.*

ADAMS. Hour after hour went by. The fields, the towns ticked off, one by one. The lights changed. I knew now that I was going to see him again. And though I dreaded the sight, I caught myself searching the side of the road, waiting for him to appear.

SOUND. *Auto hum up . . . car screeches to a halt . . . impatient honk two or three times . . . door being unbolted.*

SLEEPY MAN'S VOICE. Yep? What is it? What do you want?

ADAMS (*breathless*). You sell sandwiches and pop here, don't you?

VOICE (*cranky*). Yep. We do. In the daytime. But we're closed up now for the night.

ADAMS. I know. But—I was wondering if you could possibly let me have a cup of coffee—black coffee.

VOICE. Not at this time of night, mister. My wife's the cook and she's in bed. Mebbe further down the road—at the Honeysuckle Rest. . . .

SOUND. *Door squeaking on hinges as though being closed.*

ADAMS: No—no. Don't shut the door. (*Shakily*) Listen—just a minute ago, there was a man standing here— right beside this stand—a suspicious looking man. . . .

WOMAN'S VOICE (*from distance*). Hen-ry? Who is it Hen-ry?

HENRY. It's nobuddy, mother. Just a feller thinks he wants a cup of coffee. Go back into bed.

ADAMS. I don't mean to disturb you. But you see, I was driving along— when I just happened to look—and there he was. . . .

HENRY. What was he doing?

ADAMS. Nothing. He ran off—when I stopped the car.

HENRY. Then what of it? That's nothing to wake a man in the middle of his sleep about. (*Sternly*) Young man, I've got a good mind to turn you over to the sheriff.

ADAMS. But—I—

HENRY. You've been taking a nip, that's what you've been doing. And you haven't got anything better to do than to wake decent folk out of their hard-earned sleep. Get going. Go on.

ADAMS. But—he looked as through he were going to rob you.

HENRY. I ain't got nothin' in this stand to lose. Now—on your way before I call out Sheriff Oakes. *(Fades)*

SOUND. *Auto hum up.*

ADAMS. I got into the car again, and drove on slowly. I was beginning to hate the car. If I could have found a place to stop . . . to rest a little. But I was in the Ozark Mountains of Missouri now. The few resort places there were closed. Only an occasional log cabin, seemingly deserted, broke the monotony of the wild wooded landscape. I *had* seen him at the roadside stand; I knew I would see him again—perhaps at the next turn of the road. I knew that when I saw him next, I would run him down. . . .

SOUND. *Auto hum up.*

ADAMS. But I did not see him again until late next afternoon. . . .

SOUND. *Of railroad warning signal at crossroads.*

ADAMS. I had stopped the car at a sleepy little junction just across the border into Oklahoma—to let a train pass by—when he appeared, across the tracks, leaning against a telephone pole.

SOUND. *Distant sound of train chugging . . . bell ringing steadily.*

ADAMS *(very tense).* It was a perfectly air-less, dry day. The red clay of Oklahoma was baking under the southwestern sun. Yet there were spots of fresh rain on his shoulders. I couldn't stand that. Without thinking, blindly, I started the car across the tracks.

SOUND. *Train chugging closer.*

ADAMS. He didn't even look up at me. He was staring at the ground. I stepped on the gas hard, veering the wheel sharply toward him. I could hear the train in the distance now, but I didn't care. Then something went wrong with the car. It stalled right on the tracks.

SOUND. *Train chugging closer. Above this sound of car stalling.*

ADAMS. The train was coming closer. I could hear its bell ringing, and the cry of its whistle. Still he stood there. And now—I knew that he was beckoning—beckoning me to my death.

SOUND. *Train chugging close. Whistle blows wildly. Then train rushes up and by with pistons going, et cetera.*

ADAMS. Well, I frustrated him that time. The starter had worked at last. I managed to back up. But when the train passed, he was gone. I was all alone in the hot dry afternoon.

SOUND. *Train retreating. Crickets begin to sing.*

MUSIC. *In.*

ADAMS. After that, I knew I had to do something. I didn't know who this man was or what he wanted of me. I only knew that from now on, I must not let myself be alone on the road for one moment.

SOUND. *Auto hum up. Slow down. Stop. Door opening.*

ADAMS. Hello, there. Like a ride?

GIRL. What do you think? How far you going?

ADAMS. Amarillo . . . I'll take you to Amarillo.

GIRL. Amarillo, Texas?

ADAMS. I'll drive you there.

GIRL. Gee!

SOUND. *Door closes—car starts.*

MUSIC. *In.*

GIRL. Mind if I take off my shoes? My dogs are killing me!

ADAMS. Go right ahead.

GIRL. Gee, what a break this is. A swell car, a decent guy, and driving all the way to Amarillo. All I been getting so far is trucks.

ADAMS. Hitch hike much?

GIRL. Sure. Only it's tough sometimes, in these great open spaces, to get the breaks.

ADAMS. I should think it would be. Though I'll bet if you get a good pick-up in a fast car, you can get to places faster than—say, another person, in another car.

GIRL. I don't get you.

ADAMS. Well, take me, for instance. Suppose I'm driving across the country, say, at a nice steady clip of about forty-five miles an hour. Couldn't a girl like you, just standing beside the road, waiting for lifts, beat me to town after town—provided she got picked up every time in a car doing from sixty-five to seventy miles an hour?

GIRL. I dunno. Maybe she could and maybe she couldn't. What difference does it make?

ADAMS. Oh—no difference. It's just a— crazy idea I had sitting here in the car.

GIRL *(laughing).* Imagine spending your time in a swell car thinking of things like that!

ADAMS. What would you do instead?

GIRL *(admiringly).* What would I do? If I was a good-looking fellow like yourself? Why—I'd just *enjoy* myself— every minute of the time. I'd sit back, and relax, and if I saw a good-looking girl along the side of the road . . . *(Sharply)* Hey! Look out!

ADAMS *(breathlessly).* Did you see him too?

GIRL. See who?

ADAMS. That man. Standing beside the barbed wire fence.

GIRL. I didn't see—anybody. There wasn't nothing, but a bunch of steers— and the barbed wire fence. What did you think you was doing? Trying to run into the barbed wire fence?

ADAMS. There was a man there, I tell you . . . a thin gray man, with an overnight bag in his hand. And I was trying to—run him down.

GIRL. Run him down? You mean—kill him?

ADAMS. He's a sort of—phantom.[3] I'm trying to get rid of him—or else prove that he's real. But . . . *(Desperately)* You say you didn't see him back there? You're sure?

GIRL *(queerly).* I didn't see a soul. And as far as that's concerned, mister . . .

---

3. phantom (fant′əm), a ghostlike being; an apparition

ADAMS. Watch for him the next time, then. Keep watching. Keep your eyes peeled on the road. He'll turn up again—maybe any minute now. *(Excitedly)* There. Look there—

SOUND. *Auto sharply veering and skidding. Girl screams.*

SOUND. *Crash of car going into barbed wire fence. Frightened lowing of steer.*

GIRL. How does this door work? I—I'm gettin' outta here.

ADAMS. Did you see him that time?

GIRL *(sharply)*. No. I didn't see him that time. And personally, mister, I don't expect never to see him. All I want to do is to go on living—and I don't see how I will very long driving with you—

ADAMS. I'm sorry. I—I don't know what came over me. *(Frightened)* Please—don't go. . . .

GIRL. So if you'll excuse me, mister—

ADAMS. You can't go. Listen, how would you like to go to California? I'll drive you to California.

GIRL. Seeing pink elephants[4] all the way? No thanks.

ADAMS *(desperately)*. I could get you a job there. You wouldn't have to be a waitress. I have friends there—my name is Ronald Adams—You can check up.

SOUND. *Door opening.*

GIRL. Uhn-hunh. Thanks just the same.

ADAMS. Listen. Please. For just one minute. Maybe you think I am half cracked. But this man. You see, I've been seeing this man all the way across the country. He's been following me. And if you could only help

me—stay with me—until I reach the coast—

GIRL. You know what I think you need, big boy? Not a girl friend. Just a good dose of sleep. . . . There, I got it now.

SOUND. *Door opens . . . slams.*

ADAMS. No. You can't go.

GIRL *(screams)*. Leave your hands offa me, do you hear! Leave your—

ADAMS. Come back here, please, come back.

SOUND. *Struggle . . . slap . . . footsteps running away on gravel . . . lowing of steer.*

ADAMS. She ran from me, as though I were a monster. A few minutes later, I saw a passing truck pick her up. I knew then that I was utterly alone.

SOUND. *Lowing of steer up.*

ADAMS. I was in the heart of the great Texas prairies. There wasn't a car on the road after the truck went by. I tried to figure out what to do, how to get hold of myself. If I could find a place to rest. Or even, if I could sleep right here in the car for a few hours, along the side of the road. . . . I was getting my winter overcoat out of the back seat to use as a blanket *(Hall-ooo)* when I saw him coming toward me *(Hall-ooo)*, emerging from the herd of moving steers. . . .

VOICE. Hall-ooo . . . Hall-ooo. . . .

SOUND. *Auto starting violently . . . up to steady hum.*

MUSIC. *In.*

ADAMS. I didn't wait for him to come

---

4. pink elephants, an imagined sight; an hallucination, often as the result of heavy drinking

any closer. Perhaps I should have spoken to him then, fought it out then and there. For now he began to be everywhere. Whenever I stopped, even for a moment—for gas, for oil, for a drink of pop, a cup of coffee, a sandwich—he was there.

MUSIC. *Faster.*

ADAMS. I saw him standing outside the auto camp in Amarillo that night, when I dared to slow down. He was sitting near the drinking fountain in a little camping spot just inside the border of New Mexico.

MUSIC. *Faster.*

ADAMS. He was waiting for me outside the Navajo Reservation, where I stopped to check my tires. I saw him in Albuquerque where I bought twelve gallons of gas. . . . I was afraid now, afraid to stop. I began to drive faster and faster. I was in lunar landscape now—the great arid mesa country of New Mexico. I drove through it with the indifference of a fly crawling over the face of the moon.

MUSIC. *Faster.*

ADAMS. But now he didn't even wait for me to stop. Unless I drove at eighty-five miles an hour over those endless roads—he waited for me at every other mile. I would see his figure, shadowless, flitting before me, still in its same attitude, over the cold and lifeless ground, flitting over dried-up rivers, over broken stones cast up by old glacial upheavals, flitting in the pure and cloudless air. . . .

MUSIC. *Strikes sinister note of finality.*

ADAMS. I was beside myself when I finally reached Gallup, New Mexico, this morning. There is an auto camp here—cold, almost deserted at this time of year. I went inside, and asked if there was a telephone. I had the feeling that if only I could speak to someone familiar, someone that I loved, I could pull myself together.

SOUND. *Nickel put in slot.*

OPERATOR. Number, please?

ADAMS. Long distance.

OPERATOR. Thank you.

SOUND. *Return of nickel; buzz.*

LONG DISTANCE. This is long distance.

ADAMS. I'd like to put in a call to my home in Brooklyn, New York. I'm Ronald Adams. The number is Beechwood 2-0828.

LONG DISTANCE. Thank you. What is your number?

ADAMS. 312.

ALBUQUERQUE OPERATOR: Albuquerque.

LONG DISTANCE. New York for Gallup.

(Pause)

NEW YORK OPERATOR. New York.

LONG DISTANCE. Gallup, New Mexico, calling Beechwood 2-0828. *(Fade)*

ADAMS. I had read somewhere that love could banish demons. It was the middle of the morning. I knew Mother would be home. I pictured her, tall, white-haired, in her crisp house-dress, going about her tasks. It would be enough, I thought, merely to hear the even calmness of her voice. . . .

LONG DISTANCE. Will you please deposit three dollars and eighty-five cents for the first three minutes? When you have deposited a dollar and a half, will you wait until I have collected the money?

SOUND. *Clunk of six coins.*

LONG DISTANCE. All right, deposit another dollar and a half.

SOUND.

Clunk of six coins.

LONG DISTANCE. Will you please deposit the remaining eighty-five cents?

SOUND. *Clunk of four coins.*

LONG DISTANCE. Ready with Brooklyn—go ahead please.

ADAMS. Hello.

MRS. WHITNEY. Mrs. Adams' residence.

ADAMS. Hello. Hello—Mother?

MRS. WHITNEY (*very flat and rather proper . . . dumb, too, in a frizzy sort of way*). This is Mrs. Adams' residence. Who is it you wished to speak to, please?

ADAMS. Why—who's this?

MRS. WHITNEY. This is Mrs. Whitney.

ADAMS. Mrs. Whitney? I don't know any Mrs. Whitney. Is this Beechwood 2-0828?

MRS. WHITNEY. Yes.

ADAMS. Where's my mother? Where's Mrs. Adams?

MRS. WHITNEY. Mrs. Adams is not at home. She is still in the hospital.

ADAMS. The hospital!

MRS. WHITNEY. Yes. Who is this calling, please? Is it a member of the family?

ADAMS. What's she in the hospital for?

MRS. WHITNEY. She's been prostrated

for five days. Nervous breakdown. But who is this calling?

ADAMS. Nervous breakdown? But—my mother was never nervous.

MRS. WHITNEY. It's all taken place since the death of her oldest son, Ronald.

ADAMS. Death of her oldest son, Ronald . . .? Hey—what is this? What number is this?

MRS. WHITNEY. This is Beechwood 2-0828. It's all been very sudden. He was killed just six days ago in an automobile accident on the Brooklyn Bridge.

OPERATOR (*breaking in*). Your three minutes are up, sir.

(*Pause*)

OPERATOR. Your three minutes are up, sir. (*Pause*)

Your three minutes are up, sir. (*Fade*) Sir, your three minutes are up. Your three minutes are up, sir.

ADAMS (*in a strange voice*). And so, I am sitting here in this deserted auto camp in Gallup, New Mexico. I am trying to think. I am trying to get hold of myself. Otherwise, I shall go mad. . . . Outside it is night—the vast, soulless night of New Mexico. A million stars are in the sky. Ahead of me stretch a thousand miles of empty mesa, mountains, prairies—desert. Somewhere among them, he is waiting for me. Somewhere I shall know who he is, and who . . . I . . . am. . . .

MUSIC. *Up.*

The Hitch Hiker

Responding to the Play

1. When did you realize who the hitch hiker really was? How?
2. Discuss the elements that made this play suspenseful.
3. Go through the play and indicate the music you would use wherever a new sound is called for.
4. How would you go about collecting the sounds that are required for this play?
5. Draw a poster to advertise a performance of the play.

About Life Before Television

From The New York Times, 1938. A wave of mass hysteria seized thousands of radio listeners between 8:15 and 9:30 o'clock last night when a broadcast of a dramatization of H. G. Wells's fantasy, "The War of the Worlds," led thousands to believe that an interplanetary conflict had started with invading Martians spreading wide death and destruction in New Jersey and New York. The broadcast was made by Orson Welles, who as the radio character "The Shadow," used to give "the creeps" to countless child listeners. This time at least a score of adults required medical treatment for shock and hysteria.

Back in 1938, radio was so prevalent and so believable that thousands of people listening to an evening broadcast were actually convinced that Earth had been attacked by Mars. Like television today, radio was a powerful presence in everyone's lives. Comedies, dramas, mysteries, and the news came into millions of homes every hour of the day. From the 1920s, when the first commercial radio stations began broadcasting, until the 1950s the radio was everywhere. By the 1960s, and the advent of color TV, radio had to take a back seat.

Creating and Performing

1. Now that you have thought about how you would collect the sounds for this play, choose two and create them.
2. The hitch hiker, called VOICE in the script, does not say much, but what he does say has to have intensity. Practice his lines.
3. Think about how Adams's opening and closing speeches would be similar and dissimilar. Share your interpretation with your class.

Glossary of Key Literary and Theatrical Terms

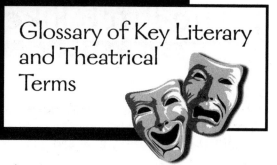

accent
the sound of speech in a particular region.

act
1. a major division in a play: *Let's read the second scene in the first act.*

2. to play the role of a character in a play: *My friend loves to act.*

actor
person who analyzes characters in relationship to a play, memorizes lines, learns blocking, and performs a role in a play.

antagonist
character who gets in the way of the protagonist, or main character; secondary character.

archetype
a stock character who represents a certain kind of person.

arena stage
stage that is surrounded by the audience; theatre-in-the-round. The stage may actually be a round shape, but it can also be a square.

aside
a side remark a character makes to the audience or another character.

audio
things that are heard, especially recordings.

audition
1. to try out for a part in a play.

2. the actual trying out itself.

backdrop
a large canvas or muslin curtain on which a scene is painted.

backstage
areas behind the stage that are not visible to the audience.

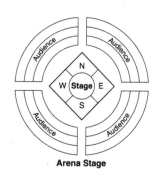

Arena Stage

beat
a special moment; actors and directors often divide scenes into beats

block
arrange the movement of people, sets, and props on the stage.

book
script, especially for a musical.

box office
place where ticket sales take place.

business manager
person who creates the production budget, coordinates publicity and ticket sales, and prepares programs.

call
time when actors should be on hand before a performance.

callback
an invitation to a second audition.

cast
choose people for particular roles in a play.

UR	UC	UL
Upstage Right	Upstage Center	Upstage Left
R	C	L
Right	Center	Left
DR	DC	DL
Downstage Right	Downstage Center	Downstage Left

center stage

center stage
the middle of a performance area.

characterization
the way in which an author reveals the characters to the reader.

choreograph
design dancing, fighting, or other specialized movements for the stage.

chorus
group of actors reciting, singing, or dancing in unison, often to comment on the action of a play.

climax
turning point of a play.

cold reading
the reading of a script for the first time.

comedy
a light or humorous play that usually has a happy ending.

comedy of manners
play that pokes fun at the actions and habits of the upper and upper middle class.

commedia dell'arte
a form of theatrical improvisation developed in Italy in the 1500s, which includes stock characters and farcical situations.

costume
clothing an actor wears onstage for a performance.

costume designer
person who designs and makes or obtains costuming for all actors.

costume plan
breakdown of the costumes characters wear in a play and the scenes in which they wear them.

credits
list of people who contributed to a production.

cross
to move from one place to another.

cue
a signal, often the last lines spoken by another actor.

curtain
the end (because the draperies open at the beginning of a play and close at the end).

dialogue
the conversation between people in a literary work

diction
the words an author chooses to use, dictated by the subject, audience, and effect intended in the literary work. Diction can be formal, informal, precise, complicated, old-fashioned, or contemporary.

direct
give suggestions to actors and crew members as to how to fulfill their roles in the production.

director
person who interprets a play, casts actors, develops blocking, and blends performances into a unified production.

down stage
the stage area closest to the audience.

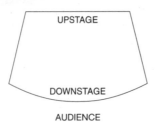

AUDIENCE

drama
a play that covers serious topics and may or may not have an unhappy ending.

dramatic monologue
a speech made by a single character that reveals something about the speaker or fills in important circumstances in the story.

dress rehearsal
final practice of a play before performance.

enter
appear on the stage.

exit
leave the stage area.

falling action
the part of a play following the turning point and approaching the resolution of the conflict

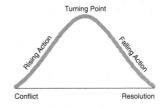

falling action

farce
comedy with exaggerated characters, physical humor, and a silly plot.

footage
a portion of a film.

foreshadowing
clues or hints given by the author as to what is to come in the literary work

fourth wall
imaginary wall between the

stage and the audience.

gesture
a movement that expresses a thought or emotion.

house
audience; place where the audience sits.

house manager
person who oversees the preparations for performance, supervises ushers, and has contact with the audience.

improvisation
to make things up as you go along; to act without a script.

irony
the contrast between what one expects or what appears to be and what actually is.

lighting
illumination of the actors and the set during a performance.

lighting designer
person who creates and carries out a lighting plan.

lobby
area where the audience waits before a performance and during intermissions.

makeup
cosmetics, hair styling, masks, wigs, etc. used by performers.

makeup designer
person who designs and applies makeup for all the actors.

mime
1. to communicate through movement and gesture rather than words

2. person who communicates in this way.

monologue
story or speech performed by an actor speaking alone.

mood
the atmosphere or overall feeling presented in a literary work.

motivation
a character's reasons for doing or saying something.

multimedia
performance including several forms of communication, such as acting, dancing, painting, audio, video, and computers.

musical
a play in which song and dance play an important part.

musical theatre
a play incorporating songs and dances throughout.

Makeup can even include feathers and masks.

Noh
a traditional form of Japanese theatre in which male actors use stylized dances and poetry to tell a story.

objective
a character's goals in a scene or play.

off book
having no need of the script.

pacing
the rate at which a play progresses.

pantomime
mime; to act out without using words or sounds.

papier-mâché
a technique for making props and masks out of torn strips of newspaper and glue made from flour and water.

pitch
high or low sound of a voice.

play
a story created for performance.

plot
story line, generally including rising action, climax, and resolution.

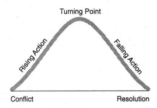
typical **plot** structure

point of view
the relationship of the teller of the story to the characters in the story.

posture
way in which one holds one's body.

producer
person who chooses the play, obtains the space, and sometimes casts actors.

production
performance of a play for an audience.

project
make one's voice loud and full enough to be heard in a big room.

prop
property; moveable objects used by actors on stage.

prop designer
person who obtains or makes props.

properties
props; moveable objects used by actors on stage.

prop table
a place offstage where all props are kept when not in use.

protagonist
character who moves the action of a play forward; usually the "good guy" or the character with whom the audience identifies.

proscenium stage
a "picture frame" stage; stage that allows audience seating on the front side only. (See diagram on facing page.)

reader's theatre
dramatic reading of a story or play script.

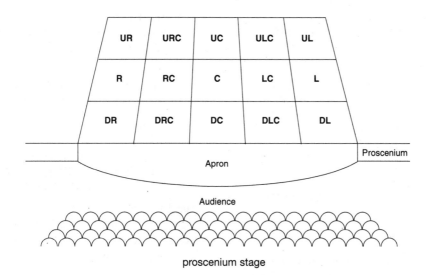

proscenium stage

realism
style of writing or acting which attempts to be as lifelike as possible.

rising action
middle part of a plot, including complications leading toward a climax.

role
a part in a play.

run
a period of time over which a play will be presented, typically four to six weeks.

scenario
a plan or outline for a plot.

scene
part of an act; segment of a play that does not require a change of scenery.

scenery
large background pieces that create a sense of place on-stage.

screenplay
a film script.

script
the text of a play.

set
the combination of scenery, furniture, and props.

set designer
person who designs and creates sets, and obtains or makes set pieces such as furniture.

set pieces
large pieces of furniture for the stage.

setting
the location in which a play takes place.

shoot
film something.

sound
all sound-producing elements of a production, including live voices, music, and sound effects.

sound designer
person who creates and carries out sound effects plan.

stage
performance area.

UR Upstage Right	UC Upstage Center	UL Upstage Left
R Right	C Center	L Left
DR Downstage Right	DC Downstage Center	DL Downstage Left

the performance area is divided into 9 distinct parts

stage crew
people handling sets, lighting, sound, costumes, or makeup.

stage left
the stage area to an actor's left when he or she faces the audience.

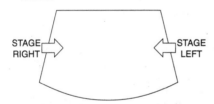

stage manager
person who holds auditions, schedules acting and technical rehearsals, and keeps track of administration.

stage right
the stage area to an actor's right when he or she faces the audience.

Stanislavski method
method of acting, named after its founder, in which actors respond according to their motivations and emotional reactions in a scene.

storyboard
series of sketches showing possible scenes in a play.

style
an author's way of writing; the way an author writes about a subject.

suspense
the way an author maintains the reader's interest, creating a mood of anxiety and uncertainty.

symbolism
words and images that represent something more than their ordinary meaning.

teleplay
television script.

theme
the underlying meaning of any literary work.

thrust stage
stage surrounded on three sides by the house, or audience.

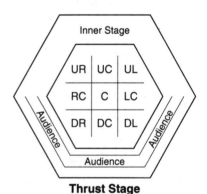

Thrust Stage

timing
pacing of particular moments in a scene.

tone
the author's attitude toward his or her subject and toward the reader.

338

tragedy
form of drama in which the main character comes to an unhappy end.

turning point
the decisive moment in a literary work.

understudy
actor who learns a role in order to substitute for an actor who is absent.

upstage
the back of the stage area, away from the audience.

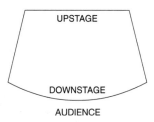

ushers
crew members who seat the audience, hand out programs, and clean up the house after each performance.

video
things that are seen, especially recordings that can be seen on television.

voice-over
recording of a voice that plays while action or other sounds are taking place, often indicated as VO in stage directions.

wings
offstage areas to the right and left of the stage, where actors often stand before entrances and after exits.

Acknowledgments

(continued from page iv)

Novio Boy by Gary Soto. Copyright © 1997 by Gary Soto. Reprinted by permission of Harcourt Brace & Company. CAUTION: Professionals and amateurs are hereby warned that this play is subject to a royalty. For information regarding performance rights, contact BookStop Literary Agency, 67 Meadow View Road, Orinda, California 94563, (510) 254-2668.

The Man in a Case by Anton Chekhov, translated by Wendy Wasserstein from *Orchards: Seven Stories by Anton Chekhov and Seven Plays They Have Inspired*, published by Knopf. Copyright © 1986 by Wendy Wasserstein. No part of this material may be reproduced in whole or in part without the express written permission of the author or her agent. CAUTION: All performance inquiries should be directed to Rosenstone/Wender 3 East 48th Street, New York, NY 10017.

Variations on the Death of Trotsky by David Ives from *All in the Timing*. Copyright © 1994 by David Ives. Reprinted by permission of Vintage Books, a Division of Random House Inc. CAUTION: All performance inquiries should be addressed to Random House Inc.

A Conversation With My Dogs by Merrill Markoe from *What the Dogs Have Taught Me*. Copyright © 1992 by Merrill Markoe. Reprinted by permission of Viking Penguin, a division of Penguin Putnam Inc.

He Who Says Yes and He Who Says No by Bertolt Brecht, translated by Gerhard Nellhaus. Copyright © 1930, 1958 Stefan S. Brecht. Reprinted by permission of Jerold L. Couture c/o Fitelson, Lasky, Aslan & Couture, Attorneys at Law. CAUTION: All performance inquiries should be directed to Jerold L. Couture c/o Fitelson, Lasky, Aslan & Couture, Attorneys at Law, 551 Fifth Avenue, New York, NY 10176-0078.

I Never Saw Another Butterfly by Celeste Raspanti. Copyright © 1971 by Celeste Raspanti. All rights reserved. CAUTION: The play printed in this anthology is not to be used as an acting script. All inquiries regarding performance rights should be addressed to Dramatic Publishing, 311 Washington Street, Woodstock, IL 60098. Phone: (815) 338-7170. Fax: (815) 338-8981.

Painted Rain by Janet Malia Allard. Copyright © 1989 by Janet Malia Allard. Reprinted by permission of the author. All rights reserved. CAUTION: Professionals and amateurs are hereby warned that the plays represented in this book are subject to a royalty. They are fully protected under the copyright laws of the United States of America, and of all countries covered by the International Copyright Union (including the Dominion of Canada and the rest of the British Commonwealth, and of all countries covered by the Pan-American Copyright Convention and the Universal Copyright Convention, and of all countries with which the United States has reciprocal copyright relations. All inquiries regarding performance rights should be addressed to the author c/o Young Playwrights, Inc., 321 West

44th Street, Suite 906, New York, NY 10036.

Nothing But the Truth a play by Ronn Smith based on the novel by Avi. Copyright © 1997 by Ronn Smith. Reprinted by permission of Avon Books, Inc. CAUTION: Performance rights are retained by Ronn Smith c/o McIntosh & Otis 310 Madison Avenue, New York, NY 10017.

This is a Test by Stephen Gregg. Copyright © 1988 by Stephen Gregg. All rights reserved. Reprinted by permission of the author. CAUTION: The play printed in this anthology is not to be used as an acting script. All inquiries regarding performance rights should be addressed to Dramatic Publishing, 311 Washington Street, Woodstock, IL 60098. Phone: (815) 338-7170. Fax: (815) 338-8981.

The Frog Prince by David Mamet. Copyright © 1982, 1983 by David Mamet. Reprinted by permission of Rosenstone/Wender. CAUTION: All performance inquiries should be directed to the author's agent: Rosenstone/Wender 3 East 48th Street, New York, NY 10017.

The Love of Three Oranges by Carlo Gozzi, adapted by Lowell Swortzell. Reprinted by permission of the author. CAUTION: For information regarding performance rights, contact Professor Lowell Swortzell, Program in Educational Theatre, New York University, Washington Square, New York, NY 10003.

Maggie Magalita by Wendy Kesselman, originally produced in New York City by The Lamb's Theatre Company, Ltd. Carolyn Rossi Copeland, Producing Director. Copyright © 1987 by Wendy Kesselman. Reprinted by permission of William Morris Agency, Inc. on behalf of the Author. All rights reserved. CAUTION: Professionals and amateurs are hereby warned that "MAGGIE MAGALITA" is subject to a royalty. It is fully protected under the copyright laws of the United States of America and all countries covered by the International Copyright Union (including the Dominion of Canada and the rest of the British Commonwealth), the Bern Convention, the Pan-American Copyright Convention and the Universal Copyright Convention as well as all countries with which the United States has reciprocal copyright relations. All rights, including professional/amateur stage rights, motion picture, recitation, lecturing, public reading, radio broadcasting, television, video or sound recording, all other forms of mechanical or electronic reproduction, such as CD-ROM, CD-I, information storage and retrieval systems and photocopying and the rights of translation into foreign languages, are strictly reserved. Particular emphasis is laid upon the matter of readings, permission for which must be secured from the Author's agent in writing. Inquiries concerning rights should be addressed to: William Morris Agency, Inc. 1325 Avenue of the Americas, New York, NY 10019 Attn: George Lane.

The Drummer by Athol Fugard. Copyright © 1989 by Athol Fugard. Reprinted by permission of Samuel French Inc. CAUTION: Professionals and amateurs are hereby warned that "THE DRUMMER," being fully protected under the copyright laws of the United States of America, the British Commonwealth countries, including Canada, and the other countries of the Copyright Union, is subject to a royalty. All rights, including professional, amateur, motion picture, recitation, public reading, radio, television and cable broadcasting, and the rights of translation into foreign languages, are strictly reserved. Any inquiry regarding the availability of performance rights, or purchase of individual copies of the authorized acting edition, must be directed to Samuel French Inc., 45 West 25 Street, New York, NY 10010 with other locations in Hollywood and Toronto, Canada.

The Big Black Box by Cleve Haubold. Copyright © 1965 by Cleve Haubold, renewed © 1993 by Dora Bond Pickard. CAUTION: Professionals and amateurs are hereby warned that "THE BIG BLACK BOX," being fully protected under the copyright laws of the United States of America, the British Commonwealth countries, including Canada, and the other countries of the Copyright Union, is subject to a royalty. All rights, including professional, amateur, motion picture, recitation, public reading, radio, television and cable broadcasting, and the rights of translation into foreign languages, are strictly reserved. Any inquiry regarding the availability of performance rights, or purchase of individual copies of the authorized acting edition, must be directed to Samuel French Inc., 45 West 25 Street, New York, NY 10010 with other locations in Hollywood and Toronto, Canada.

The Hitch Hiker by Lucille Fletcher. Copyright © 1947 by Lucille Fletcher. Reprinted by permission of William Morris Agency, Inc. on behalf of the Author. CAUTION: Inquiries concerning rights should be addressed to: William Morris Agency, Inc. 1325 Avenue of the Americas, New York, NY 10019.

Photo and Art Credits

Half-title Page: David Hockney, Two Punchinellos, © 1983 by David Hockney. The David Hockney Trust, Los Angeles, CA.

Page ix: Anthony Barboza, © 1999 Anthony Barboza. Anthony Barboza Photography.

Page 2: Milton H. Greene, Marcel Marceau, Dancing, © 1999 The Archives of Milton H. Greene, LLC. All rights reserved. www.archivesmhg.com.

Page 27: Dorothea Lange, Mother's Day Daisies, © 1934 by the Dorothea Lange Collection, The Oakland Museum of California, city of Oakland. Gift of Paul S. Taylor.

Page 47: © David Diaz.

Page 62: © David Diaz.

Page 100: William Wegmam, © 1992. 20 x 24 inch Polaroid.

Page 106: Noh Mask © Art Resource, New York.

Page 119: Butterfly, © American Friends of the Jewish Museum in Prague.

Page 129: Dita Valentikova, © American Friends of the Jewish Museum in Prague, detailed sketch.

Page 140: Helena Schanzerova, © American Friends of the Jewish Museum in Prague, watercolor.

Page 147: Stella Zee, Untitled © Stella Zee.

Page 165: Francisco Cruz, American Flag, © Francisco Cruz, SuperStock.

Page 298: © David Diaz.

Page 320: Jane Scherr, A woman was raped here... © Jane Scherr, Jerobaum.

Page 335: NanC Meinhardt.

Page 336: Noh Mask © Art Resource, New York.